Biology: A Human Perspective

A Wiley Canada Custom Publication for

Brock University

BIOL1F25

WILEY

Wiley Canada Custom Services

JOHN WILEY & SONS CANADA, LTD.

Huffman Cover Photos: Main Photo: © iStockphoto.com/Vasiliy Yakobchuk. Bottom Inset Photos (left to right): Huy Lam Photography/First Light; © Copyright Media Bakery; Cary Wolinsky/National Geographic Stock; Jimmy Chin/National Geographic Stock; LWA-JDC/Corbis
Ireland Cover Photos: Centre Photo: ©Juliet White/Getty Images, Inc. Bottom Inset Photos (left to right): ©MedicalRF.com/Getty Images, Inc.; ©Jason Edwards/NG
Image Collection; ©A. Syred/Photo Researchers, Inc; ©Tim Evans/Photo Researchers, Inc; ©Don Farrall/ Digital Vision/Getty Images, Inc.
Boyer Cover Photo: © Howard Sochurek/CORBIS

Marketing Manager: Patty Maher
Custom Coordinator: Sara Tinteri

Printed and bound in Canada

John Wiley & Sons Canada, Ltd
6045 Freemont Blvd.
Mississauga, Ontario
L5R 4J3
Visit our website at: www.wiley.ca

CONTENTS

Process Diagram

Cycle continues →

Step 1
Literature review
The scientist conducts a *literature review*, reading what has been published in major professional, scientific journals on her subject of interest.

Cycle begins →

Step 6
Theory
After one or more studies on a topic, researchers generally advance a *theory* to explain their results. This new theory then leads to new (possibly different) hypotheses and new methods of inquiry.

Step 2
Operationally defined hypothesis
The scientist makes a testable prediction or *hypothesis* about how one factor or variable interacts with another. To be scientifically testable, the variables must be *operationally defined*—that is, stated very precisely and in measurable terms.

SCIENTIFIC METHOD

Step 5
Peer-reviewed scientific journal
The scientist writes up the study and its results and submits it to a *peer-reviewed scientific journal.* (Peer-reviewed journals ask other scientists to critically evaluate submitted material before publication.) On the basis of these peer reviews, the study may then be accepted for publication.

Step 3
Research design
The scientist chooses the best *research design* to test the hypothesis and collect the data. She might choose naturalistic observations, case studies, correlations, surveys, experiments, or other methods.

Step 4
Statistical analysis
The scientist performs *statistical analyses* on the raw data to describe, organize, and numerically summarize them. Additional statistical analyses are performed to make inferences about the study to the more general population. This allows the researcher to determine whether the findings support or refute the hypothesis.

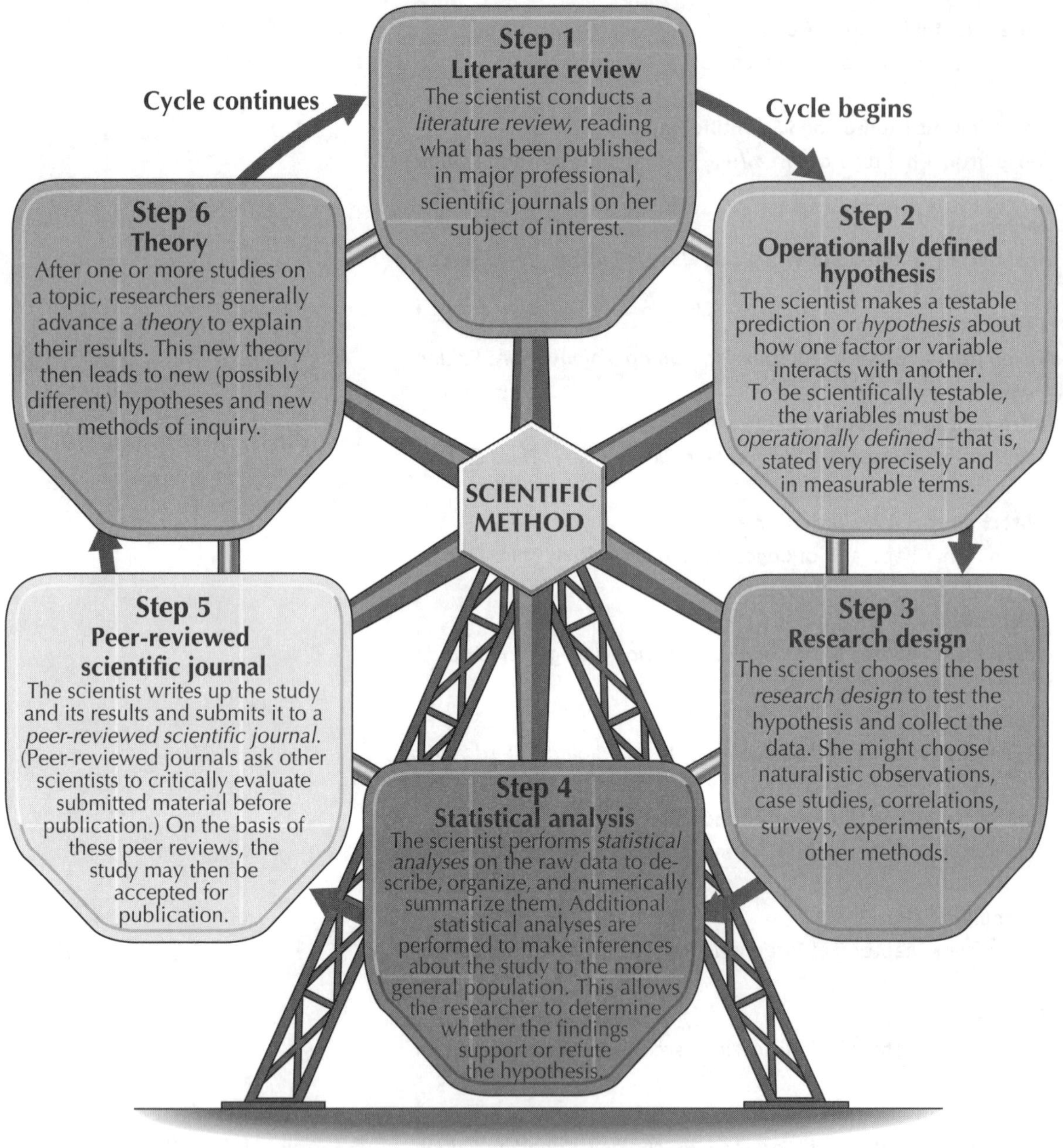

Process Diagram

To test the hypothesis that watching violent television increases aggression, experimenters might randomly assign children to one of two groups: **experimental group** participants, who watch a prearranged number of violent television programs, and **control group** participants, who watch the same amount of television, except the programs that they watch are nonviolent. (*Having at least two groups— a control group and an experimental group— allows the performance of one group to be compared with that of another.*)

Experimenters then observe the children and count how many times—say, within one hour—each child hits, kicks, or punches a punching bag (an operational definition of aggression).

■ **experimental group** The group that receives the experimental manipulation.

■ **control group** The group that does not receive the experimental manipulations but is treated the same way as the experimental group in all other areas.

Hypothesis
"Watching violence on TV increases aggression."*

Participants are **randomly selected** from the population and **randomly assigned** to the experimental group or control group.

Experimental Group

Control Group

Independent Variable (IV)
(Violent or nonviolent program)

Dependent Variable (DV)
(Number of times child hits the punching bag)

Groups Compared

* If this were a real experiment, we would operationally define the type and amount of violent TV and what is meant by "aggression." In this example, aggression is the number of times the child hits the bag.

VIEW THIS IN ACTION
in your WileyPLUS course

1

1.3 Scientists Approach Questions Using the Scientific Method

LEARNING OBJECTIVES

1. **List** the steps in the scientific method in order.
2. **Define** hypothesis and theory.

Science is a field with specific goals and rules. The overall goals are to provide sound theories regarding the phenomena we observe, using rules embodied by the **scientific method**. When a question arises about the natural world, the scientific method provides the accepted, logical path to the answer, as shown in **Figure 1.6**.

A scientific experiment is an exercise in logic: Our goal is to prove our hypothesis wrong. For example, our hypothesis is that the rooster's crow causes the sun to rise within the next 20 minutes. How could we test this

THE PLANNER

The scientific method • Figure 1.6

The scientific method is rooted in logic. If we can show that our hypothesis does not apply to even one situation, then our hypothesis is wrong. After we analyze the data and draw conclusions from them, we may have to junk our hypothesis, or conclude that it applies to a more limited range of circumstances.

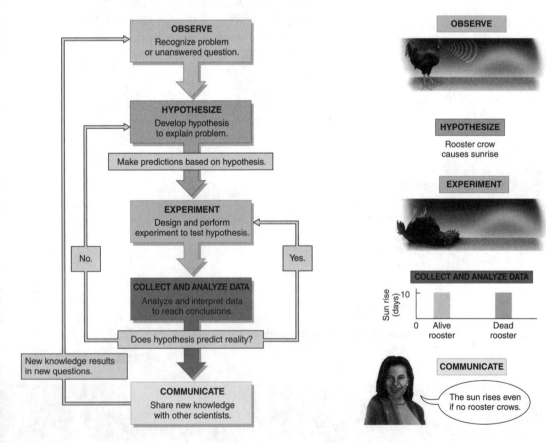

12 CHAPTER 1 What Is Life?

hypothesis? Could we force the rooster to crow at midnight, and wait 20 minutes for a glow on the eastern horizon? Could we prevent the rooster from crowing in the morning? In either case, if the sun rose as usual, our hypothesis would be disproved, and we would need to find a better hypothesis.

This silly example shows how scientists may manipulate factors that (according to the hypothesis) seem related to the observation, all in an attempt to disprove the hypothesis. We develop a hypothesis using **inductive reasoning**—creating a general statement from our observations. We design the experiment, however, with **deductive reasoning**, moving from the general hypothesis to a specific situation. An "if, then" statement is an ideal basis for a scientific experiment: "If situation A (rooster crows) occurs, then result B (sunrise) will follow." In our experiment, we changed situation A and monitored any changes in result B.

When designing and running the experiment, we must control all potential **variables**. Otherwise, we cannot draw any valid conclusions. In the rooster example, it would be a good idea to muzzle all nearby roosters. Otherwise, how would we know whether our bird or a bird in the next chicken coop had caused the sunrise? Similarly, in testing new medicines, scientists use a "double-blind" experiment: Nobody knows whether each research participant is getting real medicine or a fake, called a "placebo." This prevents expectations that the drug will work from actually causing a change in the participant's health. The "placebo effect" can be powerful, but the goal is to test the drug, not the research participant's expectations.

Finally, our hypothesis must be testable and falsifiable. If we cannot think of a situation where we could disprove it, there is no experiment to devise. Learning to assess situations with the scientific method takes some practice, but it's a skill that can be useful throughout life.

Let's take an example from human biology to show the process of testing a hypothesis. Have you seen those hand lotions that claim to be "skin firming"? Sounds great, but how would we test this claim? Under the scientific method, we consider the marketing claim to be the observation, so we must develop a testable hypothesis from the observation: "Using this hand cream

> **variable** A factor that can be changed in an experiment to test whether and how it affects the outcome.
>
> **statistical significance** An experimental result that would occur by chance in less than 1 experiment in 20; the accepted level in modern science.

for one month will cause measurable tightening of the skin on the back of the hand." Now we restate the hypothesis as an "if, then" statement: "If the cream does firm the skin, then using the cream on the back of the hand for one month will reduce the skin-fold measurement." This is a testable statement that lends itself to controlled experimentation. First, we will assess each person's skin tautness by measuring the skin fold that can be pulled up on the back of the hand. Then we will randomly divide the participants into two groups: a control group and an experimental group. We will treat each group in an identical manner, except that the control group will use Brand X hand cream without the firming agent and the experimental group will get Brand X with the firming agent. After using the cream for one month, we will repeat the skin-fold measurements and analyze our data, looking for changes in skin tautness between the two groups as evidence for either accepting or refuting the hypothesis. If the experimental group displays a change in tautness that would occur by chance in less than 1 experiment in 20, the change is said to have **statistical significance**, and the hypothesis is supported: The cream does tighten the skin.

It is important to note that any conclusions drawn from a scientific experiment must be supported by the data. If the results of your experiment could have happened by chance, you cannot say that the results were due to the experimental design. In that case, a new experiment must be designed and run.

The Scientific Method Leads to Theories

Because biologists cannot always control all factors, or variables, that might affect the outcome, they often use observation as a form of experimentation. If you were interested in the effects of mercury on the human brain, it would not be ethical to dose people with mercury, but you could perform an observational study. You could measure blood levels of mercury, or you could ask your research participants about past diet (food, especially fish, is the major source of mercury exposure). Then you would use statistical tests to look for a relationship between mercury exposure and intelligence. Finally, you could try to confirm or refute your results with controlled experiments in lab animals. Does mercury make rats faster or slower at negotiating a maze (a standard test for rat intelligence)? Observational studies are also a mainstay of field biology.

Observation, experimentation, and analysis are the basis for scientific reasoning. Once a group of related hypotheses have survived rigorous testing without being disproved, they are accepted as a **theory**. Theories are not facts but rather extremely well-supported explanations of the natural world that nobody has disproved. To a scientist, a theory is much more than a hypothesis or a belief—it's our best effort to date to explain nature. Many fields of science may be involved in supporting a theory. The theory of evolution through natural selection, for example, is supported by taxonomists, geologists, paleontologists, geneticists, and even embryologists. Many scientists have tried, but none has refuted the basic hypothesis first described by Charles Darwin in 1859. We will discuss another key theory, the cell theory, in Chapter 4.

> **theory** A general uniting principle of science, upheld by observation and many experiments.

Science is not a perfect, set-in-stone answer to questions about the natural world but rather a dynamic, ever-changing collection of ideas. New information can change or destroy accepted explanations for the natural world. For example, doctors once blamed contagious disease on ill humors, miasmas, and evil spirits. Through the work of nineteenth-century biologist Louis Pasteur, it became clear that many diseases were caused by microscopic organisms. In his breakthrough experiment, Pasteur sterilized some grape juice and showed that it did not ferment into wine. Then he added yeast, and the juice fermented. When Pasteur showed through experiment that invisible organisms can also cause disease, he helped establish the germ theory of disease. Although it's called a theory, the germ theory is the universally accepted scientific explanation for infectious disease. More recently, the accepted role of the cell nucleus has come into question. Based on experiments, biologists used to consider the nucleus the cell's control center, but new evidence suggests it actually functions more like a library for genetic data. The actual control of gene expression and cellular activity seems to reside outside the nucleus, in specific RNA molecules. The theory of nuclear control in the cell is under serious scrutiny, and further experiments could alter it.

Scientific studies are part of the daily news. As technology advances, humans confront scientific hypotheses and experimental results almost every day. We see advertisements for new drugs. We hear that fossil fuels are warming the globe. We see countless new technologies in the field of consumer electronics. In medicine, we hear about a steady stream of new surgeries and wonder drugs. We are told of many ways in which humans are causing the loss of rain forests, coral reefs, natural forests, and plains, as well as the animals that live there. We worry about the causes of animal extinction (see *Ethics and Issues: Why Should Endangered Species Matter to Me?* for a discussion of this). About the only way to wade through the morass of information in the media is to understand and use the scientific process. Responsible citizens living in technological cultures sometimes must make decisions about contested scientific issues they read about in the media. Some reports have linked the radiation from cell phones to brain tumors, but other reports find no connection. A few concerned citizens have demanded that manufacturers produce "safer" cell phones, with lower radiation emissions. Can you think of an experiment that would resolve this issue, at least in principle? As you read about the scientific studies on this issue, ask yourself: What types of controlled and observational experiments underlie the claims about cell phones and cancer? Are the experiments convincing?

Critical Reasoning Is Useful in Human Biology

The ability to question and criticize—for example, our constantly changing understanding of obesity or the dangers posed by food additives or environmental chemicals—is useful in many aspects of human biology. Critically analyze the data, experiments, and claims before you accept what you read. There are plenty of opinions out there; don't accept any until you consider the evidence and reach an informed decision. Form your own opinion based on what you understand to be true.

In other words, become a critical reasoner! Critical reasoners are skeptical, logical, and open to new information, enjoying the way it changes their previous assumptions and ideas. Critical reasoners question assumptions and stated facts, using logic to arrive at their own conclusions. They find good analogies for information that they find to be true, often helping others make sense of the new information. Taking on the role of a critical thinker means recognizing that you don't have to settle for a story or a very

ETHICS AND ISSUES

Why Should Endangered Species Matter to Me?

About 20 years ago, biologists began to realize that they would start to run out of things to study due to the accelerating wave of extinctions shaking the planet. Extinctions occur for many reasons; overhunting, destruction of habitat by fire, construction, or ecological change, and invasion of exotic species can all play a role.

What's the big deal? Some extinction is natural, after all. Why is it important to prevent endangered species from going extinct? The answers range from scientific to economic to spiritual:

- Organisms can be useful. A species of plant called the rosy periwinkle was the source of a key drug that defeats one type of leukemia. Scientists are actively looking in many unusual ecosystems for useful chemicals that organisms have evolved for specific reasons. Many antibiotics, for example, were derived from fungi that evolved these compounds for protection against bacteria.

- Life is unique. As far as we know, this is the only planet with life. If we respect life, we should respect its myriad forms as well: the whales, swans, lobsters, and even the endangered fish and mussels in our streams.

- Life has scientific value. To understand the wonders of evolution, we need to study the results of evolution.

- Life is a web. Organisms in the wild have complex interactions that we are only beginning to understand. Extinguishing one organism can have cascading effects throughout an ecosystem.

It's hard to know exactly how far along we are in the current wave of extinction because biologists are not even sure how many species inhabit the Earth. So far, about 1.9 million species have been described, but it is estimated that the total number is several times that. The World Conservation Union reports that 748 species are already extinct, and another 16,119 are threatened with extinction. These threatened organisms include one in three amphibians, one in four coniferous trees and mammals, and one bird in eight. The group also notes that "56% of the 252 endemic fresh-water Mediterranean fish are threatened with extinction."

Critical Reasoning Issues Different organizations and governmental agencies may use different data to define "endangered." For some, the term may refer to species of which fewer than 500 breeding pairs

are known in a certain country; for others, the data set may encompass the whole continent. Knowing the expertise and motives of an organization or agency may be crucial to understanding how it uses and presents data. However, regardless of technical definitions of "endangered," some of the organisms that are currently becoming extinct are ones we have not even yet identified, let alone studied. Their beauty and utility will go completely unrecognized as they fade from existence. Although evolution may eventually restore biodiversity to its current levels, that will take millions of years. Thus, in biodiversity, as in so many things, a gram of prevention is worth a kilo of cure!

Think Critically

1. What examples can you find of a governmental agency or organization that does not specify its definition of "endangered" and "threatened with extinction"?
2. What are some other reasons to value biodiversity besides the ones mentioned?

NATIONAL GEOGRAPHIC

small sample size when looking for facts about an issue. You should ask yourself, "Were there enough trials done to see that the results were repeated consistently?" Also, critical reasoners know that there are limits to certainty but do not allow this knowledge to prevent them from seeking as full an understanding of an issue as possible.

People have the ability not only to communicate in complex ways but also to record the past. We can consult studies, relate current affairs to similar historical events, and use statistics to support our reasoning. In so doing, we understand that the past proves the law of unintended consequences—that actions often have unexpected effects. For example, using naturally cool stream water as an industrial plant coolant saves money and seems to be a good use of the available resources. However, the practice dramatically increases the temperature of these streams below the plant. The temperature increase, in turn, changes the population of organisms that are able to survive there and often alters the productivity of the entire watershed below the plant.

Critical reasoning is not the kind of thinking illustrated by the fact that 87% of people rate themselves above average in intelligence. It is also not illustrated by the notion that because a woman was cured of her epilepsy after being bitten by a rattlesnake, the venom caused the cure. Rather, critical reasoning is the best way to understand complex interactions such as those that take place within the human body and between the body and its external environment. Studying human biology is the perfect way to practice your critical reasoning skills, as you will be investigating the most complex system we know—ourselves and our relationship to our environment.

CONCEPT CHECK **STOP**

1. **What** are the steps of the scientific method?
2. **What** is the difference between a hypothesis and theory?

1.4 Scientific Findings Often Lead to Ethical Dilemmas

LEARNING OBJECTIVES

1. **Define** altruistic behavior.
2. **Briefly describe** why a basic knowledge of science is essential to being a productive citizen.

Humans have evolved as social animals, following the rules and expectations that make life possible in groups. This cultural structure that overlies the biological structure of human life certainly adds interest to our study of human biology. Culture generally requires that people accept responsibility for other individuals within the population, rather than merely surviving and protecting their young. Although **altruistic** behavior does appear among some primates, it helps distinguish humans from other life-forms and creates one basis for the governments and laws people have established.

> **altruistic** Putting the needs of others ahead of, or equal to, personal needs.
>
> **ethical decision** A decision based on the principles of right and wrong, rather than on financial, personal, or political gain.

When individuals must make judgments and act for the good of the group rather than the individual, they must make **ethical decisions**, and ethical decisions should be informed decisions. Where does that information come from? Scientific research provides our basic understanding of the natural world. Although humans can and do add their interpretations and values to the results of science, science itself is judgment free. Scientific results are neither good nor bad; they are just the best current idea of how the material world operates. The discovery by Pasteur and his peers that germs cause many diseases was neither good nor bad—it was just true. The ability to analyze scientific issues is essential in an informed society and turns out to be more important as scientifically based issues become even more common and complex. Science seeks to explain the natural world, but

Nuclear power • Figure 1.7

Nuclear power poses an interesting mix of scientific and political issues. Atomic fission can provide a large amount of electricity, and it does not create greenhouse gases, which warm the globe and threaten harm to the biosphere. However, radioactive waste is dangerous, and nuclear plants can melt down and spew vast amounts of radiation, as one did at Chernobyl in the Soviet Union in 1986. The decision to use nuclear power is a political decision, not a scientific one, so it is imperative that each member of society understands the scientific data on nuclear reactors, as well as the social ramifications of that information.

Nuclear power has its pluses and minuses. To take a position, you should know about global warming, radioactive waste, and the costs and benefits of other technologies for making electricity—all scientific issues.

Hiding from the truth and not engaging in personal critical thought • Figure 1.8

Is this any way to run an informed citizenry?

the uses of science, both beneficial and harmful, grow from human choices. Sometimes people choose to use scientific discoveries to improve the environment and the human condition, and sometimes they use them to carry out seemingly evil designs. One example of this can be seen in **Figure 1.7**. Another example of this dual edge is the understanding that germs cause disease. Pasteur's germ theory of disease can be used to help cure disease—or to invent biological warfare.

Many ethically charged scientific issues, such as stem cell research, environmental conservation, or genetically modified food, have both personal and political ramifications. Each of these requires an understanding of the science and the societal issues. An informed voting public requires that each individual draw logical and defensible conclusions from scientific information. The alternative is **Figure 1.8**.

CONCEPT CHECK

1. **What** is altruistic behavior?
2. **Why** is it important to understand scientific information?

There Are Four Main Categories of Organic Chemicals

LEARNING OBJECTIVES

1. **Identify** the main categories of organic compounds.
2. **Define** the roles of carbohydrates, lipids, proteins, and nucleic acids in the human body.
3. **Explain** the function of ATP in energy storage and usage.

When we discuss life, we are discussing organic chemistry. Scientists used to think that all organic chemicals were made by organisms. Although that's not true, organic chemicals are usually made by organisms, and they always contain carbon. In terms of bonding, carbon is astonishingly flexible. With four valence electrons, it can bond covalently with four other atoms, leading to an almost infinite set of carbon structures, from simple methane, CH_4, to highly complex rings and chains. In organic compounds, carbon often bonds with two carbons and two hydrogens. The resulting hydrocarbon compounds can be chain or ring structures. Attached to the carbon/hydrogen core are **functional groups** that determine the compound's reactivity (see **Figure 3.8**).

Organic compounds are grouped into four main categories: **carbohydrates**, **lipids**, **proteins**, and **nucleic acids**.

> **functional group**
> Subunit on an organic molecule that helps determine how it reacts with other chemicals.

Functional groups • Figure 3.8

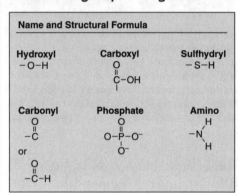

Name and Structural Formula		
Hydroxyl −O−H	**Carboxyl** O ‖ C−OH	**Sulfhydryl** −S−H
Carbonyl O ‖ −C or O ‖ −C−H	**Phosphate** O ‖ O−P−O⁻ ｜ O⁻	**Amino** H ｜ −N ｜ H

These functional groups are found on a variety of organic molecules. Each group is usually found attached to a long string of carbon molecules.

Carbohydrates Are the Best Energy Source for the Human Body

Carbohydrates are organic molecules that are quite abundant in organisms. A carbohydrate is composed of carbon, hydrogen, and oxygen in a ratio of 1:2:1. Many carbohydrates are **saccharides** (sugars). Glucose, as shown in **Figure 3.9**,

Glucose, glycogen, and cellulose • Figure 3.9

a. The glucose molecule, $C_6H_{12}O_6$, can be diagrammed in two ways.

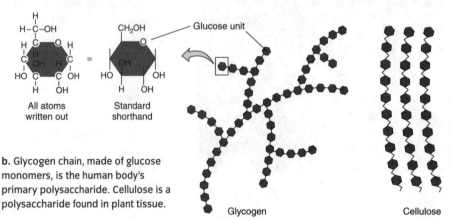

All atoms written out

Standard shorthand

Glucose unit

b. Glycogen chain, made of glucose monomers, is the human body's primary polysaccharide. Cellulose is a polysaccharide found in plant tissue.

Glycogen

Cellulose

Saturated and unsaturated fats • Figure 3.10

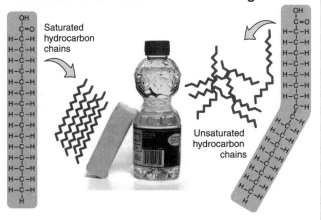

Saturated fats usually have animal origins. At room temperature, these fats are composed of tightly packed, straight lipid molecules. Unsaturated fats are usually plant products and have kinked lipid molecules that will not pack together tightly at room temperature.

and fructose are both simple sugars. They are called **mono-saccharides** because they have one ring of 6 carbons, with 12 hydrogens and 6 oxygens attached. **Oligosaccharides** and **polysaccharides** are longer sugar chains (*oligo* = few, and *poly* = many). **Disaccharides**, such as sucrose and lactose, are common in the human diet. **Glycogen,** also in Figure 3.9, is a polysaccharide sugar molecule stored in animal tissue. It is a long chain of glucose molecules, with a typical branching pattern. Glycogen is stored in muscles and the liver, where it is readily broken down when needed.

Unlike glycogen, **starch** is a fairly long, straight chain of sugars. Plants store energy in starch, often in roots, tubers, and grains. **Cellulose**, another polysaccharide, has a binding pattern similar to glycogen. Cellulose is often used in structural fibers in plants and is the main component of paper. The difference between cellulose and glycogen depends on which particular carbon on the sugar ring connects the branches to the main chain. This small difference makes cellulose indigestible to humans, whereas glycogen is an easily digestible source of quick energy.

Despite the hoopla surrounding the high-protein Atkins diet, carbohydrates are the best energy source for the human body: We are efficient carbohydrate-burning machines. Restricting intake of carbohydrates and increasing intake of other organic compounds puts biochemical stress on the whole body. When digesting proteins, for example, we generate nitrogenous wastes, which can release potentially harmful nitrogen compounds into our blood.

Water is needed to digest carbohydrates. In the process of **hydrolysis**, digestive enzymes insert a water molecule between adjacent monosaccharides in the chain, disrupting the covalent bond between sugars and releasing one sugar molecule. To add a sugar molecule to a chain, the opposite of hydrolysis must occur. In **dehydration synthesis**, a molecule of water is removed from adjacent glucose molecules, allowing them to bond. By adding water, digestive enzymes separate glucose molecules from glycogen and starch. Once glucose enters a cell, it can be completely metabolized into carbon dioxide and water, producing energy through the process of cellular respiration described in Chapter 15. Because we lack the enzymes needed to remove sugar molecules from cellulose, all the cellulose we eat travels through our digestive system intact. This "fiber" is not converted into fuel, but it is essential for proper digestion and defecation.

Lipids Are Long Chains of Carbons

Lipids, such as oils, waxes, and fats, are long-chain organic compounds that are not soluble in water. Although most of the human body is aqueous, it is divided into cells, as described in Chapter 4. Because water does not dissolve lipids, they form a perfect barrier between these aqueous compartments. Lipids, like other organic compounds, are composed of carbon, hydrogen, and oxygen, but NOT with the 1:2:1 ratio of carbohydrates. The carbon–hydrogen ratio is often 1:2, but lipids have far fewer oxygens than do carbohydrates. Lipids have a high energy content (9 kcal/g), and most people enjoy the "richness" they impart to food.

Humans store excess caloric intake as fats, so reducing lipids is a common dietary tactic. As the proportion of stored lipids in the body rises, people become overweight or obese, as discussed in Chapter 14.

Fatty acids are energy-storing lipids. A fatty acid is a long chain of hydrogens and carbon, sometimes with more than 36 carbons. A carboxyl (acid) group is attached to the end carbon, which gives it the name "fatty acid." The other carbons are almost exclusively bonded to carbons or hydrogens. These chains are hydrophobic; the carboxyl group is the only hydrophilic location. Generally, the longer the hydrocarbon chain, the less water soluble the fatty acid will be.

You have no doubt heard about two types of fatty acid: **saturated** and **unsaturated** fats (**Figure 3.10**). Saturated fats have no double bonds between carbons in the fat chains. For this reason, they are completely *saturated* with hydrogens and cannot hold any more. The straight chains of hydrocarbons in a saturated fat allow the individual chains to pack close together. Saturated fats, such as butter and other animal fats, are solid at room temperature. Unsaturated fats have at least one double bond between adjacent carbons. This puts a crimp in the straight carbon chain, preventing close packing of the molecules. As a result, unsaturated fats are liquid at room temperature. Examples of unsaturated fats include vegetable oils and the synthetic fats added to butter substitutes. Some vegetable oils are "hydrogenated" to remain solid at room temperature. Hydrogenating adds hydrogens, removes double bonds, and straightens the molecular arrangement of the fats. This process allows the lipid to act like an animal fat and to be solid or semisolid at room temperature.

A **triglyceride** is three fatty acids attached to a glycerol backbone. Triglycerides, the most abundant fat in the body, can store two to three times as much energy per gram as carbohydrates. The body manufactures triglycerides as nonpolar, uncharged storage molecules. In adipose (fat) tissue, excess calories are stored in droplets of triglycerides.

Eicosanoids are essential lipids that serve as raw materials for **prostaglandins**. Prostaglandins are short-chain fatty acids that regulate local signaling processes. When nearby cells detect prostaglandins, they respond immediately with the sensation of pain. Aspirin blocks prostaglandins from reaching their cellular target, whereas ibuprofen competes for the site where prostaglandins bind to cells. Ibuprofen acts more like the game of musical chairs, with the pain receptor as the chair and prostaglandin as the other player. Because aspirin blocks prostaglandins entirely, it is more effective against some pain.

Phospholipids are another key group of lipids. As shown in **Figure 3.11**, phospholipids are fats that have two fatty acids and one phosphate group attached to a glycerol backbone. The fatty acids comprise the hydrophobic tail, whereas the phosphate group serves as a hydrophilic head. This unique structure allows phospholipids to form double layers (bilayers) that attract water on their edges and yet repel water from their center. The cell membrane, explored in the next chapter, is one such bilayer.

Steroids are a final group of lipids that often makes news. These are large molecules with a common four-ring structure, important to normal growth and development. Steroids include cholesterol, sex hormones, and metabolism regulators, as shown in **Figure 3.12**.

Cholesterol is an integral part of cell membranes that allows for

> **cholesterol** A class of steroids found in animals; aids in membrane fluidity.

Phospholipids • Figure 3.11

A phospholipid molecule has a polar head and a nonpolar tail.

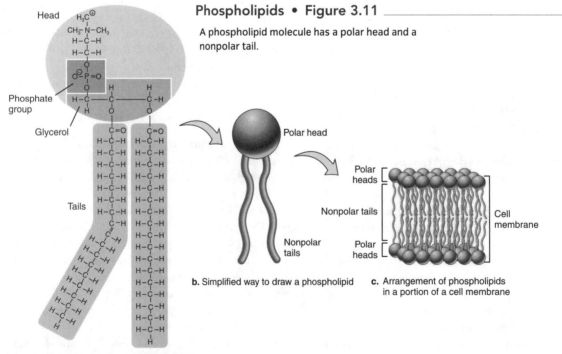

a. Chemical structure of a phospholipid

b. Simplified way to draw a phospholipid

c. Arrangement of phospholipids in a portion of a cell membrane

56 CHAPTER 3 Everyday Chemistry of Life

Steroids • Figure 3.12

The body synthesizes cholesterol into other steroids, which play essential regulatory roles as hormones. Regulatory hormones, such as cortisone, maintain salt and calcium balance in the fluids of the body.

Hydrocarbon tail

H₃C   CH₃

CH₃

CH₃

CH₃

HO

4 rings

Hydroxyl group

a. Cholesterol

OH

CH₃

HO

b. Estradiol (an estrogen or female sex hormone)

OH

CH₃

CH₃

O

c. Testosterone (a male sex hormone)

CH₂OH

C=O

CH₃   OH

HO

CH₃

O

d. Cortisol

flexibility and growth. High blood cholesterol has been linked to heart disease, so dietary restriction of cholesterol is often suggested. However, because your body synthesizes cholesterol, it is often difficult or even impossible to manage cholesterol levels solely by diet.

The sex hormones **estrogen** and **testosterone** are two steroids that are responsible for the enormous changes of puberty. Anabolic steroids, which are related to testosterone, stimulate growth of the muscles. Anabolic steroids have important medical value as replacement hormones for males and females with low levels of testosterone or human growth hormone. Although many athletes have taken anabolic steroids to increase muscle mass and improve performance, these substances are banned in most sports.

The health concerns of environmental estrogens are discussed in *Ethics and Issues: Environmental Estrogens: Are We Feminizing the Planet?* on page 58.

Proteins Are Both Structural and Functional

Proteins contain carbon, hydrogen, oxygen, and nitrogen and are the most abundant organic compounds in your body. You contain more than 2 million different proteins. Some provide structural support, and others function in physiological processes. Proteins provide a framework for organizing cells and a mechanism for moving muscles. They are responsible for transporting substances in the blood, strengthening tissues, regulating metabolism and nervous communications, and even fighting disease.

Millions of different proteins are all formed from just 20 amino acids. An amino acid is composed of a central carbon atom with four groups attached to it: (1) a hydrogen atom, (2) an amino group ($—NH_2$), (3) a carboxyl group ($—COOH$), and (4) a radical group or side chain (R). The R group determines the activity of the amino acid, as shown in **Figure 3.13**.

Amino acid structure • Figure 3.13

Amino acids are the building blocks of proteins. Twenty amino acids combine to form millions of proteins. Note that the only difference between these amino acids is the composition of the "R" side chain. Each amino acid has a different side chain, and each side chain has different reactive properties.

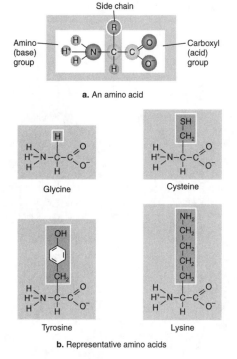

Side chain

R

Amino (base) group

H⁺   N—C—C   O   O⁻

Carboxyl (acid) group

a. An amino acid

H

H⁺—N—C—C   O   O⁻

Glycine

SH

CH₂

H⁺—N—C—C   O   O⁻

Cysteine

OH

CH₂

H⁺—N—C—C   O   O⁻

Tyrosine

NH₂

CH₂

CH₂

CH₂

CH₂

H⁺—N—C—C   O   O⁻

Lysine

b. Representative amino acids

ETHICS AND ISSUES

Environmental Estrogens: Are We Feminizing the Planet?

Estrogens are female sex hormones, present in both males and females. Together with male steroid hormones, they help control the development of numerous body systems and are responsible for sexual maturation and reproduction. However, if they are present in overly high concentrations in either females or males, estrogens have been shown to cause birth defects in offspring, abnormal sexual development, immune and organ system problems, and some forms of cancer.

Because most people's bodies produce estrogens in the proper amount, the question arises: Where is the estrogen overload in some people coming from? The answer is that environmental estrogens are all around us. Some are naturally occurring, while others are present in commonly used chemicals or byproducts of industrial processes.

Phytoestrogens, which are naturally occurring, are found in fruits, vegetables, grains, legumes, and seeds. Estrogens are also associated with heavy metals, such as lead, mercury, and cadmium. There are estrogens in products as diverse as pesticides and fungicides, plastics, ordinary household cleaners and solvents, and pharmaceuticals.

These products may add enough estrogens to the environment to cause birth defects and reproductive failures in many animal species. For example, the Florida panther population suffers from sterility, thought to be caused by high levels of environmental estrogen in their prey.

Human beings, along with other animals, have been exposed to phytoestrogens for thousands of years, but only in the last 100 years or so have chemical estrogens been released into the environment through product development and manufacturing processes. It is tempting to say that because much environmental es-

trogen is either naturally occurring or the byproduct of products and processes that are important to human health and well-being, it is impossible to avoid and therefore not worth worrying about. From a critical perspective, however, the issue of environmental estrogen warrants closer examination.

Critical Reasoning Issues A critical reasoner develops the habit of doing a risk-benefit analysis on issues like this. The key to such an analysis is knowing as much as possible about both the risks and the benefits. What if limiting human exposure to environmental estrogen may cause more harm than would be caused by allowing such exposure to occur? Consider an example: A commonly used estrogen-carrying drug is cimetidine, which is used to treat acid reflux disease. Do the risks associated with exposure to residual estrogen override the benefits of using cimetidine for patients with acid reflux disease?

Think Critically

1. Plastics also contain estrogens. Should plastics therefore be banned or drastically limited? After all, when properly recycled into sturdy replacements for picnic tables, park benches, and footbridges on walking paths, plastics greatly reduce the need for pressure-treated lumber, which uses chemicals that may indeed be more dangerous than environmental estrogens.
2. Another way of looking at the problem is to consider whether a better solution might be for individuals to limit their own exposure to environmental estrogens through the choices they make about products they use. Would such a solution be effective, or should we seek broad-based public-policy solutions?

NATIONAL GEOGRAPHIC

Estrogen

Individual amino acids combine to form proteins, using **peptide bonds** that form between the amino group of one amino acid and the carboxyl group of the next. The resulting two-amino-acid compound is called a dipeptide.

peptide bond
Covalent bond between the carboxyl group of one amino acid and the amino group of the adjacent amino acid.

As more amino acids join the growing chain, it becomes a **polypeptide**. As a rule of thumb, when the amino acid count exceeds 100, the compound is called a protein. **Figure 3.14** shows the formation of proteins from amino acids.

The making of a protein • Figure 3.14

✓ THE PLANNER

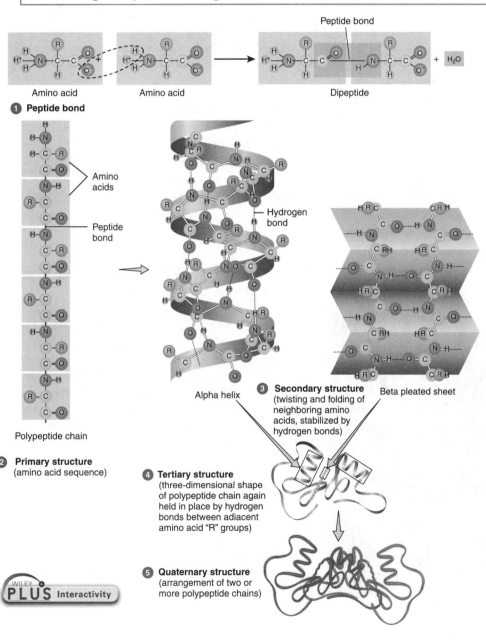

Peptide bond

Amino acid   Amino acid   Dipeptide   + H_2O

1 Peptide bond

Amino acids

Peptide bond

Polypeptide chain

2 Primary structure
(amino acid sequence)

Alpha helix

Hydrogen bond

3 Secondary structure
(twisting and folding of neighboring amino acids, stabilized by hydrogen bonds)

Beta pleated sheet

4 Tertiary structure
(three-dimensional shape of polypeptide chain again held in place by hydrogen bonds between adjacent amino acid "R" groups)

5 Quaternary structure
(arrangement of two or more polypeptide chains)

WILEY PLUS Interactivity

Insulin, the hormone that stimulates the cellular uptake of glucose, was the first polypeptide whose sequence of amino acids was determined. Frederick Sanger and his coworkers determined the sequence in 1955, and Sanger earned the first of two Nobel Prizes for chemistry in 1958. (His second Nobel was awarded in 1980 for his work in determining the nucleotide sequence of a virus that attacks bacteria.) Insulin is a short polypeptide, with only 51 amino acids. Titin, the largest protein isolated so far from humans, is found in muscles and contains over 38,000 amino acids.

59

The folding and interacting of adjacent amino acids determine the shape of a protein. The folding brings different amino acids together. If they repel one another, the protein bends outward. If they attract via weak hydrogen bonds, they bend inward, as shown in Figure 3.14.

Proteins have four levels of structural complexity. Their **primary structure** is the unique order of amino acids in the chain. Nearby amino acids interact via hydrogen bonds to form either alpha helixes or beta, pleated sheets, which is the **secondary structure**. The **tertiary structure** emerges from interactions between adjacent amino acids of the helical or pleated sheets, creating a complex coiling and folding. Tertiary structure is a result of the hydrophobic and hydrophilic portions of the molecule twisting to either associate with water or to "hide" from it inside the molecule. The **quaternary structure** emerges from the looping of two or more strands around one another. Some proteins have only one strand, but many, including hemoglobin, are composed of two or more polypeptide chains.

The final shape of a protein is either **globular** or **fibrous**. Globular proteins are round and usually water-soluble. These are often functional proteins, such as enzymes and contractile proteins. Fibrous proteins are stringy, tough, and usually insoluble. They provide the framework for supporting cells and tissues.

The shape of a protein molecule determines its function, and the final shape is determined by its primary structure. Changing even one amino acid can alter the folding pattern, with devastating effects on the protein's function, as shown in **Figure 3.15**.

In sickle cell anemia, a change of one amino acid from the normal hemoglobin protein creates a protein that fails to deliver oxygen correctly. When normal hemoglobin releases its oxygen to a tissue, the protein remains globular. A "sickled" hemoglobin molecule becomes sharp, deforming the entire red blood cell into the sickle shape. These cells can get lodged in small blood vessels, causing pain and interfering with oxygen flow to the tissues.

Proteins and their bonds are susceptible to minor changes in the environment, such as increased temperature or decreased pH. When a protein unfolds, or radically alters its folding pattern in response to environmental changes, we say it is **denatured**. This happens when we cook. As we heat eggs, proteins in the clear whites unfold, forming a cloudy mass. This reaction is not reversible; denaturing is often permanent.

Enzymes are a special class of functional proteins. Enzymes serve as **catalysts** for biochemical reactions—meaning that they facilitate a specific reaction without being altered during it. Catalysts bring the reactants, or substrates, together, so a reaction can occur much more quickly. Enzymes rely on shape to function properly. The **active site** of the protein is shaped to bind to one specific substrate. After the substrate binds, the enzyme provides an environment for the specific chemical reaction to occur. See **Figure 3.16**. Most enzymes are proteins, although some reactions are catalyzed by RNA, a form of nucleic acid.

Most Nucleic Acids Are Information Molecules

The fourth and final class of organic compounds is the **nucleic acid**. These are large molecules composed of carbon, hydrogen, oxygen, nitrogen, and phosphorus. Nucleic acids store and process an organism's hereditary information.

Microscan of normal and sickled red blood cells (sickle cell anemia) • Figure 3.15

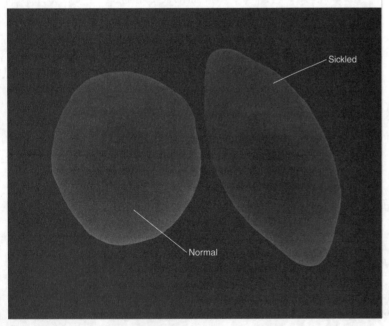

Sickled

Normal

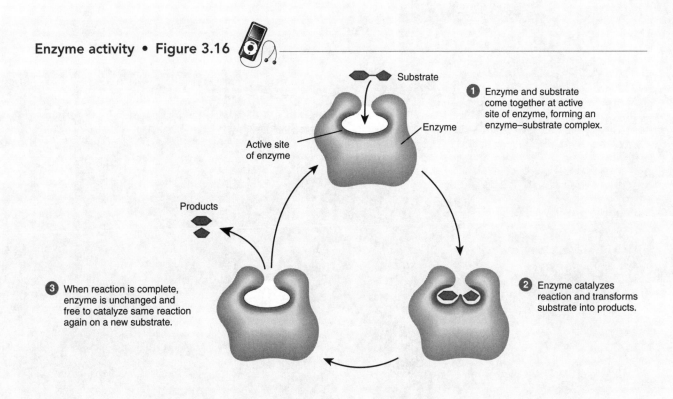

Substrate

1 Enzyme and substrate come together at active site of enzyme, forming an enzyme–substrate complex.

Enzyme

Active site of enzyme

Products

3 When reaction is complete, enzyme is unchanged and free to catalyze same reaction again on a new substrate.

2 Enzyme catalyzes reaction and transforms substrate into products.

The two types of nucleic acid are **deoxyribonucleic acid (DNA)** and **ribonucleic acid (RNA)**.

DNA exists in the nucleus of our cells. It contains the hereditary (genetic) information of the cell. DNA encodes the information needed to build proteins, to regulate physiological processes, and to maintain homeostasis. The genes that make each individual and each organism unique are carried as codes in the DNA; see **Figure 3.17** on the next page.

The sugar in DNA is a deoxyribose, meaning it lacks an oxygen, whereas RNA contains a simple ribose sugar. DNA has four bases: adenine (A), thymine (T), cytosine (C), and guanine (G). RNA also has these four bases, with one change: in RNA, uracil (U) appears instead of thymine. DNA is a double-stranded molecule. To fit the two DNA strands of one macromolecule together neatly and precisely, the strands lie antiparallel to one another—meaning that although they lie parallel, they run in opposite directions. The phosphate end of one strand opposes the hydroxyl end of the other. James Watson and Francis Crick, who discovered DNA's structure, could not make their model mathematically fit without the antiparallel configuration. The antiparallel

arrangement of DNA strands is paramount to the entire molecule—one strand must be upside down in relation to the other.

During DNA replication, this antiparallel configuration provides a logical explanation for why one strand is replicated with ease, whereas the other one is copied in "fits and starts." The enzyme responsible for duplicating the DNA can read in only one direction. It replicates DNA just as you read easily from left to right. The enzyme cannot read in the opposite direction, slowing the replication process. Imagine how much more slowly you would read these words if they made sense only from right to left.

The two chains of DNA nucleotides wrap around one another in a doubled **alpha helix**, held together by hydrogen bonds between bases. In naturally occurring DNA, the ratio of adenine to thymine is usually 1:1 and the ratio of cytosine to guanine is again approximately 1:1. These ratios indicate that A bonds to T and C to G. Every time you find an adenine base on one strand of DNA, you will most likely see it base-paired to a thymine on the complementary strand.

> **alpha helix** Spiral chain of monomers, resembling an old-fashioned telephone cord.

A nucleotide consists of a base, a pentose sugar, and a phosphate group.
The paired bases of DNA project toward the center of the double helix. The structure is
stabilized by hydrogen bonds (dotted lines) between each base pair. There are two
hydrogen bonds between adenine and thymine and three between cytosine and guanine.

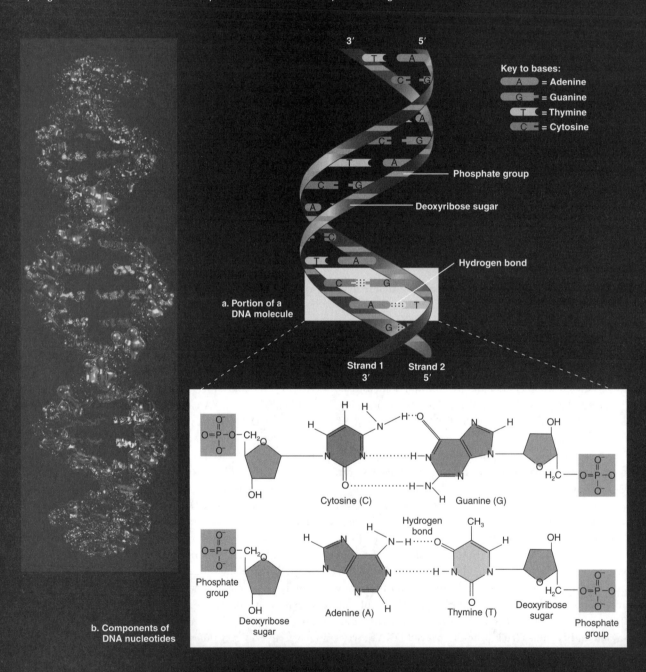

Key to bases:
A = Adenine
G = Guanine
T = Thymine
C = Cytosine

Phosphate group

Deoxyribose sugar

Hydrogen bond

a. Portion of a
DNA molecule

Strand 1
3′

Strand 2
5′

Cytosine (C)   Guanine (G)

Hydrogen
bond

Phosphate
group

Deoxyribose
sugar

Adenine (A)   Thymine (T)   Deoxyribose
sugar

Phosphate
group

b. Components of
DNA nucleotides

Adenosine triphosphate (ATP) and adenosine diphosphate (ADP) • Figure 3.18

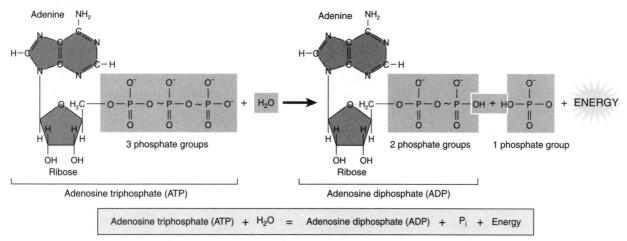

$$\text{Adenosine triphosphate (ATP)} + H_2O = \text{Adenosine diphosphate (ADP)} + P_i + \text{Energy}$$

RNA is not a storage unit, and it may occur inside or outside the nucleus. RNA serves to regulate cellular metabolism, produce proteins, and govern developmental timing. RNA is usually a single-stranded molecule. However, nucleic acids are more stable when paired. To achieve stability, RNA strands will fold back on themselves, pairing up A:U and C:G, similar to DNA. The shape of the RNA molecule often dictates its function.

High-Energy Compounds Power Cellular Activity

Life requires energy. Most often energy is available in spurts, rather than as a continuous stream all day long. We eat food, which our bodies convert to usable energy. Soon after a meal, lots of this energy circulates in the blood, but without a way to store the excess, we would have to eat almost continuously. Our energy storage system provides short- and long-term storage. Short-term energy storage uses a high-energy system that is reversible and instantly available. The most common storage is **ATP**, or **adenosine triphosphate**. ATP powers all cellular activity, from forming proteins to contracting muscles (see **Figure 3.18**). Long-term storage includes glycogen in muscles and liver, and triglycerides packed into specialized storage cells called **adipocytes**.

> **adenosine triphosphate (ATP)** The primary energy molecule that can be used to perform cellular functions.
>
> **adipocytes** Specialized cells (fat cells) that store large quantities of lipid.

ATP is composed of an adenine bonded to a ribose sugar with three phosphates attached. These phosphate bonds carry a lot of energy in their covalent bonds. When ATP is hydrolyzed, the third phosphate bond breaks, releasing inorganic phosphate (P_i) and the energy that held the ATP molecule together, forming **adenosine diphosphate (ADP)**. This released energy drives cellular activity. The ATP–ADP energy storage system is readily available and renewable. When glucose is broken down, the released energy can be used to recombine the inorganic phosphate to the ADP, generating a new ATP molecule.

> **adenosine diphosphate (ADP)** The molecule that results when ATP releases one phosphate group.

Without chemistry, there is no life, but how does life emerge from the many molecules we have examined? In the next chapters, we will look further up the hierarchy—to cells, tissues, and organs—to see the basic organization of an organism.

CONCEPT CHECK

1. **What** are the four main categories of organic compounds?
2. **What** are the main roles of carbohydrates, lipids, proteins, and nucleic acids in the body?
3. **How** does ATP store energy?

4.1 The Cell Is Highly Organized and Dynamic

LEARNING OBJECTIVES

1. **Outline** the cell theory.
2. **Describe** the difference between organelles and cytoplasm.
3. **Differentiate** between prokaryotic and eukaryotic cells and between plant and animal cells.

ells are the building blocks of life. Every living thing is composed of cells, from the smallest bacterium to the blue whale or the coast redwood. These giants have vastly more cells than single-celled bacteria, and more organization, both inside their cells and out, than do those bacterial cells. All animals' structure, regardless of their anatomy, ultimately comes down to cells. This is because all animals are multicellular.

You can think of cells as packages. Because life requires certain chemical conditions, organisms must concentrate some chemicals and exclude others. Those tiny compartments with the right conditions for the many chemical reactions that sustain life are called cells (see **Figure 4.1**).

The study of cells is called **cytology**, and scientists who study cells are called **cytologists**. All cells, regardless of source, have similar characteristics, as defined by the **cell theory**. This represents the latest version of our centuries-old understanding about cells:

1. All living things are composed of cells.
2. All cells arise from preexisting cells through cell division.
3. Cells contain hereditary material, which they pass to daughter cells during cell division.
4. The chemical composition of all cells is quite similar.
5. The metabolic processes associated with life occur within cells.

Idealized animal cell • Figure 4.1

This diagram is useful in studying all the organelles. However, no one cell in the human body contains all the organelles depicted here.

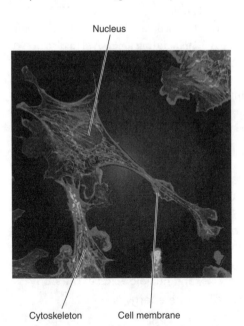

Nucleus

Cytoskeleton   Cell membrane

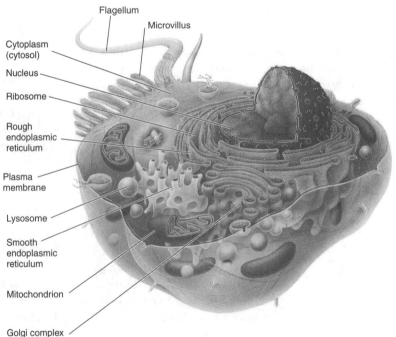

Flagellum

Microvillus

Cytoplasm (cytosol)

Nucleus

Ribosome

Rough endoplasmic reticulum

Plasma membrane

Lysosome

Smooth endoplasmic reticulum

Mitochondrion

Golgi complex

Sectional view

Although all cells share these characteristics, they can be remarkably different in shape and size. A cell can be as large as an ostrich egg or smaller than a dust speck (a typical liter of blood, for example, contains more than 4.9×10^{12} red blood cells). Because most cells are microscopic, you need trillions to make up a typical mammal: The human body contains trillions of cells representing a few hundred different kinds, and virtually all but one type is invisible without a microscope. Our egg, the only human cell visible to the naked eye, is approximately as big as this period.

The Cell Is a Highly Organized Structure

Cells have three basic parts, as shown in Figure 4.1.

1. It is defined by a barrier called the **plasma membrane** (in animals) or cell wall (and plasma membrane in plants and bacteria).

2. Inside the plasma membrane is a fluid called **cytosol**, which supports multiple types of **organelles**, each with a function vital to the life of the cell.

3. The most prominent organelle is usually the nucleus. The cytosol and the organelles other than the nucleus are often referred to as **cytoplasm**.

The cytosol contains water, dissolved compounds, and small molecules called **inclusions**. These molecules vary with the type of cell, and may include **keratin** for waterproofing, **melanin** for absorbing ultraviolet light, and **carotenes**, which are precursors to vitamin A. See *I Wonder… What Makes a Stem Cell Different from a "Regular Cell"?* for further discussions of cells.

organelle Typically, a membrane-bound structure suspended in the cytosol; hair-like projections from the cell may also be called organelles.

keratin Tough, fibrous proteins that form hard structures, such as hair and nails.

melanin A dark brown, UV-light-absorbing pigment produced by specific cells.

carotene A yellow-orange pigment.

I WONDER...

THE PLANNER

What Makes a Stem Cell Different from a "Regular Cell"?

The term "stem cell" refers to a cell that has not yet matured and specialized. Stem cells, therefore, have the capacity to mature into any of a variety of cell types. The cells that make up your skin, muscles, heart, and intestine, for example, have specialized to perform the functions required of them. During early embryological development, however, you did not have skin cells or intestinal cells. Instead you were a mass of undifferentiated, or "pluripotent," cells, each with the capacity to develop into one of the over 200 specific types of cell that make up your body. As development proceeds, the microenvironment surrounding each of these cells becomes slightly different. Even the placement of the cell can stimulate developmental changes. One cell will be completely surrounded by other cells, while another will be on the periphery of the developing mass. This subtle difference, along with chemical cues inside the cell, begins the process of differentiation. As the tissues of the body form, the cells that make up that tissue become fully committed to that developmental pathway.

Because stem cells have not yet committed to a particular tissue type, they can be coerced into forming just about any tissue of the body. Putting stem cells into a portion of the brain, and exposing them to the microenvironment of the brain, may cause them to become new brain cells. Interestingly, it is nearly impossible to cause a mature cell to reverse this process. Thus far, scientists have not been successful in creating a group of stem cells from mature precursors by altering the cell's microenvironment.

The high degree of organization and the dynamic character of the cell are evident. Inside the cell, membrane-bound compartments can be seen. These compartments are the organelles, small structures whose overall goal is to maintain cellular homeostasis. Some organelles are microscopic power plants that break down nutrients and combine them with oxygen to make electrical energy, and others are tiny chemical factories that churn out proteins. Still other organelles extend through the plasma membrane to the surface of the cell and circulate the surrounding fluid so that waste materials and nutrients can diffuse into or out of the cell.

Not only is the dynamic character and pervasive organization of cells a model of molecular engineering, but also the countless processes in the cell take place at a rate that is hard for us to comprehend. Millions of reactions happen every second. Water movement and storage is one such reaction, as described in *What a Scientist Sees: "This Baby Needs Water!"*

Millions of Years Ago, Cells Adapted to Their Environments

The first cells were less organized and less dynamic than the cells described above, lacking a nucleus and distinct organelles. They are called **prokaryotic** cells, and do not compartmentalize cell functions. Early life-forms were prokaryotic, adapting to the extreme environments of the early Earth. Today, they survive as bacteria and archaebacteria.

Plant, animal, and fungal cells are described as **eukaryotic** cells, which almost certainly adapted by taking in smaller, energy-producing prokaryotic cells. Eukaryotic cells have a nucleus and organelles. However, not all eukaryotic cells are the same—plant cells differ slightly from human cells. Because plants lack

prokaryotic Type of cell with no internal membrane-bound compartments, usually having only genetic material as organelles.

eukaryotic Cell that contains a distinct membrane-bound nucleus.

WHAT A SCIENTIST SEES

"This Baby Needs Water!"

Any medical professional can easily determine this from looking at the skull of this baby. The sunken appearance of the "soft spot" in the front of the baby's skull is a dead giveaway for a trained scientist. Normally the soft area of a baby's skull is plumped outward by an abundance of cerebrospinal fluid circulating around the brain and spinal cord. Cerebrospinal fluid is formed by filtering the liquid portion of the blood. With less water taken into the body, there will be less water available to hydrate the blood and the cells of the body. The cytoplasm of the cells will equilibrate with the water in the blood, causing the body cells to lose water. With less water in the blood, there will be less fluid available for the formation of cerebrospinal fluid. Because infants have a larger surface area to volume ratio than adults, a lack of water intake is far more critical to their health.

Using what you know of osmosis, describe the effects on the cells of the body when not enough water is present in the diet. In which direction would you expect water to move—into or out of the cells? What would you expect to occur, at the cellular level as water is added to this baby's system?

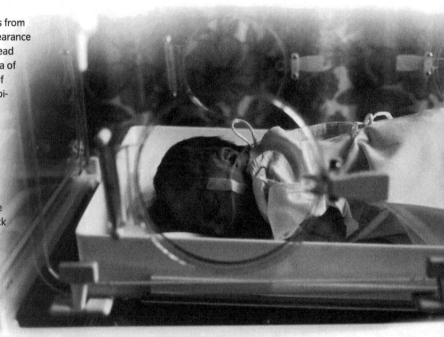

the skeletal support found in most animals, their support arises from cell walls that surround their cells. Plant cells have an organelle not found in animal cells, a central vacuole that maintains cell pressure. Many plant cells have chloroplasts—organelles where photosynthesis and energy production occurs—and many believe that chloroplasts originated as bacteria that were "adopted" by the plant cell.

4.2 The Cell Membrane Isolates the Cell

LEARNING OBJECTIVES

1. **Discuss** the structure of the cell membrane.
2. **Explain** movement across the membrane, both passive and active.
3. **Define** osmosis, and relate it to the actions of hypotonic and hypertonic solutions.
4. **Compare** the subtle differences in the main categories of active transport.

phospholipids
Compounds containing phosphoric acid and a fatty acid.

glycoprotein
Protein plus a carbohydrate.

glycolipid Lipid plus at least one carbohydrate group.

The obvious place to start studying cellular anatomy is the plasma membrane, the structure that separates the cell from the extracellular fluid. This membrane is composed of two layers of **phospholipids**, interspersed with proteins, fats, and sugars, as shown in **Figure 4.2**. The phospholipids are arranged in a double layer, or bilayer, with the **hydrophilic**, water-loving heads (the charged, phosphate ends of the molecule) oriented toward the aqueous environment both inside and outside the cell. The **hydrophobic**, water-fearing, nonpolar, lipid portions of the molecules are sandwiched in the center. Some of the proteins and lipids associated with the cell membrane have sugars attached to their external surface and are called **glycoproteins** and **glycolipids**.

Cell membrane • Figure 4.2

The cell membrane is composed of a phospholipid bilayer supporting embedded proteins. Sugar attached to lipids (glycolipids) or attached to proteins (glycoproteins) coat the surface of the cell.

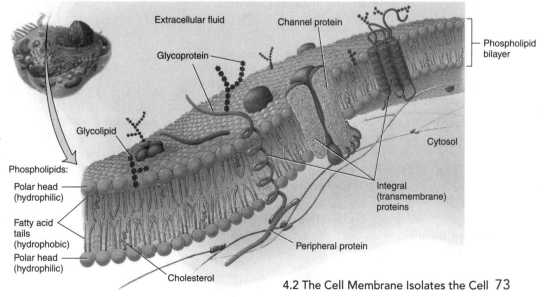

The glycoproteins and glycolipids form a layer called the **glycocalyx**, which is unique and defines the cell as belonging to a specific organism. Both blood type and tissue type are defined by the specific structures on the glycocalyx. For example, each person's white blood cells carry a group of identifying proteins called the human leukocyte antigens (HLAs) that serve as markers indicating that our cells belong to us. HLA is used to match tissues before organ transplants. Because HLA is inherited, if we need a transplant, we can often find a close tissue match within our immediate family.

The cell membrane is not a static structure. At 37°C, its phospholipids are liquid, not solid, so the basic structure of the membrane is a continually swirling fluid with a consistency similar to olive oil or light machine oil. Cholesterol, a necessary component of the cell membrane, helps to maintain this viscosity by interfering with the movement of the fatty acid tails of the phospholipid. The proteins embedded in the membrane are in constant motion, floating around in the fluid phospholipid bilayer. Picture a beach ball covered in Vaseline and rolled in the sand. As the Vaseline "membrane" warms in the sun, it will begin to flow around the ball (representing the cytosol of the cell), causing the embedded sand grains to swirl with it. Similarly, the glycocalyx and embedded proteins in the fluid phospholipid bilayer swirl around the cell membrane.

Movement Across the Membrane Can Be Passive or Active

The phospholipid bilayer defines the cell and protects it from the aqueous environment. Without membrane lipids, the cell would literally disintegrate, much like a cracker dropped into a glass of juice. However, the plasma membrane cannot maintain cellular homeostasis unless it allows some compounds into and out of the cell. In fact, rather than being a simple plastic bag, the membrane is a selectively **semipermeable** barrier that allows nutrients to enter the cell and waste and secretory products to exit it. Some ions and molecules cross freely; others can be moved across the membrane with the expenditure of energy; and still others cannot cross at all. Movement across the membrane can be either passive or active.

Passive movement includes **filtration**, **diffusion**, and **facilitated diffusion**. None of these activities requires

the cell to expend energy. Filtration is the movement of solutes in response to fluid pressure. Your kidneys separate waste products from the blood via filtration.

Diffusion Moves Molecules from High Concentrations to Low Concentrations

Diffusion is the movement of a substance toward an area of lower concentration. Open a perfume bottle and set it in the corner of a room. Within a short time, the perfume will diffuse from the bottle and permeate the room. Warm the room or the perfume in the bottle, and the diffusion speeds up. Diffusion results from the random movement of the molecules, which eventually tends to balance out the molecule's concentrations, as shown in **Figure 4.3**. The same phenomenon occurs

Diffusion • Figure 4.3

At equilibrium, net diffusion stops, but the random movement of particles continues.

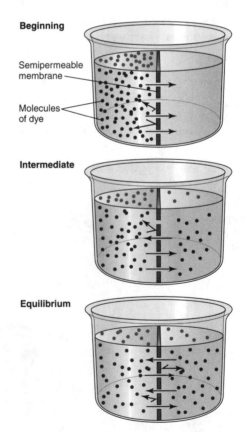

Beginning

Semipermeable membrane

Molecules of dye

Intermediate

Equilibrium

Isotonic
solution

Normal RBC
shape

Hypotonic
solution

RBC undergoes
hemolysis

Hypertonic
solution

SEM

RBC undergoes
crenation

Hypotonic and hypertonic solutions • Figure 4.4

Osmosis can occur quite rapidly when cells are placed in hypotonic or hypertonic solutions. Hemolysis is an almost instantaneous process when a red blood cell (RBC) is placed in a hypotonic solution. Crenation (the shriveling of red blood cells) in hypertonic solutions takes less than two minutes.

continuously in your cells. Lipid-soluble compounds and gases can diffuse across the cell membrane as if it weren't there, traveling right through the phospholipid bilayer. The driving force for the movement of oxygen from the atmosphere into the deepest tissues of the body is simple diffusion.

While lipid-soluble molecules can diffuse freely through it, the phospholipid bilayer blocks the diffusion of **aqueous**, or water-soluble, solutes. This is a potential problem, as many aqueous solutes, such as glucose, are essential compounds that must be able to penetrate the cell membrane. To solve this problem, the lipid bilayer has **integral** and **peripheral proteins** that serve as channels and receptors for dissolved substances to enter and exit the cell.

integral protein A protein that spans the plasma membrane.

peripheral protein A protein that sits on the inside or the outside of the cell membrane.

solute Salts, ions, and compounds dissolved in a solvent, forming a solution; water is the most common solvent in the human body.

The most abundant compound in the body is water. To maintain homeostasis, cells must allow water to move between the intracellular fluid (ICF) and the extracellular fluid (ECF). Diffusion of water across a semipermeable membrane, such as the cell membrane, is termed **osmosis**. In osmosis, water moves in a direction that tends to equalize **solute** concentration on each side of the membrane. In effect, locations with higher solute concentrations and therefore lower water concentrations seem to "pull" water toward them.

Water cannot cross the phospholipid bilayer, so it must travel through proteins.
Usually, the extracellular fluid is **isotonic** to the cells, and water flows equally into and out of the cell through transport proteins. If you place a cell in a **hypotonic** solution (water with a lower concentration of solutes than the cytosol), the cell will take in water and may even burst. In contrast, a

isotonic A solution with the same concentration as the cell cytoplasm.

hypertonic solution (with a higher concentration of solutes), will remove water from the cell and cause it to shrivel up (see **Figure 4.4**). When working with individual cells, it is useful to calculate the concentration of an isotonic solution. Doing so allows you to predict water movement into and out of cells when they are placed in solutions of varying concentrations. It is worth noting that during osmosis, as water diffuses across a membrane toward areas of lower water concentration and higher solute concentration, it creates osmotic pressure. This pressure can be measured and is called **water potential**, the pressure of resting cells in an isotonic solution.

Facilitated diffusion uses transport proteins.
When solutes are transported across the membrane down their concentration gradients (from high concentration to low concentration) by **transport proteins**, no energy is expended, as is the case for simple diffusion. However, this type of movement requires a transport protein to facilitate the diffusion. This is the main avenue through which

HEALTH, WELLNESS, AND DISEASE  THE PLANNER
Malfunctioning Organelles Can Be Life Threatening

The human body is only as strong as the weakest link in its homeostatic chain. Although extremely small, organelles that do not function properly are that weak link. Two of the more problematic organelles are the mitochondrion and the lysosome.

Mitochondria carry their own DNA, coding for 37 of the approximately 900 genes required to produce ATP (Adenosine triphosphate, or cellular energy). Mutations in the mitochondrial DNA occur just as they do in human DNA. A mutated mitochondrion is capable of producing daughter mitochondria, each of which carries that same mutation. Symptoms of mitochondrial disorders are most often seen in skeletal and heart muscle, glands, and the brain. Patients experience muscle spasms, muscle weakness, and stroke-like episodes. Interestingly, these symptoms increase with age, as cell division continues. As the percentage of mutated mitochondria goes up in the

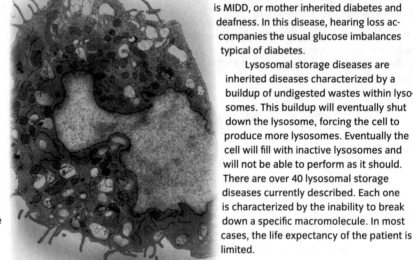

cells of a tissue, the ability of that tissue to function properly goes down. Charcot-Marie-Tooth disease is a mitochondrial disorder in which the nerves that reach the hands and feet are compromised. Another mitochondrial disease is MIDD, or mother inherited diabetes and deafness. In this disease, hearing loss accompanies the usual glucose imbalances typical of diabetes.

Lysosomal storage diseases are inherited diseases characterized by a buildup of undigested wastes within lysosomes. This buildup will eventually shut down the lysosome, forcing the cell to produce more lysosomes. Eventually the cell will fill with inactive lysosomes and will not be able to perform as it should. There are over 40 lysosomal storage diseases currently described. Each one is characterized by the inability to break down a specific macromolecule. In most cases, the life expectancy of the patient is limited.

---

glucose is moved into cells. After a meal, blood glucose is higher than cellular glucose. However, in order to diffuse into the cell, glucose needs a "doorway" through the phospholipid bilayer. It would make very little sense to expend

energy just to get glucose into the cell to make energy (see **Figure 4.5**). Once in the cell, these compounds move to organelles. See *Health, Wellness, and Disease: Malfunctioning Organelles Can Be Life Threatening* to learn more.

Facilitated diffusion • Figure 4.5

Some molecules, such as glucose, require transport proteins to provide an easier entry into the cell.

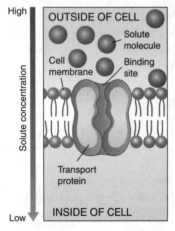
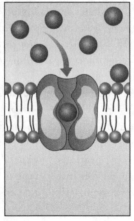
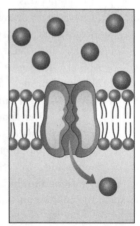

Active Transport Uses Energy to Move Molecules Across Membranes

When energy is consumed to move a molecule or ion against the concentration gradient, we call the process **active transport**, or solute pumping. Osmosis and other forms of diffusion move molecules "down" their concentration gradients without additional energy. Active transport moves molecules "up" their concentration gradients, the opposite of what you would expect from simple osmosis and diffusion. As a result, active transport is used to concentrate molecules inside cells at levels that exceed the extracellular concentration, using energy derived from the breakdown of ATP into ADP (adenosine diphosphate). Active transport accounts for the almost complete uptake of digested nutrients from the small intestine, the collecting of iodine in thyroid gland cells, and the return to the blood of the vast majority of sodium ions filtered from the blood by the kidneys.

Active transport can move atoms, ions, or molecules into the cell (**endocytosis**) or out of it (**exocytosis**) (see **Figure 4.6**). In endocytosis, extracellular molecules and particles are taken into the cell via vesicle formation. Just as punching a partially inflated balloon caves in the balloon wall, endocytosis begins with depression of the cell membrane. Particles in the extracellular fluid flow into the

Endocytosis and exocytosis • Figure 4.6

The pathway on the left indicates movement from the rough endoplasmic reticulum through the Golgi complex to the plasma membrane. This is exocytosis. The pathway to the right indicates the flow of endocytosed particles.

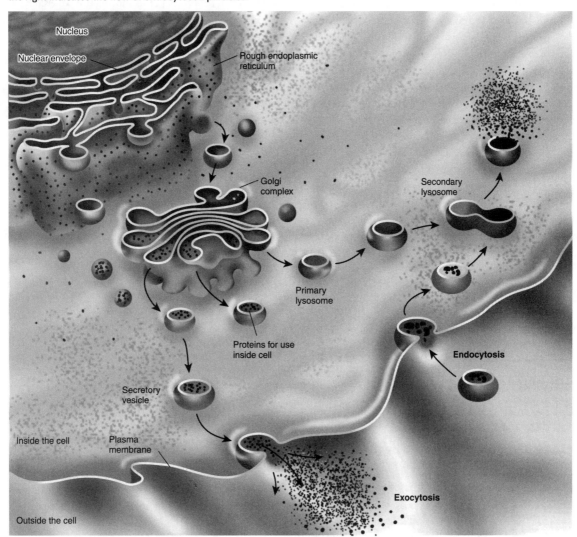

Nucleus

Nuclear envelope

Rough endoplasmic reticulum

Golgi complex

Secondary lysosome

Primary lysosome

Proteins for use inside cell

Endocytosis

Secretory vesicle

Inside the cell

Plasma membrane

Exocytosis

Outside the cell

77

Sodium/potassium pump • Figure 4.7

The sodium/potassium pump transfers two potassium ions into the cell for every three sodium ions it removes. The movement of ions happens simultaneously.

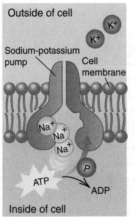
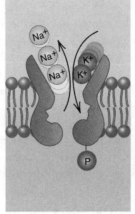
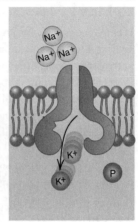

new dimple and get trapped within the vesicle that forms when the two sides touch and are pinched off inside the cell.

Exocytosis is used to remove secretory products or waste products from the cell. Vesicles form within the cell, usually from one of two organelles, the Golgi apparatus or a lysosome. Each of these vesicles travels to the inner wall of the cell membrane and fuses with it (think of two soap bubbles fusing into one larger bubble where they touch). This fusion releases the vesicle's contents into the extracellular fluid.

Often, small molecules or ions are moved by intramembrane pumps. Transport proteins may act as pumps, moving ions or small molecules in either direction across the plasma membrane. For example, calcium ions are typically transported via a pump. Pumps often have reciprocal functions—pumping one molecule or ion into the cell while simultaneously removing a second chemical species from the cell. For example,

sodium/potassium ATPase (adenosine triphosphatase) acts as a common reciprocal pump, moving two potassium ions into the cell while pumping three sodium ions out of it, as shown in **Figure 4.7**. We will discuss this pump again when we cover neurophysiology.

CONCEPT CHECK

1. **What** are the main structural components of a typical cell membrane?

2. **How** are passive and active movements across the cell membrane different?

3. **What** is osmosis, and **how** does it relate to hypertonic and hypotonic solutions?

4. **How** do the main types of active transport differ?

4.3 The Components of a Cell Are Called Organelles

LEARNING OBJECTIVES

1. **List** the main organelles of a typical animal cell and describe their function.

2. **Explain** the crucial role played by the cell nucleus.

3. **Describe** the four major steps of mitochondrial reactions.

Each of the organelles covered in this section probably evolved as the result of cellular adaptations to changing environments. Cells that lacked some or all of these organelles almost certainly had a harder time successfully competing with cells that had them, so each organelle played a role in the long-term success of the cell and, in turn, the multicellular organism.

Organelles Continue to Play a Role in Regulating the Life and Death of Our Cells

Cytologists used to view the cytosol as a water bath, but it is actually a highly organized chemical soup complete with a support structure called the **cytoskeleton**. The

> **cytoskeleton** The internal framework of a cell.

cytoskeleton lies directly underneath the plasma membrane, and is attached to it in many places. Composed mainly of three types of filaments, the cytoskeleton extends throughout the cytosol, providing shape, support, and a scaffold for suspending and moving organelles. Unlike your bony skeleton, the cytoskeleton is continuously changing shape, forming and breaking down. This gives cells a plasticity, or fluidity, that allows them to change shape or move organelles quickly.

The cytoskeleton has three types of protein structure: microfilaments, intermediate filaments, and microtubules. Microfilaments, the thinnest cytoskeletal structures, are responsible for cellular locomotion, muscle contractions, and movement during cell division. They also establish the basic shape and strength of the cell. Intermediate filaments are much stronger than microfilaments and protect the cell from mechanical stresses. Microtubules are long strings of the globular protein tubulin, coiled tightly into a tube. Microtubules are used as tracks for organelle movement, and are instrumental in chromosome movement during cell division. The different proteins of each cytoskeletal element are what give it a characteristic function. The microfilaments are composed mostly of actin, a protein that, under the proper conditions, will cause movement in a predictable fashion. We discuss this protein far more extensively when looking at skeletal muscle contraction. Intermediate filaments are composed of extremely tough, supportive proteins found nowhere else in the cell.

Flagella and Cilia Keep Things Moving

Many cells have projections from their surface that can move either the entire cell or move the extracellular fluid past the cell. **Flagella** are single, long, whip-like structures that propel the cell forward. The only human cell that moves by flagellum is the sperm.

Cilia are shorter extensions that look like hairs or eyelashes, and they are far more common in the human body than flagella (see **Figure 4.8**). They beat synchronously in what is referred to as a "power stroke" to move mucus across the surface of the cell or to circulate the extracellular fluid to increase diffusion. Cilia line the upper respiratory tract, moving mucus upward and sweeping out debris and pathogens.

Cilia movement • Figure 4.8

Cilia are formed from an inner core of microtubules, extending from the cytoskeleton.

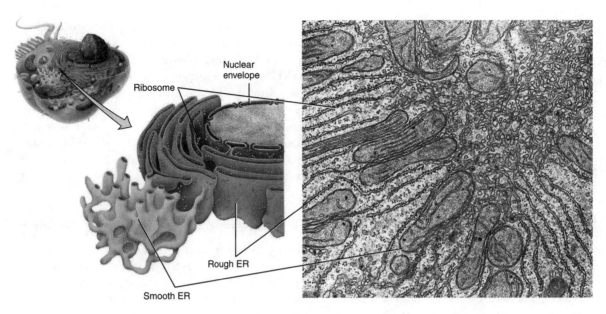

Smooth endoplasmic reticulum and rough endoplasmic reticulum • Figure 4.9 _____

The cell is packed with ER. The thin tubules without ribosomes studding their surface are the channels of the SER. The SER is concentrated in the lower left of the micrograph. As the view of the whole cell at the left shows, RER is found immediately outside the cell nucleus, while SER is a continuation of the RER tubules.

Endoplasmic Reticulum: Protein and Hormone Manufacturing Site

Within the cytosol of many cells lie networks of folded membranes, called the **endoplasmic reticulum** or **ER** (literally "within fluid network"). The membranes of the ER are directly connected to the double membrane surrounding the cell nucleus.

Human cells have two types of ER, rough and smooth. **Rough endoplasmic reticulum** (RER) is a processing and sorting area for proteins synthesized by the **ribosomes** that stud its outer membrane, as shown in **Figure 4.9**. Ribosomes are small non-membrane-bound organelles composed of protein and ribosomal RNA. They serve as protein factories, synthesizing proteins that may be included in other organelles or in the plasma membrane itself, or are exocytosed through secretory vesicles.

Smooth endoplasmic reticulum, or **SER**, is responsible for the synthesis of fatty acids and steroid hormones, such as testosterone. SER has no attached ribosomes. In the liver, enzymes that break down drugs and alcohol are stored in the SER.

In both RER and SER, the end product is a vesicle filled with product ready for the next step in processing.

These vesicles form from the ER and usually move substances from the ER to the cell membrane for exocytosis or to the Golgi complex for further packaging.

Golgi Complex: Complicated Chemical Factory

This organelle is one of the few to retain the name of its discoverer, Camillo Golgi, who discovered it in 1898. The **Golgi complex**, or Golgi apparatus, is usually found near the end of the SER and resembles a stack of pancakes called **saccules** (see **Figure 4.10**). These saccules are slightly curved, with concave and convex faces. The concave portions usually face the ER, and the convex portions face the plasma membrane. Vesicles are found at the edges of these saccules.

> **saccule** Small circular vesicle used to transport substances within a cell.

The precise role of the Golgi complex is debatable. Clearly, it is involved with processing of proteins and fatty acids, but exactly how does it do that? Some scientists believe that vesicles from the ER fuse with the lowest saccule of the Golgi complex, and then the saccules

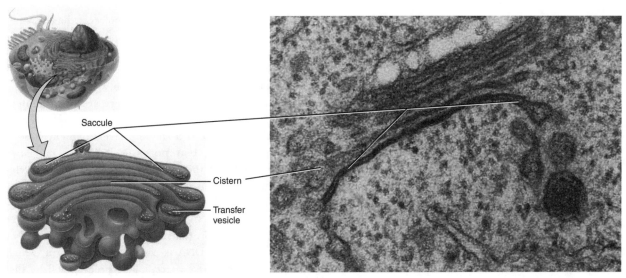

Golgi complex • Figure 4.10

The color-enhanced blue Golgi complex in this cell clearly shows the "stack of pancakes" appearance of this organelle.

Saccule

Cistern

Transfer vesicle

"move up" in ranking toward the upper saccule. From there, the Golgi complex membrane forms a second vesicle, which transports completed proteins to their destination. Other scientists believe that the original vesicles from the ER fuse with the top saccule of the Golgi complex right from the start. The enzymes within this top saccule complete the processing of the proteins or fatty acids in the vesicle, which are then transported to their functional areas.

In either case, the vesicles that leave the Golgi complex migrate all over the cell, following paths defined by the cytoskeleton. Some fuse with the cell membrane, others fuse with lysosomes, and still others become lysosomes. It seems that the Golgi complex completes the processing of proteins and fatty acids, readying the products for use in other organelles or in the cell membrane.

Lysosomes: Safe Chemical Packages

Lysosomes are chemical packages produced by the Golgi complex that contain **hydrolytic enzymes** powerful enough to digest an entire cell from the inside. The lysosome sequesters these digestive enzymes for use in decomposing macromolecules that have entered the cell via endocytosis, as shown in **Figure 4.11**. When a lysosome (*lyse* means "to break open or break

> **hydrolytic enzymes** Proteins that help decompose compounds by splitting bonds with water molecules.

Lysosome • Figure 4.11

The lysosome sequesters digestive enzymes for use in decomposing macromolecules that have entered the cell via endocytosis, or for autolysis (self-destruction).

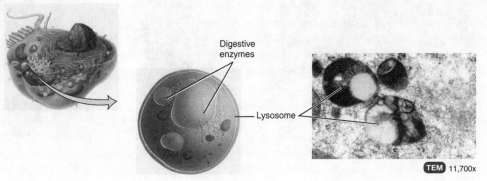

Digestive enzymes

Lysosome

TEM 11,700x

apart") fuses with an endocytotic vesicle, it pours its contents into the vesicle. The hydrolytic enzymes immediately begin breaking down the vesicle's contents. In this way, the lysosome provides a site for safe decomposition in the cell. Additionally, bacteria are routinely destroyed in the body by phagocytosis followed by lysosomal activity. If the lysosome breaks open, as happens during cell death, it will release these powerful enzymes into the cell, where they will begin to digest the cell itself. This process is called autolysis, literally self-breaking. Lysosomes can even digest parts of the body. The frog's tail is lost not by developmental changes in DNA processing but rather by lysosomes bursting and digesting cells in the tail.

The Cell's "Library" Is the Nucleus

The **nucleus** contains a cell's genetic library, and is usually the largest organelle in a cell (see **Figure 4.12**).

(Mature human red blood cells, however, have no nucleus.) This organelle is approximately 5 micrometers in diameter in most human cells. It is covered, like the cell itself, by a phospholipid membrane, called the **nuclear envelope**. The difference between this envelope and the cell membrane is that there are two complete phospholipid bilayers surrounding the nucleus, whereas the cell membrane is a single bilayer. The envelope is punctuated by **nuclear pores**, which allow molecules to enter and exit the nucleus. The DNA in the nucleus is analogous to the cell's library, which is "read" by molecules called RNA. After RNA makes a perfect impression of the DNA, it leaves the nucleus and serves as templates for proteins. The process of forming RNA copies of nuclear DNA is called **transcription**, which means to "write elsewhere." This process will be discussed in detail in Chapter 20.

The cell nucleus • Figure 4.12

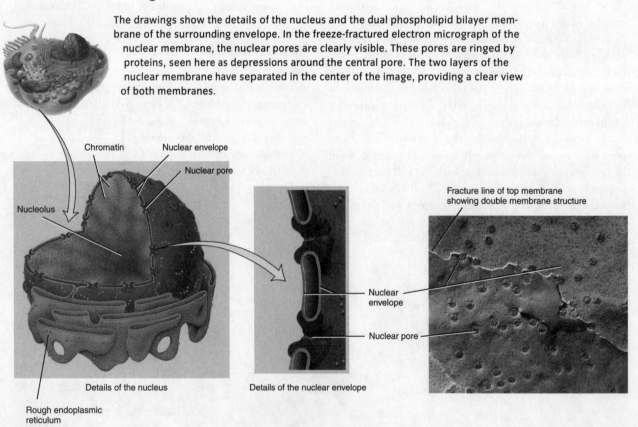

The drawings show the details of the nucleus and the dual phospholipid bilayer membrane of the surrounding envelope. In the freeze-fractured electron micrograph of the nuclear membrane, the nuclear pores are clearly visible. These pores are ringed by proteins, seen here as depressions around the central pore. The two layers of the nuclear membrane have separated in the center of the image, providing a clear view of both membranes.

Chromatin

Nuclear envelope

Nuclear pore

Nucleolus

Rough endoplasmic reticulum

Details of the nucleus

Details of the nuclear envelope

Nuclear envelope

Nuclear pore

Fracture line of top membrane showing double membrane structure

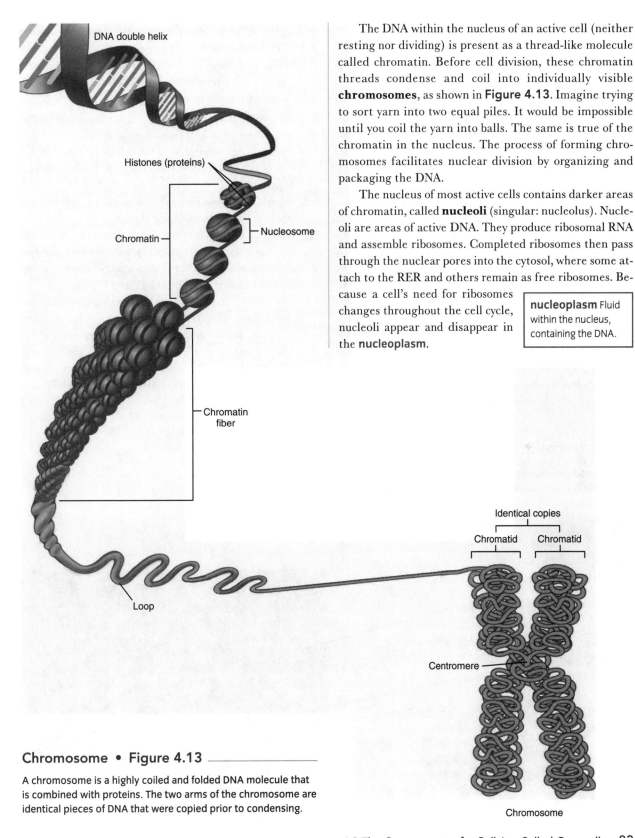

DNA double helix

Histones (proteins)

Chromatin

Nucleosome

Chromatin fiber

Loop

The DNA within the nucleus of an active cell (neither resting nor dividing) is present as a thread-like molecule called chromatin. Before cell division, these chromatin threads condense and coil into individually visible **chromosomes**, as shown in **Figure 4.13**. Imagine trying to sort yarn into two equal piles. It would be impossible until you coil the yarn into balls. The same is true of the chromatin in the nucleus. The process of forming chromosomes facilitates nuclear division by organizing and packaging the DNA.

The nucleus of most active cells contains darker areas of chromatin, called **nucleoli** (singular: nucleolus). Nucleoli are areas of active DNA. They produce ribosomal RNA and assemble ribosomes. Completed ribosomes then pass through the nuclear pores into the cytosol, where some attach to the RER and others remain as free ribosomes. Because a cell's need for ribosomes changes throughout the cell cycle, nucleoli appear and disappear in the **nucleoplasm**.

> **nucleoplasm** Fluid within the nucleus, containing the DNA.

Identical copies

Chromatid   Chromatid

Centromere

Chromosome

Chromosome • Figure 4.13

A chromosome is a highly coiled and folded DNA molecule that is combined with proteins. The two arms of the chromosome are identical pieces of DNA that were copied prior to condensing.

Mitochondria Are Energy Factories

The last of the major organelles is the **mitochondrion** (plural: *mitochondria*). This bean-shaped organelle has a smooth outer membrane and a folded inner membrane, with folds called **cristae**, as seen in **Figure 4.14**. The mitochondria convert digested nutrients into usable energy for the body, in the form of ATP. The energy in the nutrients can be released slowly, so ATP is produced in stages as needed by the cell and the body. Virtually every move you make, every step you take, can be traced to mitochondria.

Each cell has many mitochondria, all producing the ATP your cells need to survive. ATP forms within the inner membrane of the mitochondrion (**Figure 4.15**). Mitochondria require oxygen and produce carbon dioxide in their endless production of ATP, and so the processes in the mitochondria are often called **cellular respiration**. In the final analysis, we inhale oxygen to serve our mitochondria, and we exhale the carbon dioxide they produce while generating ATP. Human biologists have often described ATP as a kind of molecular battery pack that gets used up and recharged every few minutes, and the mitochondria are the recharging devices.

Mitochondria break down glucose to produce ATP in four steps.

The breakdown of glucose into ATP takes four steps, the first of which actually happens outside the mitochondrial walls. The other three steps take place within the mitochondria.

1. Glucose is brought into the cell via facilitated diffusion, where it is broken down in a series of chemical reactions called glycolysis. Glycolysis releases energy that is stored in two ATP molecules and two molecules of pyruvic acid.
2. Pyruvic acid then gets taken into the mitochondrion, where it is converted to acetyl co-A.
3. Acetyl co-A feeds into the Krebs cycle (also called the citric acid cycle or TCA cycle), another series of biochemical reactions that release energy from the acetyl co-A and stored in ATP, NADH, and $FADH_2$.
4. The NADH and $FADH_2$ formed during glycolysis and the Krebs cycle are transported to the inner membrane of the mitochondrion. There they are used to drive a final series of reactions called the electron transport chain. This final series converts the energy stored in the NADH and $FADH_2$ into usable ATP.

Mitochondrion • Figure 4.14

The cristae within the mitochondrion are a hallmark of this organelle. Here the inner membrane is colored blue to help distinguish the cristae.

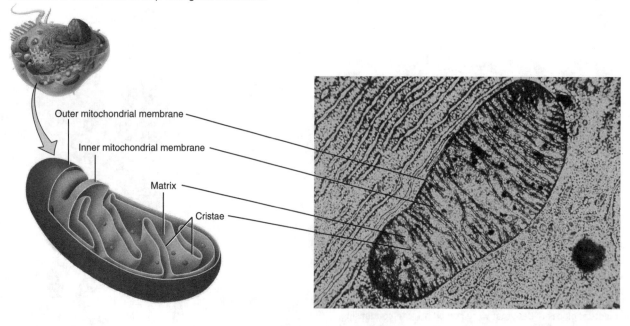

Outer mitochondrial membrane

Inner mitochondrial membrane

Matrix

Cristae

Mitochondrial reactions • Figure 4.15

THE PLANNER

1. Glucose is broken into two pyruvic acid molecules before entering the mitochondrion. This releases 2 ATP molecules and 2 NADH molecules.
2. Acetyl co-A is formed inside the matrix of the mitochondrion.
3. Energy is released from acetyl co-A during the Krebs cycle.
4. Much more energy is released as final breakdown of the initial glucose molecule occurs in the cristae membrane.

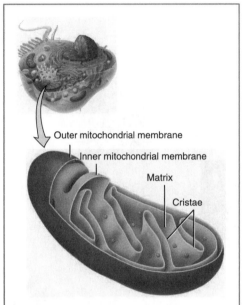

Outer mitochondrial membrane
Inner mitochondrial membrane
Matrix
Cristae

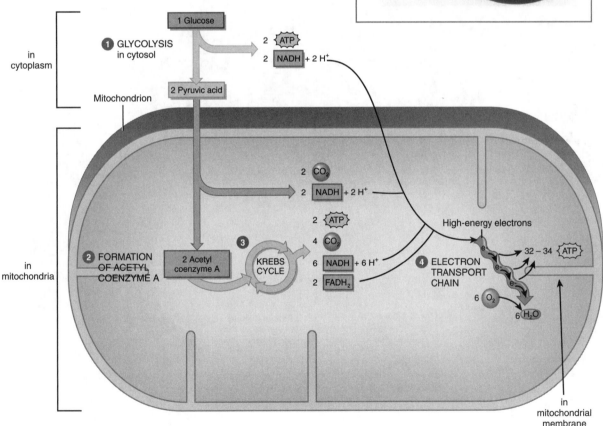

in cytoplasm

Mitochondrion

1 GLYCOLYSIS in cytosol

1 Glucose

2 ATP
2 NADH + 2 H$^+$

2 Pyruvic acid

in mitochondria

2 FORMATION OF ACETYL COENZYME A

2 Acetyl coenzyme A

3 KREBS CYCLE

2 CO$_2$
2 NADH + 2 H$^+$
2 ATP
4 CO$_2$
6 NADH + 6 H$^+$
2 FADH$_2$

High-energy electrons

4 ELECTRON TRANSPORT CHAIN

32 – 34 ATP

6 O$_2$
6 H$_2$O

in mitochondrial membrane

4.3 The Components of a Cell Are Called Organelles 85

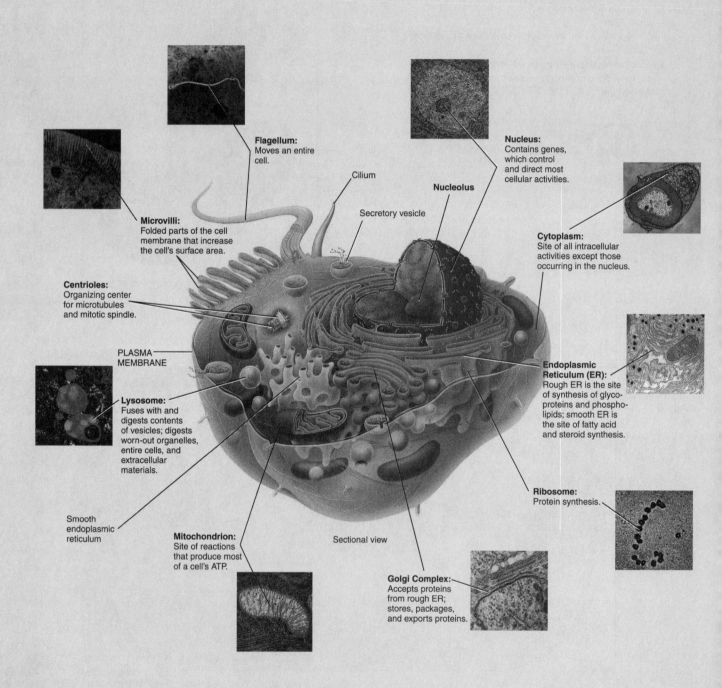

Flagellum:
Moves an entire cell.

Cilium

Nucleolus

Secretory vesicle

Nucleus:
Contains genes, which control and direct most cellular activities.

Microvilli:
Folded parts of the cell membrane that increase the cell's surface area.

Cytoplasm:
Site of all intracellular activities except those occurring in the nucleus.

Centrioles:
Organizing center for microtubules and mitotic spindle.

PLASMA MEMBRANE

Lysosome:
Fuses with and digests contents of vesicles; digests worn-out organelles, entire cells, and extracellular materials.

Endoplasmic Reticulum (ER):
Rough ER is the site of synthesis of glyco-proteins and phospho-lipids; smooth ER is the site of fatty acid and steroid synthesis.

Smooth endoplasmic reticulum

Ribosome:
Protein synthesis.

Mitochondrion:
Site of reactions that produce most of a cell's ATP.

Sectional view

Golgi Complex:
Accepts proteins from rough ER; stores, packages, and exports proteins.

Mitochondria can divide, replicating these energy-producing organelles when our cells need more ATP. Cells in active tissues, like skeletal muscle and liver, have more mitochondria than cells in less active tissue. This ability to reproduce has long intrigued cellular biologists. Mitochondria resemble bacteria in size and chemical composition, and carry their own DNA to create their proteins. Some scientists hypothesize that these organelles were once free-living bacteria that evolved from a **symbiotic** relationship into a type of ultimate, intimate symbiosis. Perhaps billions of years ago, a bacterial cell traded a free-living existence for a safe and constant environment in which to carry out its life processes. In this "you scratch my back and I'll scratch yours" arrangement, the sheltering cell receives a supply of ATP in return for protecting the mitochondria, delivering oxygen to it and disposing of its waste carbon dioxide. Interestingly, mitochondria

> **symbiotic** Intimate coexistence of two organisms in a mutually beneficial relationship.

are not constantly reshuffled through sexual reproduction and are inherited only through the egg. This means the mitochondria in your body are direct descendants of your mother's mitochondria. Because of the relatively stable DNA in mitochondria, they can help trace human migrations and evolution.

See **Figure 4.16** for a summary of animal cell parts and their functions.

CONCEPT CHECK

1. **What** are the main organelles of an animal cell and what are their functions?
2. **What** role does the nucleus play in the cell?
3. **What** are the four major steps of mitochondrial reactions?

4.4 Cell Communication Is Important to Cellular Success

LEARNING OBJECTIVES

1. **Explain** cellular signaling as it relates to the human body.

2. **Define** hormone.

To maintain stability and organization inside the human body, communication is essential. Cells must communicate with one another to function as a tissue. Tissues must send signals throughout the organ for the organ to function properly. Organs in a particular system must communicate to carry out the system's process. The importance of communication only makes sense. Think how little you could accomplish in your personal life without communication among individuals in your community. How would schooling prepare you for life if no one discussed what it means to be an educated citizen? What would become of government if there weren't any communication among constituents? On a more personal scale, how would your life fare without a cell phone or Internet connection? Just as society requires communication for survival, cells of the body require communication in order to maintain homeostasis.

Information Travels from Cell to Cell

The signals sent from cell to cell include information about the timing of cell divisions, the health of adjacent cells, and the status of the external environment. Cells communicate with one another via chemical messengers or physical contact, as seen in **Figure 4.17**. Cell signaling can be accomplished via three routes, which differ in the speed and distance of the signal transmission:

1. Circulating **hormones** can be released into the bloodstream, potentially reaching every cell. Much hormonal communication is long distance, carrying information to distant cells that will alter their functioning. For example, the pituitary gland in the center of the brain secretes a hormone that stimulates reproductive organs in the pelvic cavity.

> **hormone**
> Compound secreted in one area of the body that is active in another area; usually carried by the blood.

2. Local hormones, called **paracrines**, can be released to affect only cells in the vicinity. Neurons use paracrines to stimulate nearby nerve, muscle, or glandular cells by releasing short-lived chemicals called neurotransmitters. Paracrine communication is mostly used when quick responses are required. Neurons must respond instantly to information; therefore, they secrete neurotransmitters directly into the space between cells. Sending neurotransmitters into the bloodstream would be too slow for nerve impulses.

3. Cells of epithelial and muscular tissues can interact with other cells directly through physical connections at cell-to-cell junctions. **Gap junctions**, such as those between heart muscle cells, are used for instantaneous communications. They occur across very small distances and are extremely specific. Unlike endocrine communication, which has long-lasting effects, gap junction communications are immediate and short-lived. Cell-to-cell junctions occur in tissues like your skin, where cells are in direct contact with one another.

Our cells constantly send and receive messages—commands, corrections, updates, and requests. One of the best-coordinated, communication-rich events in a cell's life cycle is cell division, or **mitosis**. To carry out this complicated process, the cell must communicate with surrounding cells and its own organelles and biochemical pathways. During mitosis, DNA and organelles are duplicated, and DNA is condensed into manageable packets and sorted into separate nuclei. Then two intact cell membranes are formed, each containing all of the organelles and DNA of the parent cell. This process will be discussed in detail in Chapter 20. This complicated process adds to the difficulty of creating artificial cells. Read more about this in *Ethics and Issues: Artificial Life: Why Is It So Hard to Create?*

Another of the most significant communications in a cell's life cycle is the instruction it receives to die—a programmed death called **apoptosis**. Each minute countless numbers of your cells die and dismantle themselves. We know now that many cancer cells result from those cells' inability to respond to the programmed death command. We will see this in Chapter 11.

Cell signaling mechanisms • Figure 4.17

Circulating hormones are carried through the bloodstream to act on distant target cells. Paracrines act on neighboring cells. Cell-to-cell contact is the third route shown.

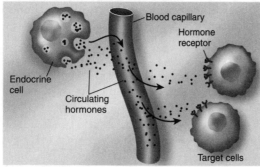

a. Circulating hormones

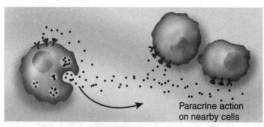

b. Local hormones (paracrine and autocrine)

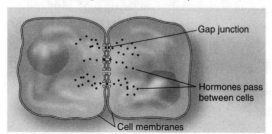

c. Gap junctions

CONCEPT CHECK   **STOP**

1. **Why** is cell-to-cell communication necessary in the human body?
2. **What** is a hormone?

ETHICS AND ISSUES

 THE PLANNER

Artificial Life: Why Is It So Hard to Create?

In 2002, scientists at the State University of New York at Stony Brook assembled the first synthetic virus. They downloaded a recipe from the Internet, bought a gene sequence from a mail-order supplier, and in their laboratory whipped up a batch of polio. They proved the virus's potency by injecting it in mice, which then became paralyzed and eventually died.

"[We] did it to prove that it can be done," Dr. Eckard Wimmer told the Associated Press (AP). Wimmer led the team that conducted the research and published the results in the prestigious journal *Science*. "This approach has been talked about but people didn't take it seriously. Now people have to take it seriously," he told AP.

Scientists are divided over whether the experiment by Wimmer's team constitutes the "creation of life" or merely the recreation of a synthetic version of something that is not a life-form. A virus, they say, is not really alive. To create artificial life, scientists must produce a life-form that is able to reproduce and change (mutate) according to evolutionary principles in response to changes in its environment.

If this could be accomplished, would the new organism truly represent life? In addition to being able to reproduce and mutate, the creation would need an artificial membrane that successfully keeps harmful molecules out while allowing nutrients in—a membrane that "knows" what a cell needs to survive. The new organism would also need a metabolism that can take in food from the environment and convert it into energy.

Whether or not the Stony Brook experiment "created life," it did call attention to a frightening possibility. While medical science and public health programs have been working for over half a century to eliminate polio as a naturally occurring menace, scientists have shown that they can recreate this dreaded disease with cookbook efficiency using off-the-shelf materials.

The Stony Brook experiment is just one of many recent efforts by scientists in the field of "synthetic biology" to recreate life or create new life-forms. In another experiment, scientists at Rockefeller University created "vesicle bioreactors"—mixtures of fat molecules from egg whites, E. coli bacteria stripped of their genetic material, and enzymes from viruses. When new genetic material was added, this jerry-rigged "cell" was able to produce proteins. Some genetic sequences caused changes to occur in the vesicle's wall, making the wall more like a true cell's membrane.

Critical Reasoning Issues Whether or not a virus or a vesicle bioreactor constitutes the creation of new life, the key question remains: What happens when more scientists have the ability to create or recreate life-forms in a laboratory? Will they unleash alien life-forms, causing untold environmental damage? Although scientific advancement is inherently value neutral, some fear the unintended consequences of creating life where there was none. Could it be that, in the wrong hands, such knowledge could lead to bioterrorism on a massive scale?

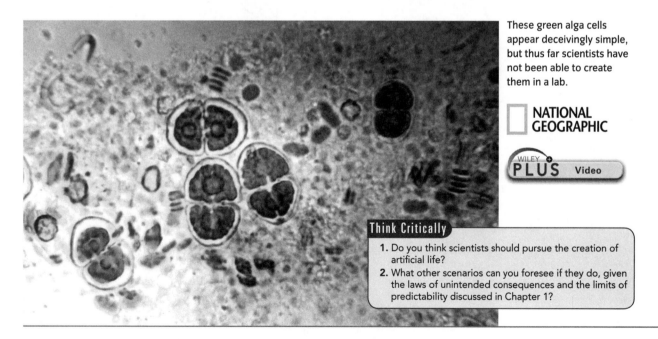

These green alga cells appear deceivingly simple, but thus far scientists have not been able to create them in a lab.

NATIONAL GEOGRAPHIC

WILEY **PLUS** Video

Think Critically

1. Do you think scientists should pursue the creation of artificial life?
2. What other scenarios can you foresee if they do, given the laws of unintended consequences and the limits of predictability discussed in Chapter 1?

4.4 Cell Communication Is Important to Cellular Success 89

Many of the enzymes that catalyze the reactions of metabolism require the assistance of coenzymes, small molecules that are derived from vitamins (Section 6.1). The extended deficiency of a vitamin from the diet usually results in a specific nutritional disease. **Scurvy**, *perhaps the first nutritional disease mentioned in recorded history (Egyptian, 1500 B.C.), is caused by the lack of vitamin C (ascorbic acid) in the diet. Symptoms of the disease include loose teeth, skin lesions, anemia, and slow healing of wounds. Outbreaks of scurvy were widespread in Europe during the interval A.D. 1500–1800, especially during the winters when fresh fruits and vegetables were scarce. Scurvy was an ever-present enemy of military personnel, especially sailors, who often served on ships for months and were unable to eat fresh fruits and vegetables. The link between the disease and vitamin C was discovered by a British navy physician in 1747. During a voyage, he found that sailors with scurvy were cured if lemons, limes, or oranges were added to their diets. From that time, British sailors have been given the nickname "limeys." We now know that vitamin C is relatively abundant not only in the citrus fruits, but also peppers, tomatoes, potatoes, and broccoli. The vitamin is essential in biochemical reactions that add hydroxyl groups to the amino acid residues proline and lysine in collagen. The chemistry and biochemistry of vitamin C were celebrated in a British stamp issued in 1977. In the chemical structure of ascorbic acid, carbon atoms are black, oxygen atoms are blue, and hydrogen atoms are red.*
(Courtesy of Professor C. M. Lang/ Photography by Gary J. Shaffen, University of Wisconsin-Stevens Point.)

Basic Concepts of Cellular Metabolism and Bioenergetics

In Parts I, II, and III of this book, we have focused on the structures and functions of important biomolecules and their assembly into membranes, cellular organelles, and cells. We have paid little attention to the maze of reactions that degrades and/or produces the molecules or to the energy requirements of biological processes. In Part IV our studies target the overall process of **metabolism**: how cells acquire, transform, store, and use energy. Metabolism is often described as the "sum total of all chemical reactions in an organism"; however, this definition is incomplete and is a great oversimplification. Metabolism is indeed a study of the thousands of reactions in a cell, but the study also includes exploring their coordination, regulation, and energy requirements.

Introduction to Metabolism   It is not uncommon for chemists to expose molecules to an environment of high temperatures, several atmospheres of pressure, strong chemical catalysts, and extreme pH values to achieve desired chemical reactions. By chemical standards, the internal conditions in most cells and organisms are relatively mild: one atmosphere pressure, a moderate temperature, and neutral pH. (Some exceptions exist, for example, very acidic pH in the stomach and intestines of animals; bacteria living in hot springs and ocean vents.) We have already explained part of the reason cells can carry out reactions under these mild conditions: the presence of catalysts, called enzymes, that function by bringing a reaction more rapidly to equilibrium. Catalysis by enzymes is an absolute necessity for life to exist—enzymes increase the rate of reactions needed for cell growth, and they are selective, allowing only certain types of molecules to enter into metabolism (thus unwanted, nonproductive reactions do not occur).

Organisms and cells are similar to machines in that they require an input of energy to function. The machine changes one form of energy into other forms. In humans and many other nonphotosynthetic organisms, the energy input is in the form of organic molecules: fats and carbohydrates. In photosynthetic organisms, light is the source of energy. Both types of organisms then convert the energy to a different form for use in biosynthesis, transport of nutrients, and other energy-requiring processes.

Thus we begin to explore the myriad of integrated biochemical reactions whereby cells extract useful energy from foodstuffs and use that energy to drive thermodynamically unfavorable reactions and carry out other critical functions. Specific questions to answer include these: How do organisms transform the potential energy in carbohydrates and fats into useful energy for biosynthesis, membrane transport, and muscle contraction? How much energy is associated with the important energy transfer molecule ATP? How do cells regulate the metabolic processes so as not to deplete some resources or produce too much of others? How do photosynthetic organisms harness energy from the sun to make carbohydrates? In addition, we shall discover the answers to practical questions such as, How much energy is available in glucose? Why does the metabolism of fats provide more energy per gram than carbohydrates? What are the roles of the vitamins in metabolic reactions?

Fortunately for us, most organisms use the same general pathways for extraction and utilization of energy. The reactions of glycolysis (glucose degradation) in humans are the same as those in bacteria and other organisms, including higher plants. However, we will encounter differences in the relative importance of metabolic pathways, regulation, enzyme structure, and reaction mechanisms. Also, we will observe compartmentation of metabolism within an organism; that is, some types of cells are used for energy production and others for energy utilization.

Autotrophs and Heterotrophs   Metabolic differences among organisms can best be studied by dividing all living organisms into two major classes (Figure 14.1). **Autotrophs** ("self-feeding" organisms) can use atmospheric carbon dioxide as the sole source of carbon, from which they build complex carbon-containing biomolecules.

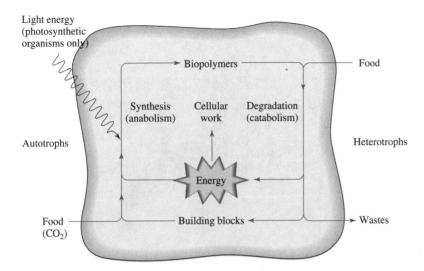

Figure 14.1 Most autotrophs use energy from the sun and CO_2 to synthesize biopolymers. Heterotrophs obtain energy by ingesting and degrading complex carbon compounds. Autotrophs and heterotrophs break down biopolymers by similar pathways.

Most autotrophs, including photosynthetic bacteria and higher plants, use the sun's energy for biosynthetic purposes and are therefore relatively self-sufficient (see Section 17.5 and 17.6). **Heterotrophs** ("feeding on others") obtain energy by ingesting complex carbon-containing compounds such as carbohydrates and fats. The heterotrophs, which include higher animals and most microorganisms, are dependent on the autotrophs for these compounds. Heterotrophic organisms can be further divided into two subclasses depending on their need for molecular oxygen. **Aerobes** live in air and use molecular oxygen for metabolic reactions. The **anaerobes** do not require oxygen for survival; in fact, for some, the strict anaerobes, molecular oxygen is toxic.

This introductory chapter focuses on the heterotrophs. We do this because the important metabolic paths have been discovered using microorganisms and animal tissue and in some ways are less complicated than those in plants. Figure 14.2 summarizes the aspects of metabolism in a heterotrophic cell.

14.1 Intermediary Metabolism

Learning Objective
Have a fundamental understanding of the principles, coordination, and bioenergetics of intermediary metabolism.

In a typical prokaryotic cell, like *Escherichia coli*, there are at least a thousand biochemical reactions that make up metabolism. A human cell may contain as many as 3000 different enzymes, each catalyzing a specific chemical reaction. The process of metabolism in all organisms takes place via organized sequences of consecutive enzyme-catalyzed reactions. Each step is usually a single, highly specific, chemical change leading to a product that becomes the reactant (substrate) for the next step. The sum of these small, discrete, but related steps usually results in a major chemical transformation of the original substrate that entered the process. This is called **intermediary metabolism** because each reaction leads to a stable product or intermediate. (Metabolic intermediates, also called **metabolites**, should not be confused with the unstable variety of intermediates often used in detailed reaction mechanisms.) A sequence of reactions that has a specific functional purpose, for example, the degradation of glucose to pyruvate (glycolysis), is called a **metabolic pathway**.

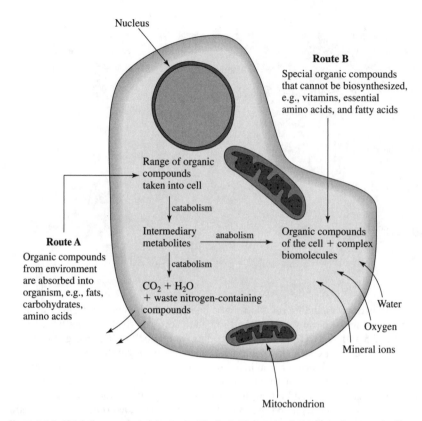

Figure 14.2 Metabolic processes in heterotropic cells. Route A is for entry of all carbon, nitrogen, and sulfur; most organic hydrogen and oxygen; and some phosphorus. Route B is for entry of specific organic compounds that are required by the cell but cannot be synthesized by the cell (vitamins, essential amino acids, essential fatty acids). Catabolism refers to degradation processes with release of energy; anabolism refers to biosynthetic processes that require energy.

The format of a pathway may be linear (glycolysis), branched (biosynthesis of amino acids), cyclic (citric acid cycle), or spiral (fatty acid degradation). These possibilities are outlined in Figure 14.3.

Metabolons—Functional Units of Metabolism

A metabolic pathway as shown in Figure 14.3 usually comprises several steps, each chemical transformation catalyzed by an enzyme. At first glance, it would appear that once a reaction is complete, the product, which becomes the substrate for the next step, must diffuse to the appropriate enzyme active site. As we learned in Chapter 1 (Section 1.4), the cell's interior is a gel-like matrix with extensive ultrastructural organization. This mazelike medium greatly hinders the movement of small substrate molecules from enzyme to enzyme in a pathway. Studies of metabolism and cell structure are showing that the enzymes in a specialized metabolic sequence are organized into functional units called **metabolons**. Metabolic intermediates can literally be passed from one enzyme active site to the next. The extent to which the enzymes in a metabolically related sequence are held together in

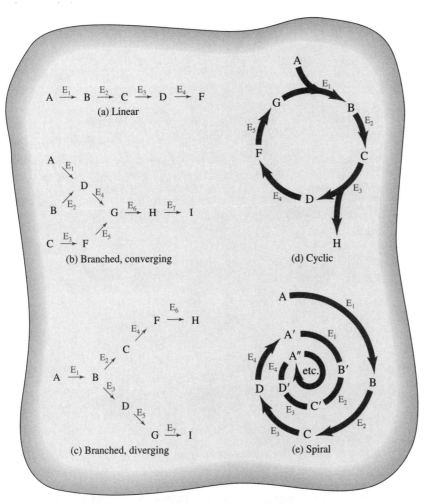

Figure 14.3 Possible sequential arrangements for metabolic pathways: (a) linear; (b) branched, converging; (c) branched, diverging; (d) cyclic; (e) spiral. A, B, C, D, F, G, H, and I refer to metabolic intermediates. Primed letters refer to modifications of A, B, C, and D. E_n refers to enzymes that catalyze the reactions.

metabolons varies greatly (Figure 14.4). The enzymes of some pathways, for example, glycolysis, are only loosely held together by a few weak noncovalent bonds (Figure 14.4a). In some pathways, the enzymes are tightly associated to form a **multienzyme complex** (for example, the pyruvate dehydrogenase complex; Section 16.1, Figure 14.4b). The functional metabolic units may be in several cell locations including the cytoplasm, in cell membranes (Figure 14.4c), or in organelles like the nucleus, mitochondria, peroxisomes, and chloroplasts. The purpose of metabolons should be obvious—they organize the enzymes of a pathway into a functional unit and the metabolites can be channeled from one enzyme to the next. This assures the efficient transfer of intermediates between enzymes. Reactants are less likely to be lost by diffusion. As more metabolic pathways are studied, we may find that most (if not all) of the enzymes of a specific pathway are physically united into some type of functional unit like a metabolon.

Two Directions of Metabolism

Metabolic pathways can be organized into two paths depending on their overall biochemical purpose. **Catabolism** is the degradative path, whereby complex organic molecules such as fats, carbohydrates, and proteins are degraded to simpler molecules such as lactate, pyruvate, ethanol, CO_2, H_2O, and NH_3 (see Figures 14.1 and 14.2). Catabolism is characterized by oxidation reactions and, because foodstuffs contain potential energy, by release of free energy, which is captured eventually in the form of ATP.

The other part of metabolism is **anabolism** or biosynthesis, which is characterized by the construction of large, complex biomolecules from smaller precursor molecules. The synthesis of proteins from individual amino acids, the formation of glucose from two pyruvate molecules, and the synthesis of DNA from nucleotides represent anabolic processes. In contrast to catabolism, anabolism is generally characterized by reduction reactions and energy input. Energy is supplied by ATP, NADH, and NADPH molecules, which contain energy released from catabolism.

It is not possible to label every individual reaction as catabolic or anabolic because some individual steps in metabolism neither release nor require energy. In addition, not all reactions are oxidations or reductions. (The first step in the catabolic process of glycolysis involves a phosphoryl group transfer from ATP to glucose. This reaction is not an oxidation and it requires the input of energy; however, the *overall* process of glycolysis is one of oxidation and energy release.) The division into the two parts is not meant to separate metabolism into unrelated processes but to facilitate the learning of each pathway and defining its role in the overall process.

The general characteristics of catabolism and anabolism are compared in Table 14.1. In biological cells, anabolic and catabolic processes are regulated to

Table 14.1
Contrasting characteristics of catabolism and anabolism

Catabolism
Leads to degradation of biomolecules
Overall process of chemical oxidation and formation of reduced cofactors of NADH, NADPH, $FADH_2$
Release of chemical energy (exergonic) and production of ATP from ADP
Convergence of pathways

Anabolism
Synthesis of biomolecules
Overall process of chemical reduction and formation of oxidized cofactors NAD^+, $NADP^+$, FAD
Requirement for energy input (endergonic) and use of ATP
Divergence of pathways

be nonsynchronous; that is, there is a flow or **flux** of metabolites in one direction or the other depending upon the cell's energy state. For example, when a muscle cell is in a resting state with no need for energy, there is no need for catabolism of glucose to CO_2 and H_2O. Instead, glucose is stored in its polymeric form, glycogen.

ATP Energy Cycle   Anabolism and catabolism are linked together by their contrasting but coordinated energy requirements (bioenergetics): *Catabolic processes release the potential energy from food and collect it in the reactive intermediate, ATP; anabolic processes use the free energy stored in ATP to perform work.* The two processes are coupled by the **ATP energy cycle** (Figure 14.5). ATP serves as the *universal carrier of biochemical energy.* In a later section of this chapter we explain the special

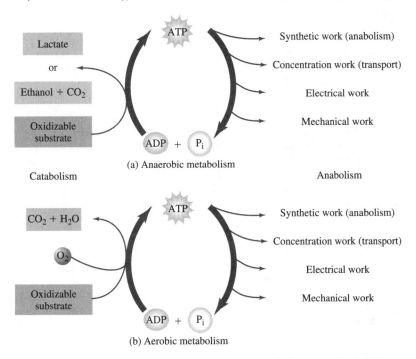

Figure 14.5 The ATP energy cycle, which links together anabolic and catabolic processes of metabolism. Catabolism provides the primary source of energy by producing ATP by the phosphorylation of ADP. (a) Anaerobic metabolism (no use of oxygen) leads to fermentation, with formation of lactate or ethanol or other products. (b) Aerobic metabolism (use of oxygen) leads to more complete degradation of organics (CO_2 + H_2O). The cellular activities that can be driven by ATP are also listed.

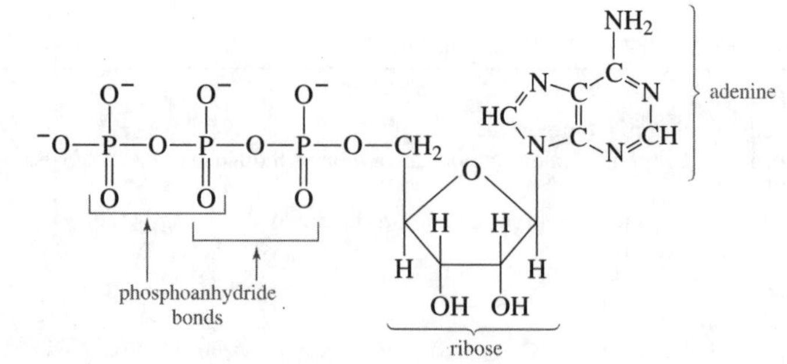

Figure 14.6 The structure of adenosine triphosphate (ATP). ATP is a typical nucleotide consisting of an adenine ring, a ribose, and three phosphate groups.

Adenosine triphosphate (ATP)

chemical and thermodynamic properties of ATP and how it effectively performs as an agent of energy transfer. From an energy standpoint, the *recycling of ATP is the central theme of metabolism*. The molecular structure for ATP is shown in Figure 14.6.

Before You Go On. . .

1. The chemical structure of ATP is shown in Figure 14.6. The two reactive phosphoanhydride bonds are identified in the structure. What kind of chemical bond holds the first phosphorus atom (called the α-phosphorus) to the 5′ carbon of ribose? How does it differ from a phosphoanhydride bond?

Stages of Metabolism

Catabolism and anabolism form a coordinated network of reactions, but for practical and pedagogical reasons, we divide each into three major stages (Figure 14.7). This is done at the risk of taking pathways and individual steps "out of context" from the whole picture of metabolism.

Stage I. Stage I of catabolism is the breakdown of macromolecules [proteins, fats (triacylglycerols), polysaccharides] into their respective building blocks. All proteins are hydrolyzed to their component amino acids; triacylglycerols are hydrolyzed to fatty acids plus glycerol; and polysaccharides are hydrolyzed to monosaccharides, primarily glucose. Essentially all reactions in stage I of catabolism involve the cleavage of chemical bonds by hydrolysis with no release of useful energy in the form of NADH or ATP.

Stage II. Stage I is preparation for the next level of reactions, where the diverse amino acids, fatty acids, and monosaccharides are oxidized to a common metabolite, acetyl-CoA (stage II). Some energy is released and captured in the form of NADH and ATP during stage II.

Stage III. In stage III acetyl-CoA enters the **citric acid cycle**, where it is oxidized to CO_2, the end product of aerobic carbon metabolism. The oxidation of citric acid cycle intermediates leads to the formation of reduced and reactive cofactors, NADH and $FADH_2$, which eventually give up their electrons. The electrons are transported via the **respiratory assembly** to molecular oxygen, ultimately producing energy and water. The energy released in electron transport is coupled directly to ATP synthesis from ADP and P_i. Stage III of catabolism is the location of most ATP production by a process called **oxidative phosphorylation**.

Catabolism is characterized by a convergence of three major routes toward a final common pathway. Many different kinds of proteins, fats, and polysaccharides enter unique pathways that converge at the citric acid cycle. Convergence of pathways is

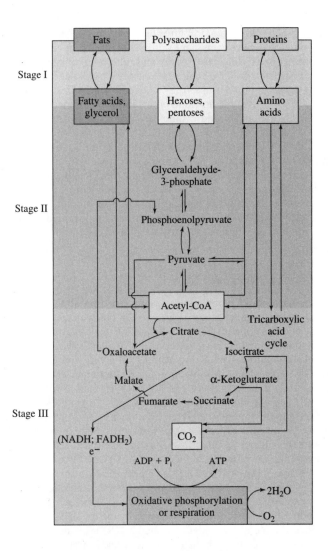

Figure 14.7 The stages of catabolism and anabolism.

efficient and economical for the cell because it greatly reduces the number of different enzymes necessary for degradation of foods.

Anabolism can also be divided into three stages; however, in contrast to catabolism, the pathways are characterized by divergence. Monosaccharide and polysaccharide syntheses may begin with CO_2, oxaloacetate, pyruvate, or lactate. The amino acids for protein synthesis are formed from acetyl-CoA and by the amination of pyruvate and α-keto acids from the citric acid cycle. The triacylglycerols are constructed using fatty acids synthesized from acetyl-CoA. Several metabolites such as oxaloacetate, acetyl-CoA, and pyruvate are common precursors for proteins, triacylglycerols, and polysaccharides; however, they branch from their starting points, leading to hundreds more of these diverse proteins, triacylglycerols, and polysaccharides.

Many anabolic pathways require energy in the form of ATP and NADPH. By noting the use of curved dual arrows in Figure 14.7, it can be seen that anabolism and catabolism are not just the reverse of each other. The two processes are *similar* in terms of intermediates and enzymes, but they are not *identical*. Catabolism and anabolism of glucose illustrate the relationships. Glucose is degraded by glycolysis to pyruvate, a pathway requiring a sequence of 10 enzyme-catalyzed steps. The reversal of glycolysis or synthesis of glucose from pyruvate requires 11 steps, of which 8 are the exact reverse of those in glycolysis. Three steps in glycolysis are thermodynamically irreversible and their reverse requires three different steps in glucose synthesis. It does not seem economical to have even slightly different pathways for anabolism and catabolism, but distinct routes are a thermodynamic and regulatory necessity. Catabolic processes are energetically like a boulder taking the most direct route as it rolls downhill. Carrying the same boulder uphill, as in anabolism, requires some changes in the route; however, portions of the downhill pathway may be retraced. Distinct but coordinated paths for anabolism and catabolism also allow for metabolic regulation. Regulation of metabolic pathways often occurs at thermodynamically irreversible steps. Since irreversible steps in catabolism are replaced by different steps in anabolism, sites of regulation will differ in the two processes.

Anabolic and catabolic pathways also differ in types of cells, intracellular location, and regulation. For example, glucose degradation predominates in active muscle cells, whereas glucose synthesis takes place primarily in liver cells. Fatty acid synthesis occurs in the cytoplasm of adipose cells; the enzymes for fatty acid degradation occur in the mitochondria of resting muscle cells. A detailed discussion on tissue specificity and integration of pathways is presented in Chapter 20.

Deciphering Metabolic Pathways

To understand a metabolic pathway, it is essential to know all the details of the reaction steps: (a) biochemical characteristics including enzymes, coenzymes, substrate, products, intermediates, kinetics, and mechanisms; (b) control of the pathway including the regulation at the reaction level (presence of allosteric enzymes) and the control by cellular conditions (regulation at the gene level), and (c) the physiological function of the pathway and how it coordinates with the overall metabolism of the organism. Several approaches for gathering this information will be outlined here and described in greater detail in later chapters.

Some of the earliest studies of metabolism were done in whole organisms by feeding various foods and collecting and analyzing waste products in urine and feces. These kinds of studies only identified final products and did not provide details of individual metabolic pathways. The introduction of radioisotopes near the middle part of the 20th century allowed biochemists to feed labeled biochemicals to animals, sacrifice the animals, and analyze tissue for the presence of the isotopes. Radioisotopes were used in the 1940s to elucidate the pathway for cholesterol synthesis in rats (Section 18.4). Other metabolic pathways and details were uncovered by the use of tissue slices. For example, the citric acid cycle was elucidated in the late 1930s by incubating thin slices of pigeon liver and heart tissue with the biochemical acids citrate, malate, oxaloacetate, and succinate. The sequence of the citric acid cycle reactions was determined by adding metabolic inhibitors to the tissues and analyzing the buildup of certain intermediates.

Today, biochemists are more likely to use genetics and even sophisticated instrumentation to study metabolism. With genetic engineering, it is possible to prepare specific bacterial mutants that lack an enzyme because of an inactivated or deleted gene. Higher organisms that lack a particular gene can also be produced. These so-called **gene knockouts** are particularly useful if a single missing gene results in a metabolic defect that can be characterized.

An experimental approach still used by today's biochemists is to prepare **cell-free extracts**. The Buchners in their studies of glucose metabolism in yeast in the 1890s were first to use cell-free extracts. Animal and plant cells are homogenized in a buffer to release cell components and **fractional centrifugation** is used to separate organelles (see Window on Biochemistry 1-2). For example, these methods were used to locate the enzymes of the citric acid cycle, respiration, and fatty acid catabolism in the mitochondria. Automated chromatography and electrophoresis procedures may be applied to cell-free extracts in order to purify and characterize enzymes and other molecules essential in metabolism (see Section 3.5). The techniques of NMR and MS are now being used to study metabolism (see Window on Biochemistry 14-1 and Biochemistry in the Clinic 14).

The search for the miracle diet pill is not just a current fad, but actually began in the early part of the twentieth century. Many scientists and physicians believe that the very first drug prescribed for weight loss was **2,4-dinitrophenol (DNP).** *In the 1920s and 1930s, biochemists at Stanford University discovered that DNP caused increased oxygen consumption and an increased metabolic rate (up to 50%), but a decline in ATP production. Instead of being used for ATP synthesis, the energy from metabolism was given off as heat. Hence the body was able to break down excess stored fats at a rapid rate. Individuals on the drug could lose up to 12 pounds in eight days. Body fat seemed to melt away. Physicians began to prescribe the chemical as a diet aid and by 1935 at least 100,000 Americans had used it. Some of the side effects noted by patients included headaches, high fever, weakness, and diarrhea. Unfortunately, it also caused several deaths and was banned by the FDA in the late 1930s. It became popular again in the 1990s when it was used by athletes for quick weight loss. Controlled toxicity studies with experimental animals have proved that DNP is a deadly poison. We now know that DNP acts as an* **uncoupling agent;** *it breaks the link between electron transport/respiration and ATP synthesis (see Section 17.3).*
(Courtesy FDA History Office.)

ATP Formation by Electron-Transport Chains

513

In the previous three chapters we have studied fundamentals of the early stages of metabolism. The oxidation steps in catabolism have been defined as stepwise processes designed to remove electrons from substrates and collect them in the reduced cofactors, NADH, NADPH, and $FADH_2$. Another important event is the substrate-level formation of ATP. During the study of each metabolic pathway we have kept a tally of these important metabolic products (see Tables 15.2 and 16.3). For example, the oxidation of glucose by glycolysis, pyruvate oxidation, and the citric acid cycle generates a total of ten NADH, two $FADH_2$, and four substrate-level phosphoanhydride bonds (two ATP and two GTP) while each of the six carbon atoms of glucose is oxidized to CO_2. We will see in Chapter 18 that fatty acids travel

Figure 17.1 Convergence of preliminary metabolic pathways into aerobic metabolism. Pyruvate from glycolysis is decarboxylated to acetyl-CoA, which enters the citric acid cycle. Acetyl-CoA is also produced by the oxidation of fatty acids. NADH and $FADH_2$, generated in the pathways, bring electrons to the electron-transport chain. Here their electrons are used to reduce O_2 to water. The oxidized cofactors NAD^+ and FAD return to be reduced by nutrient oxidation. ATP is generated during electron transport. All entering nutrients including glucose and fatty acids are oxidized to CO_2 and H_2O.

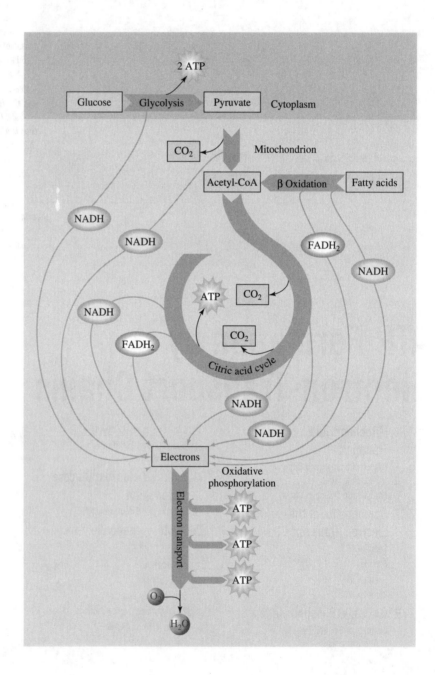

the β-oxidation pathway leading to acetyl-CoA, which enters the citric acid cycle to oxidize each carbon atom to CO_2 with production of NADH, $FADH_2$, and substrate-level ATP (or GTP).

Only a small amount of energy in the form of reactive phosphoanhydride bonds (ATP or GTP) is extracted from fuel molecules during the transfer of electrons from substrates to cofactors in stages I and II and the citric acid cycle. The remainder of the oxidative energy from food resides in the form of electrons with high transfer potential in the reduced cofactors, NADH and $FADH_2$. The energy in the reduced cofactors is recovered by employing molecular oxygen as a terminal electron acceptor (oxidizing agent). The participation of O_2 allows more complete oxidation of substrates than is possible in anaerobic metabolism. The electrons from NADH and $FADH_2$ are not passed directly to O_2 but are transferred through a series of electron carriers that undergo reversible reduction and oxidation. The series of carriers, located in the inner mitochondrial membrane of plant and animal cells, is called an **electron-transport chain**. Electron transport results in the availability of large amounts of free energy. Part of the energy released by electron transport is used to pump protons through the inner mitochondrial membrane, thus generating a transmembrane proton gradient. Energy from the gradient drives the synthesis of ATP ($ADP + P_i \rightleftharpoons ATP + H_2O$). The chemical reaction of phosphorylation is catalyzed by the enzyme complex **ATP synthase**. The combined processes of electron transport and ATP synthesis (called **oxidative phosphorylation**) are the final stages of aerobic metabolism (Figure 17.1).

Electron-transport chains are universal metabolic features found in all aerobic organisms, including plants. Oxidative phosphorylation occurs in the mitochondria of plants for catabolic metabolism; however, plants use another type of electron-transport chain to provide energy for **photosynthesis**. Photosynthetic organisms use light-absorbing pigments to collect energy from the sun and specialized electron-transport chains to drive electrons to a higher energy level. A goal of photosynthesis is to generate ATP and reducing power as NADPH in order to make glucose by fixing CO_2. The molecular system for photosynthesis is present in plant organelles called chloroplasts. In bacteria, ATP is synthesized by energy coupling of electron-transport chains in the cell membrane.

17.1 Mitochondrial Electron Transport

Learning Objective
Understand the fundamentals of biological oxidation–reduction processes.

Our primary objective in previous chapters of Part IV was to outline the catabolism of carbohydrates. After preliminary reactions in stages I and II, the catabolic pathways of these primary nutrients converge to stage III, the citric acid cycle, electron transport, and oxidative phosphorylation. The important metabolic processes of stage III occur in mitochondria (see Figure 16.2). The components of the biochemical apparatus for **respiration** (uptake of O_2, electron transport, and ATP synthesis) are present as integral proteins in the folded inner membrane or as peripheral proteins on the membrane. The extensive folding of the membrane provides a large surface area on the matrix side for placement of many molecular systems for high levels of ATP production. Components of the electron-transport chain are arranged in the membrane in packages called **respiratory assemblies**. The inner membrane also possesses knoblike spheres projecting from its surface into the matrix. These protrusions, called F_1 particles, contain the components of the ATP synthase complex and are the sites for coupling electron transport and ATP production. Mitochondria are complete biochemical factories that can independently carry out respiration if provided with O_2, ADP, P_i, reducible cofactors (NAD^+ and FAD), and oxidizable substrates such as pyruvate, fatty acids, and citric acid cycle intermediates.

Electron Transport and Oxidative Phosphorylation

Now that we have described the cellular location of aerobic metabolism, we turn to a discussion of the biochemical components and characteristics of electron transport and oxidative phosphorylation. Electrons removed from nutrients and metabolic intermediates during oxidative reactions are transferred by dehydrogenases to the cofactors NAD^+ and FAD. The general reaction displaying this oxidation–reduction process is

$$AH_2 + NAD^+ \xrightleftharpoons{\text{dehydrogenase}} A + NADH + H^+$$

where AH_2 and A represent reduced and oxidized metabolites from glycolysis, pyruvate dehydrogenation, and the citric acid cycle. A similar process occurs with FAD, where BH_2 and B represent metabolites from the citric acid cycle and other pathways:

$$BH_2 + FAD \xrightleftharpoons{\text{dehydrogenase}} B + FADH_2$$

Important dehydrogenase-catalyzed reactions from various pathways are reviewed in Table 17.1.

Table 17.1
Reactions catalyzed by NAD- and FAD-linked dehydrogenases

NAD Linked

1. Glyceraldehyde-3-phosphate + P_i + NAD^+ $\rightleftharpoons$
   $$\text{1,3-bisphosphoglycerate} + NADH + H^+$$
2. Pyruvate + CoA + NAD^+ $\rightleftharpoons$ acetyl-CoA + CO_2 + NADH + H^+
3. Isocitrate + NAD^+ $\rightleftharpoons$ α-ketoglutarate + NADH + H^+ + CO_2
4. α-ketoglutarate + CoA + NAD^+ $\rightleftharpoons$ succinyl-CoA + CO_2 + NADH + H^+
5. Malate + NAD^+ $\rightleftharpoons$ oxaloacetate + NADH + H^+

FAD Linked

1. Succinate + FAD $\rightleftharpoons$ fumarate + $FADH_2$

Before You Go On. . .

1. As a means of reviewing metabolic pathways from previous chapters, identify the pathway and the enzyme system that catalyzes each of the reactions in Table 17.1. Also identify the cellular location for each enzyme. For example, the first reaction in the NAD-linked category is in glycolysis and the enzyme is glyceraldehyde-3-phosphate dehydrogenase. The glycolytic enzymes are located in the cellular cytoplasm.

2. What type of chemical process occurs in all of the reactions in Table 17.1 and what is the common enzyme class for all the reactions?

Thus, electrons from substrates are collected in NADH and $FADH_2$. Cells contain only a limited supply of the oxidized cofactors NAD^+ and FAD. Their reduced products must be recycled if metabolism is to be continuous. Recycling is accomplished by oxidation brought about by transfer of electrons from NADH and $FADH^+$ to the terminal electron acceptor, O_2:

$$NADH + H^+ + \tfrac{1}{2}O_2 \xrightarrow{\quad ADP + P_i \;\; ATP \quad} NAD^+ + H_2O$$

$$FADH_2 + \tfrac{1}{2}O_2 \xrightarrow{\quad ADP + P_i \;\; ATP \quad} FAD + H_2O$$

There are two important consequences shown in these reactions:

1. The oxidized cofactors that are reformed (NAD^+ and FAD) are thus available for continued oxidative metabolism (they are recycled).
2. Energy released during electron transport is coupled to ATP synthesis.

The Electron-Transport Chain

Although the above reactions for cofactor oxidation are rather simplistic, they do show how the two processes of electron transport and ATP synthesis are combined. The reactions are written as single steps, but each represents a net reaction obtained by addition of several reactions. In fact, electrons are shuttled from NADH and $FADH_2$ to O_2 through a series of carriers called the respiratory electron-transport chain (Figure 17.2). The chain is composed of four large protein complexes called NADH-coenzyme Q reductase (complex I), succinate-coenzyme Q reductase (complex II), cytochrome c reductase (complex III), and cytochrome c oxidase (complex IV). Most of the carriers within each complex are integral membrane proteins with prosthetic groups that can accept and donate electrons. In other words, the carriers can undergo reduction and oxidation reactions.

The carriers are arranged in order of increasing electron affinity; hence, electrons can flow spontaneously from one carrier to the next. (The electrons flow "downhill" in terms of energy.) Electrons in NADH are at the highest energy level of any among the carriers. Stated in different terms, NADH is a strong reducing agent (in fact, the strongest of the carriers). Electrons from NADH pass to complex I (NADH-CoQ reductase), which is composed of proteins with FMN and iron–sulfur (Fe–S) clusters. $FADH_2$ is oxidized by Fe–S clusters that are part of succinate-CoQ reductase (complex II) and also acyl-CoA dehydrogenase.

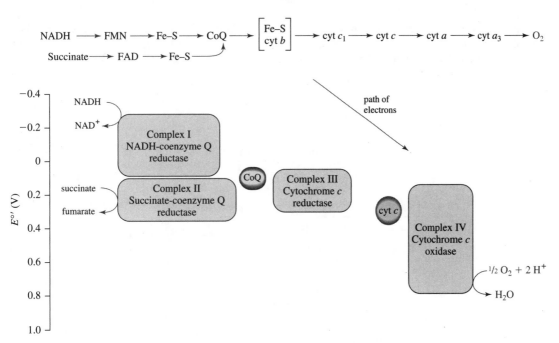

Figure 17.2 The four complex carriers in the mitochondrial electron-transport chain. The relative energy level of each is noted on the scale of $E^{\circ\prime}$ to the left. $E^{\circ\prime}$ refers to the standard reduction potential measured in volts. The four complexes transfer electrons from reduced cofactors NADH and $FADH_2$ to molecular O_2. The flow of electrons is shown in the reaction sequence at the top. CoQ refers to coenzyme Q, which exists in two forms: ubiquinone, the oxidized form, and ubiquinol, the reduced form.

Bioenergetics of Redox Processes

The energy released in electron transfer processes (redox reactions) is dependent on the energy levels of the oxidizing agent and the reducing agent. The relative energy levels of all oxidizing and reducing agents, including the components of the mitochondrial electron transport chain, are quantified by using **standard reduction potentials**, $E^{\circ\prime}$. The reduction potential is a measure of how easily a compound can be reduced (how easily it can accept electrons). $E^{\circ\prime}$ is measured under standard temperature and pressure conditions and at a pH of 7, just as we did for $\Delta G^{\circ\prime}$ (see Section 14.3).

All compounds are compared to the redox potential of H^+/H_2 which is assigned an $E^{\circ\prime}$ of 0.0 V. Compounds with positive $E^{\circ\prime}$ values are better electron acceptors than H^+. The more positive the value of $E^{\circ\prime}$ for the oxidized form of a carrier, the better it functions as an electron acceptor. The final and best electron acceptor of the mitochondrial electron chain is O_2, which has an $E^{\circ\prime}$ of $+0.82$ V. The more negative the $E^{\circ\prime}$ of a carrier, the weaker it acts as an oxidizing agent and the better it acts as a reducing agent (electron donor). The $E^{\circ\prime}$ for NADH, the best reducing agent in the chain, is -0.32 V. The $E^{\circ\prime}$ for each carrier in the transport chain is given in the table below. Note that the $E^{\circ\prime}$ values for respiratory carriers range between the limits of -0.32 V ($NAD^+/NADH$) and $+0.82$ V (O_2/H_2O).

The following equation may be used to calculate the standard free energy change for redox reactions:

$$\Delta G^{\circ\prime} = -nF\Delta E^{\circ\prime}$$

where

n = number of electrons transferred from one carrier to another (usually one or two)

F = the faraday constant, 96.5 kJ/volt·mole (this is a unit conversion factor to change units of volts to kJ/mol)

$\Delta E^{\circ\prime}$ = the difference in reduction potential between the two carriers, in volts
$(\Delta E^{\circ\prime} = E^{\circ\prime}{}_{acceptor} - E^{\circ\prime}{}_{donor})$

We will use this equation to calculate the amount of energy available when electrons are transferred from NADH through the chain to O_2. Normally two electrons pass from an NADH ($E^{\circ\prime}{}_{donor} = -0.32$V) to O_2 ($E^{\circ\prime}{}_{acceptor} = +0.82$V). The total energy released during this transfer is calculated as follows:

$$NADH + H^+ + \tfrac{1}{2}O_2 \longrightarrow NAD^+ + H_2O$$

$$\Delta G^{\circ\prime} = -(2)\left(96.5\,\frac{kJ}{V\cdot mol}\right)[+0.82 - (-0.32)]V$$

$$\Delta G^{\circ\prime} = -(2)(96.5)(1.14)\ kJ/mol$$

$$\Delta G^{\circ\prime} = -220\ kJ/mol$$

Standard reduction potentials, $E^{\circ\prime}$ for mitochondrial electron carriers

Redox Reaction[a]	$E^{\circ\prime}$ (V)
$NAD^+ + 2\,H^+ + 2\,e^- \rightarrow NADH + H^+$	-0.32
$FMN + 2\,H^+ + 2\,e^- \rightarrow FMNH_2$	-0.30
$FAD + 2\,H^+ + 2\,e^- \rightarrow FADH_2$	-0.18
$2\,H^+ + 2\,e^- \rightarrow H_2$	0.00
Ubiquinone $+ 2\,H^+ + 2\,e^- \rightarrow$ ubiquinol	0.05
Cytochrome $b_{(ox)} + e^- \rightarrow$ cytochrome $b_{(red)}$	0.08
Cytochrome $c_{1(ox)} + e^- \rightarrow$ cytochrome $c_{1(red)}$	0.22
Cytochrome $c_{(ox)} + e^- \rightarrow$ cytochrome $c_{(red)}$	0.25
Cytochrome $a_{(ox)} + e^- \rightarrow$ cytochrome $a_{(red)}$	0.29
Cytochrome $a_{3(ox)} + e^- \rightarrow$ cytochrome $a_{3(red)}$	0.55
$\tfrac{1}{2}O_2 + 2H^+ + 2e^- \rightarrow H_2O$	0.82

[a] (ox), oxidized; (red), reduced.

Thus electrons from the two cofactors enter the electron-transport chain through separate branches that converge at CoQ. Electrons from reduced CoQ ($CoQH_2$) are transported by complex III to cytochrome c (via cytochrome c reductase) and finally through cytochrome c oxidase (complex IV) to O_2. (The order of carriers also represents their physical proximity to one another in the inner membrane of the mitochondria.)

The quantitative amount of energy released on electron transfer from one carrier to another is of significance because it tells us if enough energy is available to make ATP from ADP and P_i. The energy released from electron transport may be calculated in terms of the familiar constant, the standard free energy change, $\Delta G^{\circ\prime}$ (see Section 14.3 and Just in Time Review 17.1).

It is important to note that all the energy is released not in a *single* step of electron transfer, but in incremental amounts at each redox step. The quantity of energy released can be calculated between adjacent carriers or over any interval of the chain. The energy released at three specific steps in the chain is collected in the form of a transmembrane proton gradient and used to drive the synthesis of ATP:

$$ADP + P_i \rightleftharpoons ATP + H_2O$$

Before You Go On...

1. Calculate the amount of energy available, in terms of $\Delta G^{\circ\prime}$, when two electrons are transferred from $FADH_2$ to O_2. Is this enough energy to make ATP?

17.2 Components of the Electron-Transport Chain

Learning Objective
Know the physiological location, role, and components of the electron-transport chain.

The electron-transport chain is composed of several serially ordered components that participate in electron flow. Each component is capable of undergoing reduction and oxidation; that is, it can accept electrons from the preceding carrier and pass them to the next carrier in line. The flow of electrons is spontaneous and thermodynamically favorable because the next carrier has a greater affinity for electrons than the previous one. To aid our chemical study of these carriers, we divide the chain into four segments referred to in the previous section: NADH-CoQ reductase (complex I), succinate-CoQ reductase (complex II), cytochrome c reductase (complex III), and cytochrome c oxidase (complex IV). There are four molecular types of redox centers in the complexes (in addition to NADH and $FADH_2$): flavin mononucleotide (FMN), iron–sulfur clusters (Fe–S), ubiquinone (CoQ), and **cytochromes**.

Complex I

The carriers in complex I are shown in Figure 17.3. Electrons flow from NADH to the first carrier in the complex, **flavin mononucleotide** (Figure 17.4). FMN, a relative of FAD, is reduced by accepting two electrons from NADH. Electrons from the product, $FMNH_2$, pass next to a prosthetic group composed of an **iron–sulfur cluster** (Figure 17.5). The most common forms have equal numbers of iron and sulfur (Fe_2S_2 and Fe_4S_4). Sulfur atoms either are from those in cysteine residues in proteins or are from inorganic sulfur. The iron atoms in these complexes cycle between the oxidized ferric state (Fe^{3+}) and the reduced ferrous state (Fe^{2+}).

Figure 17.3 Components of NADH-CoQ reductase, complex I. The proteins in complex I have the prosthetic groups FMN and Fe–S. Electrons enter the complex from NADH and flow to CoQ.

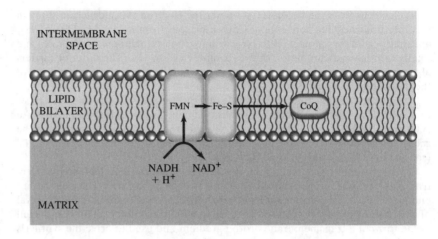

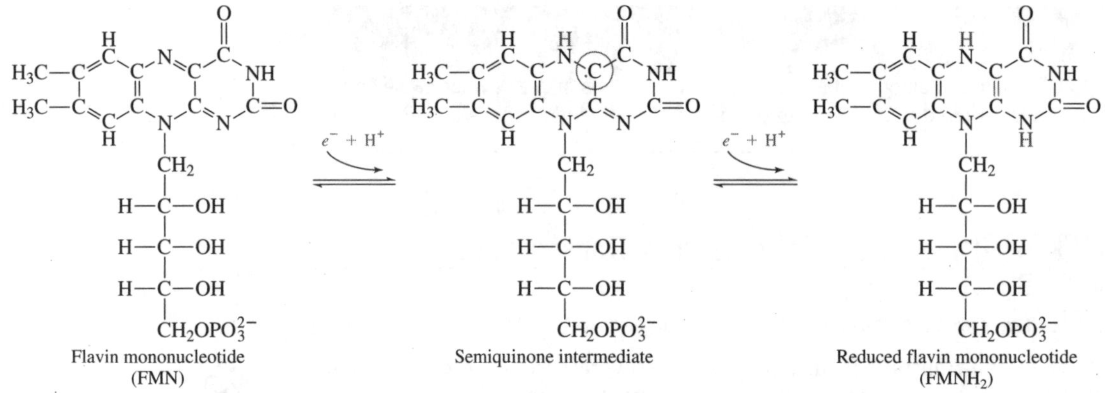

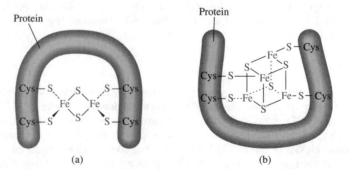

Flavin mononucleotide
(FMN)

Semiquinone intermediate

Reduced flavin mononucleotide
(FMNH₂)

Figure 17.4 Structures of the redox cofactors FMN and FMNH₂. FMN accepts one electron and a proton to form a semiquinone intermediate. The location of the radical (free electron) is circled. A second electron and proton produce FMNH₂.

(a)

(b)

Figure 17.5 The structures of iron–sulfur complexes in electron-transport proteins: (a) Fe_2S_2 and (b) Fe_4S_4. In addition to inorganic sulfide ions (S^{2-}), sulfur atoms from cysteine residues in the proteins also bind to iron. The iron atoms can undergo reversible oxidation–reduction, $Fe^{3+} + e^- \rightleftharpoons Fe^{2+}$.

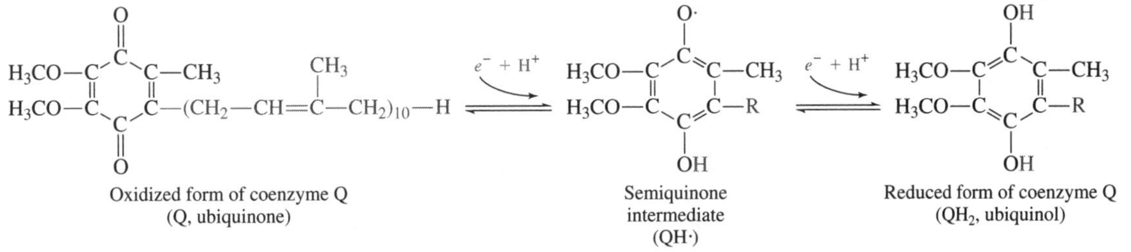

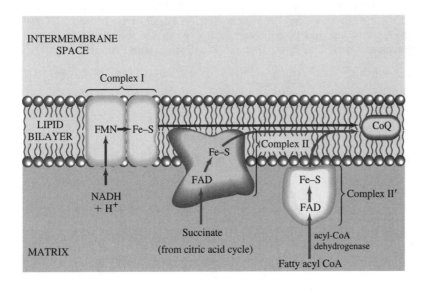

Figure 17.6 The structures and redox action of the three forms of coenzyme Q: ubiquinone, semiquinone, and ubiquinol. The oxidized form, CoQ, accepts two electrons and two protons to produce $CoQH_2$. A semiquinone intermediate is produced after transfer of one electron and one proton.

Complex I terminates at the carrier **ubiquinone**, also called **coenzyme Q** or **CoQ**. (The name is derived from its ubiquitous presence in nature.) The structure of the CoQ found commonly in mammalian systems is shown in Figure 17.6. CoQ is the smallest and most hydrophobic of all the carriers. The long hydrocarbon side chain of CoQ acts as an anchor to hold it in the nonpolar inner mitochondrial membrane. When ubiquinone (CoQ) accepts two electrons and two protons it is reduced to ubiquinol ($CoQH_2$; Figure 17.6). A semiquinone intermediate is formed after transfer of one electron.

Complex II

Coenzyme Q also serves as the entry point for electrons from the cofactor $FADH_2$. At least two forms of complex II are present in the mitochondrial membrane. The enzymes succinate dehydrogenase (citric acid cycle) and acyl-CoA dehydrogenase (β oxidation; see Chapter 18) direct the transfer of electrons from their substrate molecules (succinate and acyl-CoA) to CoQ via $FADH_2$. Both of these enzymes have iron–sulfur clusters as prosthetic groups and are present as integral proteins in the inner mitochondrial membrane (Figure 17.7). All electrons that enter the transport chain from NADH and $FADH_2$ must pass through the ubiquinone/ubiquinol pair (coenzyme Q). Some nutritionists recommend daily supplements of CoQ as an antioxidant and to help prevent heart disease and some cancers (see Biochemistry in the Clinic 17).

Figure 17.7 Entry of $FADH_2$ electrons into electron transport (complexes II and II′). Electrons from succinate and fatty acyl-CoA substrates are transported by specific FAD-linked dehydrogenases to CoQ.

Figure 17.8 Complex III transfers electrons from CoQH₂ to cytochrome *c* (cyt *c*), which acts as a mobile shuttle to carry electrons to complex IV. The electron carriers in Complex III are iron–sulfur clusters and cytochromes.

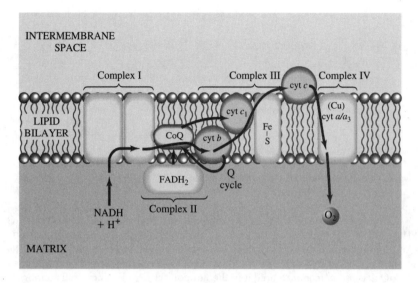

Complex III

In the next segment of the chain, complex III, electrons are transferred from ubiquinol to cytochrome *c* (Figure 17.8). The electron carriers in complex III are iron–sulfur clusters and cytochromes. The iron–sulfur clusters are similar to those already described. **Cytochromes** are electron-transferring proteins that contain a heme prosthetic group (Figure 17.9). Note that the cytochromes resemble the oxygen-carrying proteins myoglobin and hemoglobin. Cytochromes are highly colored because of the presence of the heme prosthetic group. The red-brown color in animal muscle is due to cytochromes (and myoglobin). Wild game birds have dark breast meat because of a high concentration of mitochondrial cytochromes in active flight muscle. Domestic birds (chickens, turkeys, etc.) have white breast meat because of a lower concentration of cytochromes in less active flight muscle.

Each cytochrome molecule, with its heme group, is able to accept and donate only one electron per redox cycle. The iron atom in the heme cycles through the reduced (Fe^{2+}) and oxidized (Fe^{3+}) forms. The heme structures in their different protein environments lead to slightly different reduction potentials for the cytochromes (see the table in Just in Time Review 17.1).

The transfer of electrons from reduced CoQ (CoQH₂) is not as direct as indicated in the text or figures. Complications in electron transfer arise because CoQH₂ is a two-electron donor and the cytochromes are one-electron acceptors. Electrons entering complex III via CoQH₂ separate into interlinking paths that result in the **Q cycle**

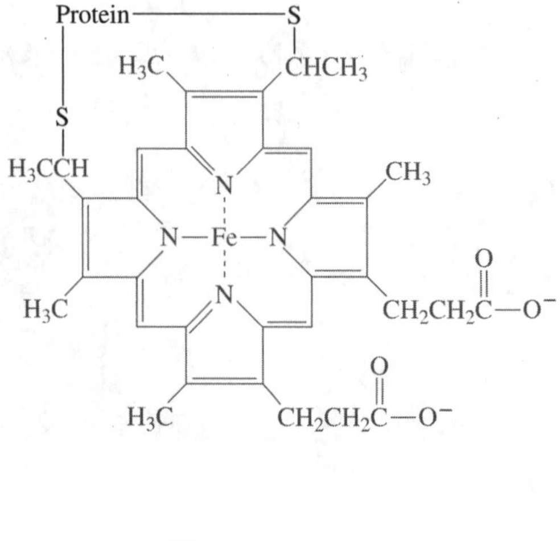

Figure 17.9 The structure of heme *c*, the kind found in cytochrome *c*.

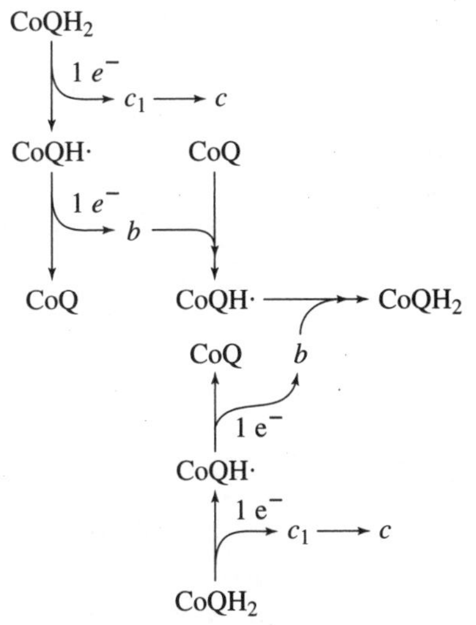

$$
\begin{array}{l}
\text{CoQH}_2 \\
\quad\downarrow 1\,e^- \\
\quad\quad\rightarrow c_1 \rightarrow c \\
\text{CoQH}\cdot \quad\quad \text{CoQ} \\
\quad\downarrow 1\,e^- \\
\quad\quad\rightarrow b \\
\text{CoQ} \quad\quad \text{CoQH}\cdot \rightarrow \text{CoQH}_2 \\
\quad\quad \text{CoQ} \quad b \\
\quad\quad\uparrow 1\,e^- \\
\quad\quad \text{CoQH}\cdot \\
\quad\quad\uparrow 1\,e^- \\
\quad\quad\quad\rightarrow c_1 \rightarrow c \\
\quad\quad \text{CoQH}_2
\end{array}
$$

Figure 17.10 The Q cycle of electron transport in complex III.

(see Figure 17.10). Some electrons from $CoQH_2$ are used to reduce cytochrome c (via cytochrome c_1). In the figure, two $CoQH_2$ molecules each transfer a single electron to a cytochrome c. The two $CoQH\cdot$ semiquinone products then each transfer an electron to a cytochrome b. The two electrons from the cytochrome b are used to generate a new $CoQH_2$. The net result is that two $CoQH_2$ molecules, bringing in four electrons, are oxidized. Two electrons are used to reduce two cytochrome c molecules and two electrons are used to regenerate a $CoQH_2$:

$$2CoQH_2 + 2cytc_{(ox)} + CoQ \rightleftharpoons 2CoQ + 2cytc_{(red)} + CoQH_2 + 2H^+$$

The Q cycle is thought to assist in maintaining the proton gradient necessary for ATP synthesis.

Complex IV

The final complex in the electron-transport chain is composed of cytochromes a and a_3, combined into a carrier called **cytochrome c oxidase**. It consists of ten protein subunits with two types of prosthetic groups, two hemes (a and a_3), and two copper atoms (see Figure 17.8). Electrons passing from cytochrome c to O_2 flow through the iron atoms in the two hemes and the copper atoms. Copper cycles through cuprous (Cu^+) and cupric Cu^{2+} ions. Of all the carriers in the chain, cytochromes a and a_3 are the only ones capable of *direct transfer* of electrons to O_2. A total of four electrons is necessary to reduce O_2 to H_2O:

$$O_2 + 4e^- + 4H^+ \rightleftharpoons 2H_2O$$

The flow of electrons from NADH (or $FADH_2$) through the various complexes to O_2 drives the movement of protons across the inner membrane (from matrix to intermembrane space). A proton gradient provides energy for ATP formation.

Elucidating the actual sequence of respiratory electron carriers has been a popular subject for biochemical study. Several lines of experimental evidence support the order as we have outlined here:

1. Complex studies on the unique absorption of light by the oxidized and reduced forms of each carrier. The ultraviolet–visible absorption spectrum of a carrier varies with redox state.

2. Experimental measurements of the standard reduction potentials, $E^{\circ\prime}$, for each component of the chain. This required the tedious task of isolating, purifying, and measuring each carrier.

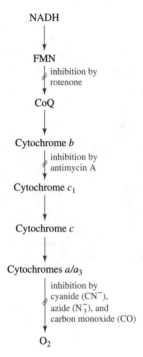

NADH

↓

FMN

↓ inhibition by rotenone

CoQ

↓

Cytochrome b

↓ inhibition by antimycin A

Cytochrome c_1

↓

Cytochrome c

↓

Cytochromes a/a_3

↓ inhibition by cyanide (CN^-), azide (N_3^-), and carbon monoxide (CO)

O_2

Figure 17.11 Inhibition of mitochondrial electron transport. Several chemicals are shown that block electron transport at specific locations. Rotenone and antimycin A have little effect on human mitochondrial electron transport except at very high concentrations; however, CN^-, N_3^-, and CO are extremely toxic to humans and other animals.

3. The use of chemicals that inhibit the flow of electrons at specific points in the chain. In Figure 17.11 are shown three types of electron flow inhibitors and their sites of action. Rotenone, a fish poison and insecticide, inhibits electron transfer between NADH and CoQ (probably between the iron–sulfur cluster and CoQ in complex I). The antibiotic antimycin A inhibits flow of electrons from cytochrome b to cytochrome c_1 (in complex III) in bacterial electron-transport chains. Cyanide (CN^-), azide (N_3^-), and carbon monoxide (CO) block electron flow from cytochromes a and a_3 to O_2. The CN^-, N_3^-, and CO may act by complexing with copper atoms in cytochrome oxidase, thereby interfering with the binding of O_2 to complex IV.

17.3 Oxidative Phosphorylation

Learning Objective

Be able to explain the process of oxidative phosphorylation, the linkage of electron transport to ATP formation.

The process of oxidative phosphorylation is the combination of two distinct activities, which can be summarized in reaction form:

1. The flow of electrons from NADH (or $FADH_2$) to molecular oxygen via the electron-transport chain:

$$NADH + H^+ + \tfrac{1}{2}O_2 \longrightarrow H_2O + NAD^+ \qquad \Delta G^{\circ\prime} = -220\ \text{kJ/mol}$$

The downhill flow of electrons from a high energy level in NADH and $FADH_2$ to O_2 releases large amounts of energy, measured in terms of $\Delta G^{\circ\prime}$, to drive the second process:

2. The phosphorylation of ADP by inorganic phosphate, synthesizing ATP:

$$ADP + P_i \rightleftharpoons ATP + H_2O \qquad \Delta G^{\circ\prime} = +31\ \text{kJ/mol}$$

Step 2 is catalyzed by the inner mitochondrial membrane enzyme **ATP synthase**. The energy from electron transport is collected and converted into a form appropriate to drive the reaction of ATP synthesis. In the intact mitochondrion, the two processes of electron transport and ATP synthesis are linked together or coupled. Each process is dependent on the other. Electrons do not flow from nutrients to O_2 unless there is a need for ATP synthesis (high concentrations of ADP must be present). ATP cannot be generated by oxidative phosphorylation unless there is energy from electron transport.

The stoichiometry of oxidative phosphorylation may be studied by using isolated, intact mitochondria that are supplied with O_2, oxidizable substrates such as pyruvate or succinate, ADP, P_i, and NAD^+ or FAD. Each molecule of pyruvate oxidized by the pyruvate dehydrogenase complex causes the formation of one molecule of NADH (two electrons from pyruvate are transferred to NAD^+). When the two electrons in the reduced cofactor pass through the electron-transport chain, about three molecules of ATP are made for each oxygen atom reduced. (Because of proton leakage back into the matrix, the exact number of ATP is between two and three, probably about 2.5 ATP. For ease of later calculations and for consistency, we will use 3 ATP.) Thus, the net overall reaction for mitochondrial NADH oxidation is

$$NADH + H^+ + 3ADP + 3P_i + \tfrac{1}{2}O_2 \longrightarrow NAD^+ + 4H_2O + 3ATP$$

Each molecule of succinate, on oxidation by succinate dehydrogenase, leads to the formation of one $FADH_2$. Two electrons from $FADH_2$ enter the electron-transport chain at CoQ and lead to the production of about two ATPs on reduction of O_2.

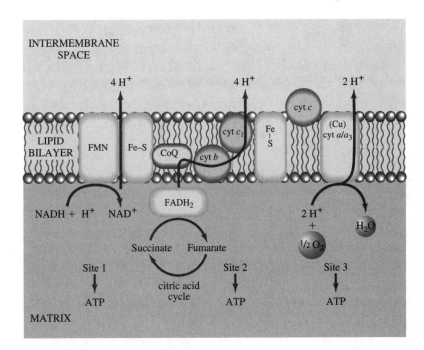

Figure 17.12 Locations of the three energy-coupling sites in the mitochondrial electron-transport chain. Site 1 is between the NADH and CoQ; site 2 is in the cytochrome c reductase region, and site 3 is in cytochromes a/a_3. As two electrons pass through each site, one ATP is produced by phosphorylation of ADP.

Coupling of Electron Transport with ATP Synthesis

The mechanistic study of oxidative phosphorylation has been an active and controversial area of biochemical research. Beginning in the early 1940s, several American and British biochemists, including S. Ochoa, A. Lehninger, D. Green, E. Racker, P. Mitchell, and P. Boyer, attempted to describe the coupling details of electron transport and ATP synthesis. One of the first experimental findings was the relationship between the number of moles of ATP generated per mole of oxygen reduced to H_2O. This is often expressed as the P/O ratio, that is, the number of molecules of ATP formed (ADP + P_i) per pair of electrons that moves through the chain to oxygen. For NADH oxidation, P/O is about 3. For $FADH_2$, P/O is about 2. (Experimental measurements show actual ratios of 2.5 and 1.5, respectively.) These results can be explained by assuming there are *three* discrete coupling sites along the electron chain between the entry of NADH and oxygen (Figure 17.12). Electrons from $FADH_2$ enter the chain at a point beyond the first coupling site. Passage of two electrons through each site leads to the formation of an ATP at that site. After years of intense study we now know that there is one coupling site in each of three main enzyme complexes: Site 1 is in NADH-CoQ reductase (complex I), site 2 is in cytochrome c reductase (complex III), and site 3 is in cytochrome c oxidase (complex IV).

After the coupling sites and their locations were identified, the next challenge for biochemists was to define the mechanism of **energy coupling**: How is energy from electron transport transduced (changed) to a form of energy that can be used to phosphorylate ADP? This requires a change from electrochemical (redox) energy to chemical (phosphoanhydride bond) energy. Several mechanisms of coupling have been proposed:

1. It was first suggested that electron transport caused the formation of high-energy covalent intermediates that transferred energy to ATP generation. No experimental evidence for such energy-rich intermediates has yet been found.

2. A second hypothesis was that electron transport energy was stored in high-energy protein conformational forms. As with the previous suggestion, no one has obtained experimental evidence for conformational intermediates.

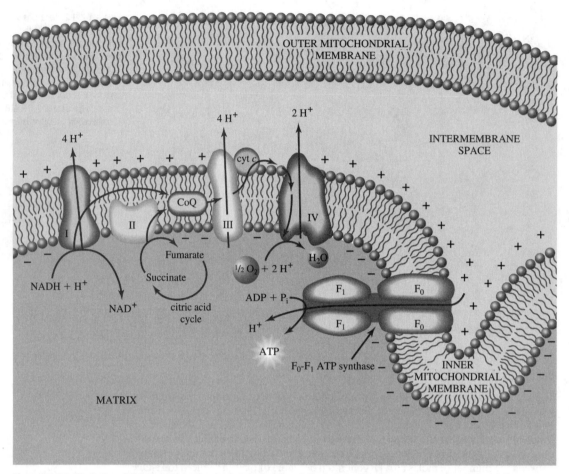

Figure 17.13 Mechanism of chemiosmotic coupling. As electrons flow through the three coupling sites, protons are pumped through the inner membrane. A proton differential or gradient is built up because proton concentration becomes higher in the intermembrane space relative to the matrix. Upon collapse, this high-energy situation provides the driving force for ATP synthesis. The F_0-F_1 ATP synthase is associated with the inner membrane. I, II, III, and IV refer to the four electron-transport complexes.

3. A very different mechanism was proposed by Peter Mitchell in 1961. His hypothesis, the **chemiosmotic coupling mechanism**, suggests that *electron transport through the carriers in the inner membrane causes the unidirectional pumping of protons from the inner mitochondrial matrix to the other side of the membrane* (into the intermembrane space; Figure 17.13). Mitchell and others, over a period of several years, obtained important experimental results that supported this idea. Proton pumping occurs at each of the three coupling sites as a pair of electrons passes the site. The concentration of H^+ becomes higher in the intermembrane space than in the matrix; that is, a proton gradient is established. In carefully designed experiments, Mitchell was able to measure a difference of about 1.4 pH units between the two sides of the membrane (a higher concentration of protons or lower pH in the intermembrane space). The proton gradient can be established and maintained because protons cannot diffuse through the inner membrane back into the matrix. With a greater positive charge on one side of the membrane, an electrochemical potential difference exists across the membrane. In terms of thermodynamics, the proton gradient is an unstable, highly energetic system. Collapse of the gradient releases free energy that is channeled to the synthesis of ATP.

Components of ATP Synthase

We turn now to the process of ATP synthesis by phosphorylation of ADP using energy from collapse of the proton gradient. This is catalyzed by the enzyme complex **ATP synthase**. The ATP synthase system is present as spheres projecting from the matrix side of the inner membrane. ATP synthase consists of two units (or factors), F_1 and F_0 (Figure 17.14). The knobs, composed of F_1 particles, can be removed from the membrane by mechanical shaking. F_1 contains a catalytic site for ATP synthesis where ADP and P_i are brought together for combination. The F_1 component is a peripheral protein that is held in place on the membrane by interaction with an integral membrane component, F_0. F_0 serves as the transmembrane channel for proton flow. The F_0-F_1 complex serves as the molecular apparatus for coupling proton movement to ATP synthesis.

In spite of extensive research, the detailed mechanism of ATP formation by the complex is still not entirely clear, but results reported by J. Walker and P. Boyer have provided new insight (Nobel Prize in Chemistry, 1997). Energy released by collapse of the proton gradient (return of protons through a channel in F_0 to the matrix region) is transmitted to the ATP synthase. The chemical energy associated with the proton gradient across the inner mitochondrial membrane is transformed into mechanical energy. Conformational changes in the subunits of the F_0-F_1 complex resemble the rotation of a motor shaft and release ATP from the bound ADP and P_i with each turn.

Regulation of Oxidative Phosphorylation

Under normal physiological conditions electron transport is tightly coupled to phosphorylation of ADP. (Recall that a major function of energy metabolism is to maintain constant ATP levels.) Electrons do not flow down the electron-transport chain to O_2 unless ADP and P_i are present for phosphorylation. Thus, the flow of electrons is regulated by the concentration of ADP. This form of regulation is similar to the control of other metabolic reactions. If high levels of ADP are present in cells ATP must have been consumed to increase ADP levels. The increased level of ADP triggers an increase in the rate of catabolic reactions on nutrients. The enzymes glycogen phosphorylase, phosphofructokinase, citrate synthase, and others are stimulated to enhance the rate of nutrient oxidation. This leads in turn to the production of substrate-level ATP and GTP but, more importantly, to NADH and $FADH_2$; these can be oxidized by the electron-transport chain, thereby producing ATP. Again, we see how all metabolic processes are coordinated to maintain a proper balance of ATP and ADP (see Section 15.5).

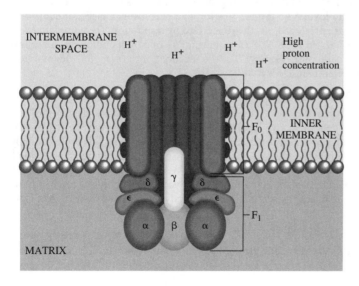

Figure 17.14 The structure of the ATP synthase (F_0-F_1 complex). F_0 acts as a channel for flow of protons back to the matrix, which results in collapse of the gradient. When protons flow through the ATPase (F_1 component) it is activated to catalyze the phosphorylation of ADP. α, β, γ, δ, and ε label protein subunits in F_1.

Uncoupling Proteins Under some specialized physiological conditions, the tight coupling of electron transport and ADP phosphorylation is disrupted (the two processes are uncoupled). The rate of electron transport is no longer controlled by the ADP concentrations but by thermodynamics. If the two processes are unlinked, electrons speed down the electron transport chain at an uncontrolled rate. Large amounts of O_2 and nutrients are consumed but no ATP is synthesized. The energy from electron transport normally used to make ATP is released in the form of heat.

The strategy of uncoupling is used by some newborn animals and hibernating mammals such as bears to maintain body heat. Some animals (including human infants) have large amounts of a specialized type of adipose tissue called **brown fat**. The color is the result of high concentrations of mitochondria containing highly colored cytochromes. In brown fat mitochondria, an integral inner membrane protein called **uncoupling protein** (UCP1) or **thermogenin** provides a channel for the return of pumped protons from the intermembrane space back into the matrix. This route of proton flow bypasses the F_0-F_1 complex; thus, the energy is released as heat instead of ATP.

Some plants use uncoupling proteins to protect sensitive tissue from freezing. The easily damaged floral spike of the eastern skunk cabbage is kept at temperatures as much as 20°F above ambient temperatures in the winter by uncoupling processes. This thermogenic organ also enhances release of volatile amines that attract insects to ensure its pollination.

For a brief period in the 1930s, the chemical 2,4-dinitrophenol was prescribed as a dieting aid. Individuals using this drug experienced heavy breathing (excessive consumption of O_2), loss of body weight (uncontrolled rate of breakdown of nutrients, fats, and carbohydrates), and excessive perspiring and fever (an increase in body temperature). Studies showed that 2,4-dinitrophenol was an uncoupling agent. Although it was effective in burning off fat, its use in diet pills was halted because of a very high level of toxicity (see p. 513).

17.4 Energy Yield from Glucose Metabolism

Learning Objective

Be able to compute the total energy from glucose metabolism in terms of ATP and understand the function of metabolic shuttles.

We now have the information needed to estimate the energy yield (in terms of ATP) on complete oxidation of carbohydrates. We have tallied the production of ATP (or GTP), NADH, and $FADH_2$ during the preliminary stages of catabolism. The amount of substrate-level ATP is quite low for glucose; however, large amounts of reduced cofactors are produced, which are recycled by respiration. The complete oxidation of glucose yields 36 or 38 ATP (assuming a P/O of 3), depending on the cellular location of its catabolism (Table 17.2). The reaction for the complete degradation of glucose in skeletal muscle is as follows:

$$\text{glucose} + 36ADP + 36P_i + 36H^+ + 6O_2 \longrightarrow 6CO_2 + 36ATP + 42H_2O$$

A brief outline of glucose oxidation and the energy yield are displayed in Table 17.2. NADH is generated by glycolysis (two molecules), pyruvate dehydrogenase (two molecules), and the citric acid cycle (six molecules). $FADH_2$ is produced only by the citric acid cycle (two $FADH_2$ per glucose). Substrate-level phosphorylation leads to a total of four ATP (in some organisms two ATP and two GTP). All of the $FADH_2$ and the NADH, except that produced in glycolysis (cytoplasm), is made in the mitochondrial matrix and can be oxidized directly by the electron-transport chain.

Recycling of Cytoplasmic NADH

NADH generated outside the mitochondria cannot be transported through the inner mitochondrial membrane into the matrix region where respiratory assemblies are

Table 17.2
Energy yield from the complete oxidation of glucose

Metabolic Stage	$NADH^a$	$FADH_2$	Substrate-Level Phosphorylation
Glycolysis	2 (cyto)	0	2 (ATP)
Pyruvate dehydrogenation	2 (mito)	0	0
Citric acid cycle	6 (mito)	2	2 (GTP)
Subtotal	2 (cyto) 8 (mito)	2	4

Oxidative Phosphorylation

Glycerol-3-Phosphate Shuttle

2 cyto NADH × 2 ATP	=	4 ATP
8 mito NADH × 3 ATP	=	24 ATP
2 FADH$_2$ × 2 ATP	=	4 ATP
Substrate level	=	4 ATP (or GTP)
Grand total		36 ATP

Malate–Aspartate Shuttle

2 cyto NADH × 3 ATP	=	6 ATP
8 mito NADH × 3 ATP	=	24 ATP
2 FADH$_2$ × 2 ATP	=	4 ATP
Substrate level	=	4 ATP (or GTP)
Grand total		38 ATP

^{a}cyto, cytoplasmic; mito, mitochondrial.

located. Cytoplasmic NADH must be recycled by electron shuttle systems, which carry electrons through the membrane in the form of reduced substrates. The **glycerol-3-phosphate shuttle** functions in skeletal muscle and brain (Figure 17.15).

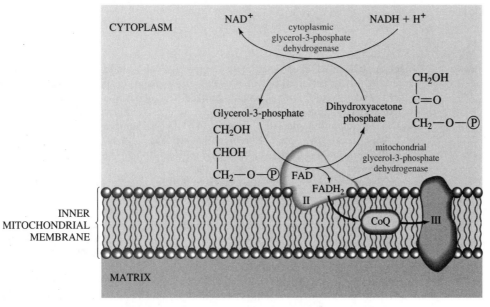

Figure 17.15 Reactions of the glycerol-3-phosphate shuttle. Cytoplasmic NADH is oxidized during the reduction of dihydroxyacetone phosphate to glycerol-3-phosphate. This reduced substrate is oxidized to dihydroxyacetone phosphate using a membrane-bound, FAD-linked dehydrogenase as catalyst. The electrons in FADH$_2$ enter the electron-transport chain at CoQ via complex II, bypassing complex I and coupling site 1.

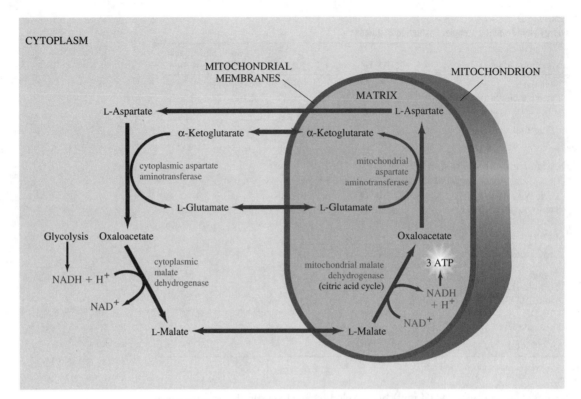

Figure 17.16 Reactions of the malate–aspartate shuttle. Cytoplasmic NADH is oxidized during the reduction of oxaloacetate to malate. Malate diffuses into the matrix, where it is oxidized to oxaloacetate using an NAD-linked dehydrogenase as catalyst. Thus, three ATP molecules are produced on oxidation of the matrix-generated NADH. Oxaloacetate is transformed to aspartate, which diffuses to the cytoplasm where it is converted back to oxaloacetate.

Electrons from NADH are used to make glycerol-3-phosphate. The dehydrogenase catalyzing the reduction of dihydroxyacetone phosphate on the cytoplasmic side is NAD linked. Glycerol-3-phosphate is oxidized by a membrane-bound, FAD-linked dehydrogenase, leading to $FADH_2$. The electrons originally in NADH are now in $FADH_2$, which enters electron transport at CoQ (via complex II), leading to two ATP. We can make the general statement that *cytoplasmic NADH produced in skeletal muscle and brain is oxidized by the glycerol-3-phosphate shuttle, resulting in only two ATP produced by oxidative phosphorylation.*

On the other hand, the **malate–aspartate shuttle**, which is present in heart and liver, leads to three ATP for each cytoplasmic NADH. Electrons from cytoplasmic NADH are carried through the inner membrane by the substrate malate, which is oxidized in the matrix by mitochondrial malate dehydrogenase, an NAD-linked enzyme (Figure 17.16). Thus, in heart and liver, cytoplasmic NADH oxidized by the malate–aspartate shuttle results in three ATP in oxidative phosphorylation. In summary, each glucose oxidized in skeletal muscle and brain produces 36 ATP; glucose oxidized by heart and liver cells yields a total of 38 ATP. Of the 36 ATP produced from glucose oxidation in skeletal muscle, only 4 come from substrate-level phosphorylation. Thirty-two ATPs are generated by oxidative phosphorylation. Therefore $32/36 \times 100$ or 89% of the ATP generated from glucose is produced during oxidative phosphorylation. (For another use of oxygen, see Window on Biochemistry 17-1.)

Nutrition: You Are What You Eat

14

Have you seen *Super Size Me*—the movie by the man who ate nothing but McDonald's food for one excruciating month? Part of the delicious delight of watching Morgan Spurlock work his way through endless Big Macs stems from pure contrariness. Your mother, after all, told you not to eat junk food, and here is Spurlock, gobbling like mad. The other delight comes from your mother's vindication. Sure enough, Spurlock suffers mightily for his excess.

Long ago, when the Beatles sang, "You know that what you eat, you are," the idea that food might affect health was revolutionary. Not anymore. Today, the idea that the food you consume can affect your health is commonplace. Indeed, many are surprised by a study that finds, for example, that eating less fat may not reduce the incidence of breast cancer or that calcium supplements may not ward off osteoporosis.

At the center of all this concern is nutrition. In an era of rising obesity in the developed world but tragically persistent starvation and undernourishment in many countries, the right to safe and nutritious food is always a critical issue. The goal of this chapter is to increase your nutritional literacy. The next chapter will discuss the digestive system—the organs and processes that convert food into simple compounds that the body can use to build and maintain cells and tissues.

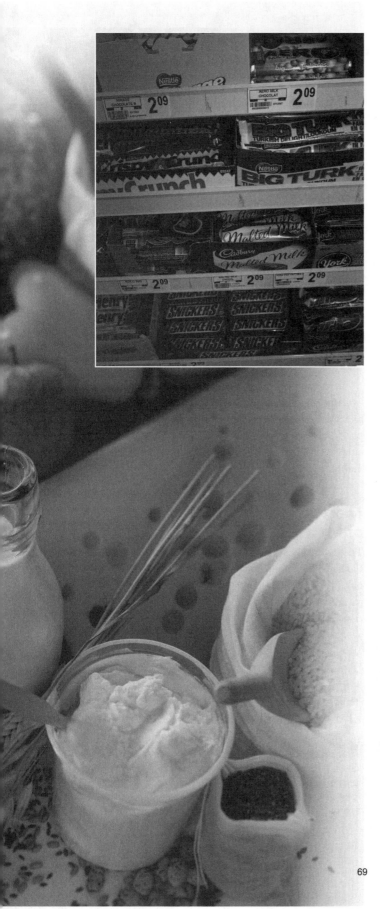

Chapter Outline

14.1 Nutrients Are Life Sustaining

LEARNING OBJECTIVES

1. **Differentiate** between macronutrients and micronutrients.

2. **Describe** how nutrients enter cells.

3. **Explain** how My Pyramid helps in making informed dietary choices.

All **aerobic** cells, and therefore all humans, need oxygen to survive. Oxygen drives the use of energy at the cellular level by serving as the ultimate electron "pull," creating the hydrogen ion concentration gradient required to form ATP. However, one cannot live by oxygen alone!

aerobic Requiring oxygen to metabolize.

nutrients Ingredients in food that are required by the body.

The cells of our body require **nutrients** in usable form to maintain homeostasis and create ATP. Because we are heterotrophs (see Chapter 2), we cannot manufacture our own organic compounds, so we must obtain them from the environment. Consequently, we spend a great deal of our time locating, preparing, and ingesting food.

Eating is so important that virtually every culture has elaborate rituals surrounding food. Think of your last Thanksgiving celebration, or even your birthday. Both of these events traditionally include a specific celebratory food: turkey with all the trimmings, or a cake with candles. In both cases, there are rituals surrounding the food. We take a moment to reflect on all the good things in our lives before eating Thanksgiving dinner, and we sing "Happy Birthday" and blow out candles before cutting the birthday cake.

Although we may not understand why, we intuitively know that we need nutrients in order to survive. What exactly are nutrients? A nutrient is defined as any compound required by the body. The two main types of nutrients are **macronutrients** (carbohydrates, lipids, and proteins) and **micronutrients** (vitamins and minerals). Both types describe organic and inorganic compounds that the body obtains from food rather than synthesizing itself. We ingest carbohydrates, lipids, and proteins to provide the necessary energy and materials for the body to create its own carbohydrates, lipids, and proteins. From these macronutrients, the body synthesizes cellular components, such as the cell membrane, enzymes, organelles, and even entirely new cells during cell division. We require micronutrients for the proper functioning of essential compounds, such as the enzymes of cellular respiration. Review Chapter 3 to refresh your understanding of carbohydrates, lipids, and proteins.

It is important to note that we take part in **nutrient cycling**, the flow of nutrients from our environment to us and back again to our environment. Bacteria and fungi play a crucial role in breaking down large organic molecules into small ones so our waste can be reused in the soil and reabsorbed by plants.

There Are Three Classes of Macronutrients

The average supermarket contains more than 20,000 food products, some of which are seen in **Figure 14.1**, but these all come down to three macronutrient groups: carbohydrates, fats, and proteins. These groupings are distinct from the six major food groups—grains, vegetables,

Three macronutrients packaged in thousands of ways • Figure 14.1

The supermarket is a marvel of macronutrient inventory management and delivery. However, some argue that supermarkets should be organized differently, and should move from a functional organization (coffee in "beverages" and cornflakes in "cereals") to a consumer organization—coffee and cornflakes in a "breakfast" section—or even a nutritional organization using food groups as the base.

fruits, milk, meat/beans, and oils—which are classified by food type rather than by their biochemical makeup (food groups are discussed later in the chapter). For example, fruits, a food group, provide us with carbohydrates in the form of fructose, and meats, another food group, are rich in protein.

Carbohydrates are our best source of energy.

One macronutrient that we often hear about in diet discussions is **carbohydrates**, and for good reason. Carbohydrates are our most efficient source of energy, meaning that when we digest carbohydrates we are left with nothing but energy, water, and carbon dioxide. With carbohydrates there are no difficult waste compounds to dispose of! Carbohydrates are composed of carbon, hydrogen, and oxygen in a 1:2:1 ratio and are in their simplest form merely carbon (*carbo*) plus water (*hydrate*). The most common carbohydrate, glucose, has the chemical formula $C_6H_{12}O_6$. Our cells are excellent at breaking down glucose to produce ATP or synthesize amino acids, glycogen, or triglycerides. Carbohydrate digestion is so efficient that we can ingest glucose and break it down completely into energy, carbon dioxide, and water. This reaction is summarized in **Figure 14.2**. Although our bodies are efficient carbohydrate-burning machines, some fad diets encourage us to avoid this energy source.

Lipids are another class of macronutrient.

Lipids—fats—are a second class of macronutrient. Fats are long chains of carbon molecules, but they have many more carbon atoms and far fewer oxygen atoms than do carbohydrates.

Fats can be either **saturated**, meaning that every space in the carbon chain is occupied with hydrogens, or **unsaturated**, meaning that there are one or more double bonds in the carbon chain, as shown in **Figure 14.3** on the following page. In the case of unsaturated fat, if one double bond is present, the fat is termed *monounsaturated;* if the fat has more than one double bond, it is *polyunsaturated*. Because double bonds make kinks in the long carbon chains, unsaturated fats cannot pack together tightly. Unsaturated fats, including vegetable oils, are liquid at room temperature. Saturated fats are solid at room temperature and are usually derived from animals.

We need a little fat in our diet; however, most of us consume more than we need because fats of various kinds are added to many foods. Fats carry flavor and add texture to food. According to marketing tests, they coat the mouth and provide much-craved oral gratification. However, the American Cancer Society reports that diets high in fat can increase the incidence of cancer; accordingly, it has developed a set of recommendations for minimizing fat intake.

Structure of glucose and digestion reaction • Figure 14.2

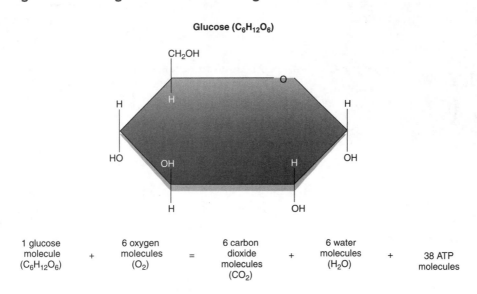

Glucose ($C_6H_{12}O_6$)

| 1 glucose molecule ($C_6H_{12}O_6$) | + | 6 oxygen molecules (O_2) | = | 6 carbon dioxide molecules (CO_2) | + | 6 water molecules (H_2O) | + | 38 ATP molecules |

Biological InSight   Saturated and unsaturated fats   •   Figure 14.3

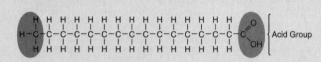

Saturated fatty acid: palmitic acid

Meats, butter, milk, and cheese are examples of foods rich in saturated fats.

Acid Group

Carbon-carbon double bonds

Polyunsaturated fatty acid: alpha-linoleic acid (omega-3)

Synthetic margarine is an example of a polyunsaturated fat that can be created as a trans fat or a cis fat.

Cis fats have the hydrogens on the same side of the main chain, whereas trans fats have one hydrogen above the chain and the other below.

Linoleic acid: *trans* configuration (*trans* isomer)

Linoleic acid: *cis* configuration (*cis* isomer)

Most animal products contain saturated fats, particularly those from beef and lamb. Most plants produce unsaturated fats, the notable exceptions being coconuts, cocoa butter, and palm kernel oils. For this reason, vegetable oil is liquid at room temperature, whereas butter and cocoa butter are solid.

Monounsaturated fatty acid: oleic acid (omega-9)

Olive oil and sunflower seeds contain monounsaturated fats. These occur as oils at room temperature.

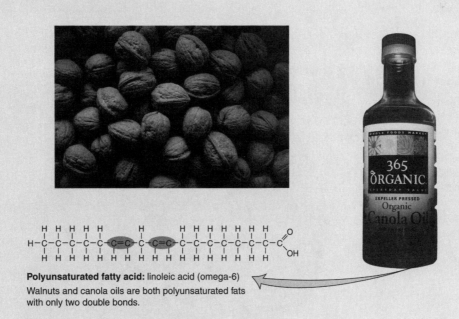

Polyunsaturated fatty acid: linoleic acid (omega-6)

Walnuts and canola oils are both polyunsaturated fats with only two double bonds.

14.1 Nutrients Are Life Sustaining **381**

These are listed in **Table 14.1**. High-fat diets are high in **calories**, leading to obesity, which is associated with increased cancer risk. Saturated fats may increase cancer risk, whereas other fats, such as **omega-3** fats from fish oils, may reduce the risk of cancer.

> **calorie** A measure of the amount of heat stored in food. One Calorie is the amount of heat needed to raise the temperature of 1 kilogram of water 1 degree Celsius.

Because fats are not soluble in water, they are not readily transported through our watery blood. They therefore combine with protein to form a **lipoprotein**, as shown in **Figure 14.4**. The lipids are "coated" with proteins, phospholipids (see Chapter 3), and cholesterol. Recall that phospholipids are polar at their phosphate end, allowing the molecule to be suspended in an aqueous environment. The technical term for molecules with both a hydrophylic end and a hydrophobic end is *amphipathic*. Low-density lipoproteins (LDLs) contain 25% protein, 20% phospholipids, 45% cholesterol, and 10% other lipids. LDLs carry most of the cholesterol in our blood and can deposit it in and around the smooth muscle fibers in arteries. This process forms fatty plaques that increase the risk of coronary artery disease. Hence, the cholesterol found in LDLs is called "bad" cholesterol. High-density lipoproteins (HDLs), on the other hand, contain about 45% protein, 30% phospholipids, and only about

Good and bad fats   Table 14.1
To limit your intake of cholesterol, *trans* fat, and saturated fat:
• Trim the fat from your steak and roast beef.
• Serve chicken and fish, but don't eat the skin.
• Try a vegetarian meal once a week.
• Limit your eggs to one or two a week.
• Choose low-fat milk and yogurt.
• Use half your usual amount of butter or margarine.
• Have only a small order of fries, or share them with a friend.
To increase your intake of polyunsaturated and monoun-saturated fats:
• Use olive, peanut, or canola oil for cooking and salad dressing.
• Use corn, sunflower, or safflower oil for baking.
• Snack on nuts and seeds.
• Add olives and avocados to your salad.
To increase your omega-3 intake:
• Sprinkle flax seed on your cereal or yogurt.
• Add another serving of fish to your weekly menu.
• Have a leafy green vegetable with dinner.
• Add walnuts to your cereal.

A lipoprotein • Figure 14.4

As the name suggests, lipoproteins are composed of a lipid attached to a protein. The relative size of each component determines the density of the lipoprotein: A higher percentage of lipid equals lower density lipoprotein.

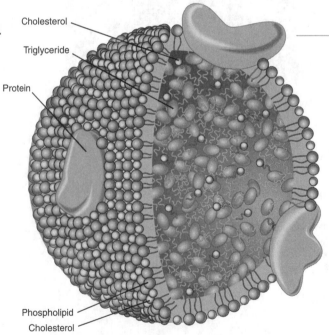

Cholesterol

Triglyceride

Protein

Phospholipid

Cholesterol

382 CHAPTER 14 Nutrition: You Are What You Eat

Essential and nonessential amino acids	Table 14.2a
Essential amino acids	**Nonessential amino acids**
Isoleucine	Alanine
Leucine	Arginine*
Lysine	Asparagine
Methionine	Aspartic acid (aspartate)
Phenylalanine	Cysteine (cystine)*
Threonine	Glutamic acid (glutamate)
Tryptophan	Glutamine*
Valine	Glycine*
Histidine*	Proline*
	Serine
	Tyrosine*

*The Institute of Medicine, Food and Nutrition Board classifies these amino acids as "conditionally essential" (*Dietary Reference Intakes for Energy, Carbohydrates, Fiber, Fat, Protein and Amino Acids*. Washington, DC: National Academy Press, 2002).

Complementary proteins	Table 14.2b
Rice and beans	
Rice and lentils	
Bread with peanut butter	
Tofu and cashew stir-fry	
Bean burrito in corn tortilla	
Hummus (chickpeas and sesame seeds)	
Black-eyed peas and corn bread	
Tahini (sesame seeds) and peanut sauce	
Trail mix (soybeans and nuts)	
Rice and tofu	

25% cholesterol and other lipids. With the lower percentage of cholesterol, HDLs are called "good" cholesterol. They are considered good because HDL removes excess cholesterol from the arterial wall and transports it to the liver for disposal or use.

Proteins are an essential part of our diet. The last class of macronutrients is **protein**. Proteins are an essential part of our diet because the amino acids they contain are not stored in the body. Instead of completely breaking down the amino acids of ingested proteins for energy, the body usually recycles them into proteins of its own. Of the 20 amino acids that make up living organisms, we can manufacture only 11. The remaining **essential amino acids** must come from our diet, as seen in **Table 14.2a**. Obtaining these amino acids is a problem only for people who choose not to consume red meat.

Complete proteins, such as those found in red meat and fish, contain all 20 amino acids. Unlike meat, no single vegetable or fruit contains all nine of the essential amino acids. For those who choose to restrict their meat intake, however, eating legumes and grains, or combining cereal with milk, will provide a full complement of amino ac-

ids. **Vegans** and vegetarians can be quite healthy, assuming that they monitor their protein intake. See **Table 14.2b** for a list of food combinations that contain complementary amino acids.

vegan A vegetarian who consumes only plant products, eating no animal products whatsoever.

MyPyramid Is a Dietary Guideline

Food groups are not nutrient classes. Rather, they are the major categories of foods: meats, dairy products, breads and pastas, vegetables, and oils or fats. Each group is important to overall health, and the recommended daily caloric intake for each group differs. For example, the recommended daily allowance (RDA) for meats is quite low, at two servings per day, or 50 grams for women and 63 for men. Most Americans consume far more than that. A "regular" hamburger from any fast-food establishment usually provides approximately 28 g of protein, so a typical "double" cheeseburger provides the entire daily protein requirement for an adult woman.

You may be familiar with the traditional **food guide pyramid**, which suggested healthy proportions of the food groups, based on the eating habits of healthy people in the United States and around the world. The pyramid offered guidelines for the number of servings of each type of food that should be eaten each day. At the bottom of the pyramid were breads, cereals, and pastas, with a recommended 6 to 11 servings per day. Fruits and vegetables were next, with a recommended 3 to 5 servings of each daily. Milk and cheese and proteins and beans constituted the next level, at 2 to 3 servings of each a day. At the top of the pyramid were fats, with a recommendation that they be used "sparingly."

The U.S. Department of Agriculture recently updated its food pyramid with MyPyramid, which can be found online at http://www.mypyramid.gov. (See **Figure 14.5**.) Although this pyramid is more in tune with current research, it is based on the same principles as the traditional pyramid. It still recommends that we get most of our caloric value from carbohydrates and limit our fat intake. Rather than being arranged horizontally, however, the food groups are

MyPyramid • Figure 14.5

It is important to note that carbohydrates remain our best source of energy.

arranged vertically. This provides a more accurate visual picture, because we require all the food groups in order to be healthy. The MyPyramid Web site is more personalized than earlier versions, giving recommendations for serving size and number based on age, gender, and activity level. When you submit your personal statistics, you receive food intake guidelines that are matched to your lifestyle, along with suggestions for improving your choices within each group. The suggested amount of whole grains is listed as a portion of the carbohydrates, and the vegetable group is divided into dark greens, orange vegetables, dry beans and peas, starchy vegetables, and others. Although this is by no means an exhaustive view of good eating, it provides a starting point for making healthier choices.

The MyPyramid graphic encourages moderation and variety. It also has a very small, uncolored section at the top for "discretionary" calories, such as those provided by candy and alcohol. It is worth noting that other organizations have produced different guidelines, created with the cultural and eating habits of other groups in mind. For example, the World Health Organization has a guideline that suggests eating about half the amount of fruits and vegetables recommended by MyPyramid. All of these guidelines are designed to help you maintain ideal body weight. See *I Wonder… How Is My Ideal Body Weight Determined?* for more on the concept of ideal body weight.

Vitamins and Minerals Are Micronutrients

A healthy diet must include vitamins and minerals. Unlike macronutrients, these micronutrients are not broken down but instead are used intact and are required for enzyme functioning or the synthesis of specific proteins. Vitamins are organic substances, such as thiamine, riboflavin, and vitamin A (see **Table 14.3** on the following page). Minerals are inorganic substances, such as calcium, zinc, and iodine (see **Table 14.4** on pages 388–389).

I WONDER...
How Is My Ideal Body Weight Determined?

When you go to a physician for your annual physical, one of the first measurements taken is your weight. This, along with your height, is entered on your chart for the physician to review. During the interview that follows, your physician may talk to you about your weight, perhaps suggesting that you drop a few pounds or even pick up a little weight.

What is the standard from which these recommendations stem? Interestingly, medical professionals do not themselves evaluate data on weight and corresponding health issues. Instead, insurance companies keep close tabs on the relationship between the two. Each company keeps its own records indicating the relationship between their clients' weight and the amount of money that client has cost them in health-related expenses. Over time, these companies build up an impressive data bank of weight and health-care correlations. Of course, this is nothing more than a business plan. Nevertheless, medical professionals use these weight and health statistics when reviewing patient data and often counsel their patients to remain within what the insurance companies deem a healthy weight range.

Another type of healthy body size calculation involves determining your body mass index (BMI). This is based on the ratio between your weight and height but does not take into account factors such as muscular development or bone mass. BMI is often used in diagnosing and tracking obesity, and is discussed further later in this chapter.

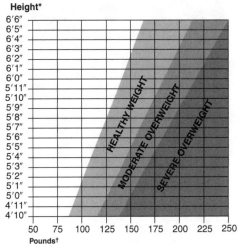

* Without shoes

† Without clothes. The higher weights apply to people with more muscle and bone, such as many men.

Vitamins   Table 14.3

Vitamins	Comment and Source	Functions	Deficiency symptoms and disorders
Fat-soluble	All require bile salts and some dietary lipids for adequate absorption.		
A	Formed from provitamin beta-carotene (and other provitamins) in GI tract. Stored in liver. Sources of carotene and other provitamins include orange, yellow, and green vegetables. *Dietary sources* of vitamin A include liver and milk.	Maintains general health and vigor of epithelial cells. Beta-carotene acts as an antioxidant to inactivate free radicals. Essential for formation of light-sensitive pigments in photoreceptors of retina. Aids in growth of bones and teeth by helping to regulate activity of osteoblasts and osteoclasts.	Deficiency results in dry skin and hair; increased incidence of ear, sinus, respiratory, urinary, and digestive system infections; inability to gain weight; drying of cornea; and skin sores. **Night blindness** or decreased ability for dark adaptation. Slow and faulty development of bones and teeth.
D	Sunlight converts 7-dehydrocholesterol in the skin to cholecalciferol (vitamin D_3). A liver enzyme then converts cholecalciferol to 25-hydroxycholecalciferol. A second enzyme in the kidneys converts 25-hydroxycholecalciferol to the active form of vitamin D. *Dietary sources* include fish-liver oils, egg yolk, and fortified milk.	Essential for absorption of calcium and phosphorus from GI tract. Works with parathyroid hormone (PTH) to maintain Ca^{2+} homeostasis.	Defective utilization of calcium by bones leads to **rickets** in children and **osteomalacia** (softened bones) in adults. Possible loss of muscle tone.
E (tocopherols)	Stored in liver, adipose tissue, and muscles. *Dietary sources* include fresh nuts and wheat germ, seed oils, and green leafy vegetables.	Inhibits breakdown of certain fatty acids that help form cell structures. Involved in formation of DNA, RNA, and red blood cells. May promote wound healing, contribute to normal structure and functioning of the nervous system, and prevent scarring. May help protect liver from toxic chemicals. Acts as an antioxidant to inactivate free radicals.	May cause oxidation of monounsaturated fats, resulting in abnormal structure and function of mitochondria, lysosomes, and plasma membranes. A possible consequence is hemolytic anemia.
K	Produced by intestinal bacteria. Stored in liver and spleen. *Dietary sources* include spinach, cauliflower, cabbage, and liver.	Coenzyme essential for synthesis of several clotting factors.	Delayed clotting time results in excessive bleeding.
Water-soluble	Dissolved in body fluids. Most are not stored in body. Excess intake is eliminated in urine.		
B₁ (thiamine)	Rapidly destroyed by heat. *Dietary sources* include whole-grain products, eggs, pork, nuts, liver, and yeast.	Acts as coenzyme for many different enzymes that break carbon-to-carbon bonds and are involved in carbohydrate metabolism. Essential for synthesis of the neurotransmitter acetylcholine.	Improper carbohydrate metabolism leads to buildup of pyruvate and lactic acids and insufficient production of ATP for muscle and nerve cells. Deficiency leads to: (1) **beriberi,** partial paralysis of smooth muscle of GI tract, causing digestive disturbances; skeletal muscle paralysis; and atrophy of limbs; (2) **polyneuritis,** due to degeneration of myelin sheaths; impaired reflexes, impaired sense of touch, stunted growth in children, and poor appetite.

Vitamins	Comment and Source	Functions	Deficiency symptoms and disorders
B$_2$ (riboflavin)	Small amounts supplied by bacteria of GI tract. *Dietary sources* include yeast, liver, beef, veal, lamb, eggs, whole-grain products, asparagus, peas, beets, and peanuts.	Component of certain coenzymes (for example, FAD) in carbohydrate and protein metabolism, especially in cells of eye, skin, intestine, and blood.	Deficiency may lead to improper utilization of oxygen resulting in blurred vision, cataracts, and corneal ulcerations. Also dermatitis and cracking of skin, lesions of intestinal mucosa, and one type of anemia.
Niacin (nicotinamide)	Derived from amino acid trypto-phan. *Dietary sources* include yeast, meats, liver, fish, whole-grain products, peas, beans, and nuts.	Essential component of NAD and NADP, coenzymes in oxidation-reduction reactions. In lipid metabolism, inhibits production of cholesterol and assists in triglyceride breakdown.	Principal deficiency is **pellagra**, characterized by dermatitis, diarrhea, and psychological disturbances.
B$_6$ (pyridoxine)	Synthesized by bacteria of GI tract. Stored in liver, muscle, and brain. *Dietary sources* include salmon, yeast, tomatoes, yellow corn, spinach, whole-grain products, liver, and yogurt.	Essential coenzyme for normal amino acid metabolism. Assists production of circulating antibodies. May function as coenzyme in triglyceride metabolism.	Most common deficiency symptom is dermatitis of eyes, nose, and mouth. Other symptoms are retarded growth and nausea.
B$_{12}$ (cyanocobalamin)	Only B vitamin not found in vegetables; only vitamin containing cobalt. Absorption from GI tract depends on intrinsic factor secreted by stomach mucosa. *Dietary sources* include liver, kidney, milk, eggs, cheese, and meat.	Coenzyme necessary for red blood cell formation, formation of the amino acid methionine, entrance of some amino acids into Krebs cycle, and manufacture of choline (used to synthesize acetylcholine).	**Pernicious anemia**, neuropsychiatric abnormalities (ataxia, memory loss, weakness, personality and mood changes, and abnormal sensations), and impaired activity of osteoblasts.
Pantothenic acid	Some produced by bacteria of GI tract. Stored primarily in liver and kidneys. *Dietary sources* include kidney, liver, yeast, green vegetables, and cereal.	Constituent of coenzyme A, which is essential for transfer of acetyl group from pyruvic acid into the Krebs cycle, conversion of lipids and amino acids into glucose, and synthesis of cholesterol and steroid hormones.	Fatigue, muscle spasms, insufficient production of adrenal steroid hormones, vomiting, and insomnia.
Folic acid (folate, folacin)	Synthesized by bacteria of GI tract. *Dietary sources* include green leafy vegetables, broccoli, asparagus, breads, dried beans, and citrus fruits.	Component of enzyme systems synthesizing nitrogenous bases of DNA and RNA. Essential for normal production of red and white blood cells.	Production of abnormally large red blood cells (**macrocytic anemia**). Higher risk of neural tube defects in babies born to folate-deficient mothers.
Biotin	Synthesized by bacteria of GI tract. *Dietary sources* include yeast, liver, egg yolk, and kidneys.	Essential coenzyme for carbohydrate metabolism and synthesis of fatty acids and purines.	Mental depression, muscular pain, dermatitis, fatigue, and nausea.
C (ascorbic acid)	Rapidly destroyed by heat. Some stored in glandular tissue and plasma. Dietary sources include citrus fruits, tomatoes, and green vegetables.	Promotes protein synthesis. As coenzyme, may combine with poisons, rendering them harmless until excreted. Works with antibodies, promotes wound healing, and functions as an antioxidant.	**Scurvy**; anemia; many symptoms related to poor collagen formation, including tender swollen gums, loosening of teeth, poor wound healing, bleeding, and retardation of growth.

14.1 Nutrients Are Life Sustaining 387

Minerals Table 14.4

Mineral	Comments and sources	Importance
Calcium	Most abundant mineral in body. Appears in combination with phosphates. About 99% is stored in bones and teeth. Blood Ca^{2+} level is controlled by parathyroid hormone (PTH). Calcitriol promotes absorption of dietary calcium. *Dietary sources* are milk, egg yolk, shellfish, and leafy green vegetables.	Formation of bones and teeth, blood clotting, normal muscle and nerve activity, endocytosis and exocytosis, cellular motility, chromosome movement during cell division, glycogen metabolism, and release of neurotransmitters and hormones.
Phosphorus	About 80% is found in bones and teeth as phosphate salts. Blood phosphate level is controlled by parathyroid hormone (PTH). *Dietary sources* are dairy products, meat, fish, poultry, and nuts.	Formation of bones and teeth. Phosphates ($H_2PO_4^-$, HPO_4^- and PO_4^{3-}) constitute a major buffer system of blood. Plays important role in muscle contraction and nerve activity. Component of many enzymes. Involved in energy transfer (ATP). Component of DNA and RNA.
Potassium	Major cation (K$^+$) in intracellular fluid. Present in most foods (meats, fish, poultry, fruits, and nuts).	Needed for formation and conduction of action potentials in neurons and muscle fibers.
Sulfur	Component of many proteins, electron carriers in electron transport chain, and some vitamins (thiamine and biotin). *Dietary sources* include beef, liver, lamb, fish, poultry, eggs, cheese, and beans.	As component of hormones and vitamins, regulates various body activities. Needed for ATP production by electron transport chain.
Sodium	Most abundant cation (Na$^+$) in extracellular fluids; some found in bones. Normal intake of NaCl (*table salt*) supplies more than the required amounts.	Strongly affects distribution of water through osmosis. Part of bicarbonate buffer system. Functions in nerve and muscle action potential conduction.
Chloride	Major anion (Cl$^-$) in extracellular fluid. *Dietary sources* include table salt (NaCl), soy sauce, and processed foods.	Plays role in acid–base balance of blood, water balance, and formation of HCl in stomach.
Magnesium	Important cation (Mg^{2+}) in intracellular fluid. *Widespread* in various foods, such as green leafy vegetables, seafood, and whole-grain cereals.	Required for normal functioning of muscle and nervous tissue. Participates in bone formation. Constituent of many coenzymes.
Iron	About 66% found in hemoglobin of blood. *Dietary sources* are meat, liver, shellfish, egg yolk, beans, legumes, dried fruits, nuts, and cereals.	As component of hemoglobin, reversibly binds O$_2$. Component of cytochromes involved in electron transport chain.
Iodine	Essential component of thyroid hormones. *Dietary sources* are seafood, iodized salt, and vegetables grown in iodine-rich soils.	Required by thyroid gland to synthesize thyroid hormones, which regulate metabolic rate.
Manganese	Some stored in liver and spleen.	Activates several enzymes. Needed for hemoglobin synthesis, urea formation, growth, reproduction, lactation, bone formation, and possibly production and release of insulin and inhibition of cell damage.
Copper	Some stored in liver and spleen. *Sources* include eggs, whole-wheat flour, beans, beets, liver, fish, spinach, and asparagus.	Required with iron for synthesis of hemoglobin. Component of coenzymes in electron transport chain and enzyme necessary for melanin formation.
Cobalt	Constituent of vitamin B$_{12}$.	As part of vitamin B$_{12}$, required for red blood cell formation.

Mineral	Comments and sources	Importance
Zinc	Important component of certain enzymes. **Widespread** in many foods, especially meats.	Important in enzyme-driven metabolism. Necessary for normal growth and wound healing, normal taste sensations and appetite, and normal sperm counts in males. Involved in protein digestion.
Fluoride	Components of bones, teeth, other tissues.	Appears to improve tooth structure and inhibit tooth decay.
Selenium	Important component of certain enzymes. **Dietary sources** are seafood, meat, chicken, tomatoes, egg yolk, milk, mushrooms, garlic, and cereal grains grown in selenium-rich soil.	Needed for synthesis of thyroid hormones, sperm motility, and proper functioning of the immune system. Also functions as an antioxidant. Prevents chromosome breakage and may play a role in preventing certain birth defects, miscarriage, prostate cancer, and coronary artery disease.
Chromium	**Found in** high concentrations in brewer's yeast. Also found in wine and some brands of beer.	Needed for normal activity of insulin in carbohydrate and lipid metabolism.

A healthy diet with plenty of fruit and vegetables will give you most of the necessary vitamins and minerals. However, many Americans now supplement their diets with moderate amounts of vitamins and minerals, just to ensure that they receive what they need on a daily basis. The usual supplement taken is an over-the-counter (OTC) multivitamin supplement. The typical ingredient list on an OTC daily multivitamin supplement includes most of what is found in Tables 14.3 and 14.4. These supplements often include vitamins E, C, and A, which help remove free radicals, thereby boosting the immune system and perhaps prolonging cell life. As with anything, excess is not healthy. Taking too large a quantity of fat-soluble vitamins can cause them to build up in the liver, hampering its functioning.

OTC vitamins usually also contain selected minerals, such as calcium, phosphorus, iodine, magnesium, and zinc, among many other micronutrients. Some minerals are found in high concentration in foods, especially prepared foods. Sodium, for example, is extremely high in most frozen and prepared foods. Because the general population consumes a large quantity of these convenience foods, sodium supplements are seldom advisable. Too much sodium in the diet may lead to hypertension.

By eating mostly whole grains, we obtain vitamins and minerals as well as glucose. Whole grain also provides **fiber**, which helps move feces along the large intestine and decreases the risk of colon cancer. **Milled** grains lose their fibrous, mineral-rich outer husk, diminishing their nutritional value. Simple carbohydrates, such as sucrose, usually provide energy and nothing else. These are sometimes called "empty calories," because they contribute more to weight gain than to homeostasis.

> **milled** Ground, as in grain that has been ground into flour.

CONCEPT CHECK

1. **What** type of nutrient is vitamin B? Is starch, a polymer of sugar, considered a macronutrient or a micronutrient?

2. **How** do nutrients enter the cell?

3. **What** personalized dietary information can be obtained from MyPyramid?

Nutrients Are Metabolized

LEARNING OBJECTIVES

1. **List** the steps of carbohydrate metabolism.

2. **Define** the difference between lipid and protein metabolism.

3. **Describe** the factors that determine how much energy our bodies expend.

The nutrients we take in must be put to work. The term **metabolism** refers to the chemical reactions in cells that break down and build up nutrients. There are two basic kinds of metabolic reactions. One kind combines molecules into more complex compounds, consuming more energy than it produces. This kind is an **anabolic** reaction. The other kind of reaction breaks molecules down, producing more energy than it consumes. This type is a **catabolic** reaction. Carbohydrates, lipids, and proteins all undergo both anabolic and catabolic reactions.

> **metabolism** The chemical reactions that take place in the body.
>
> **chemiosmosis** The diffusion of hydrogen ions across a membrane, generating ATP as the ions move from high to low concentrations.

Chemiosmosis within the inner membrane of the mitochondrion produces most of the ATP used by cells. Carbohydrate metabolism is seen in **Figure 14.6**.

Most of the glucose in our bodies is catabolized (broken down) to make ATP, but glucose can also be formed through anabolic reactions. Many glucose molecules combine to form *glycogen*, the only carbohydrate that is stored in our bodies—in the liver and skeletal muscles. The hormone *insulin* is a key to the synthesis of glycogen, a process called **glycogenesis**. There is a limit, however, to how much glycogen we can make and store. Intense athletic events such as running a marathon may completely exhaust the body's supply of glycogen, and that is why many athletes eat plenty of carbohydrates in the days before their events—a practice called "carbohydrate loading." The idea is to "load" the muscles with the maximum possible amount of stored glycogen so that energy will be readily available on the day of the race.

Carbohydrate Metabolism Can Release Energy Gradually

Carbohydrate catabolism, or cellular respiration, is actually a controlled burning of the glucose molecule through a series of enzymatic reactions that take place in our cells. Although humans do not spontaneously combust, we do release the energy in foods through a process that involves sequentially breaking chemical bonds. Burning releases energy all at once, whereas carbohydrate metabolism releases energy gradually.

The first reaction is **glycolysis**, which converts one glucose molecule into two **pyruvate** molecules, releasing a small amount of energy. Assuming that oxygen is present, the pyruvates are then passed along to a mitochondrion in the cytoplasm of the cell, where oxidation continues. The mitochondrion completes the enzymatic burning of glucose by passing the compounds through the **Krebs cycle**, in which energy-rich compounds are created, and then passing these compounds through the **electron transport chain**. These steps produce the carbon dioxide that we exhale.

> **glycolysis** The enzymatic breakdown of glucose into pyruvate, occurring within the cytoplasm.

Lipid Metabolism Is Another Source of Energy

Lipids, like carbohydrates, can be oxidized to produce ATP. If the body lacks carbohydrates, the normal source for glucose needed to produce ATP, it mobilizes fat stores and converts fat into small molecules called *ketones*. As ketones are oxidized to produce ATP, their concentration in the blood can rise above normal levels, and the body may enter a metabolic state called **ketosis**. Extreme ketosis can lead to **acidosis**, in which the pH of blood becomes very low (acidic). Acidosis is serious—it can lead to a coma or even death. A sign that a diabetic individual is critically low on insulin is sweet-smelling breath, caused by a ketone, *acetone*, diffusing from the pulmonary capillaries into the person's exhalations.

Glycolysis, the Krebs cycle, and electron transport • Figure 14.6

THE PLANNER

Glycolysis occurs in the cytoplasm, requiring two molecules of ATP to begin, but generating a total of four ATP molecules in the conversion of one molecule of glucose into two molecules of pyruvate. With oxygen present, the two pyruvate molecules are shuttled to the mitochondrion, where they are passed through a series of chemical reactions in which each step releases energy that is harvested in ATP, NADH, and $FADH_2$. These reactions are referred to as the Krebs, or TCA, cycle. The NADH and $FADH_2$ created in the Krebs cycle then drive the reactions of the electron transport chain, by which hydrogen ions are transported within the mitochondrion, creating a hydrogen ion gradient. This gradient drives chemiosmosis, the final step in this process. At this point, the energy harvested from the original glucose molecule is finally converted into about 38 ATP molecules.

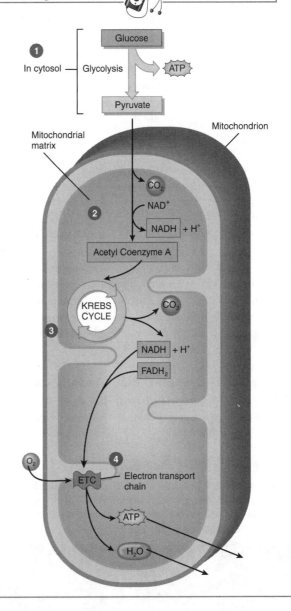

❶ Glycolysis. Oxidation of one glucose molecule to form two pyruvic acid molecules yields 2 ATPs and 2 NADH. These will form 6 ATP molecules during the ETC.

❷ Formation of two molecules of acetyl coenzyme A yields another 6 ATPs in the electron transport chain.

❸ The Krebs cycle. Oxidation of succinyl CoA to form succinic acid yields 2 ATPs, 2 molecules of $FADH_2$ and 6 molecules of NADH.

❹ The 6 NADH produced in the Krebs cycle yields 18 ATPs in the electron transport chain. The similarly produced $FADH_2$ yields 4 ATPs in the electron transport chain.

The Atkins diet keyed on lipid metabolism.

In 1972, cardiologist Robert Atkins rocked the diet world with his book about a "diet revolution" that emphasized protein and fat and discouraged eating vegetables or carbohydrates. When a revised version of the diet was published in 1992, the book became an instant best seller. Dieters waxed rhapsodic about the quick and persistent weight loss they obtained by cutting down on carbohydrates and preferring protein. However, the quick weight loss experienced in the first week is caused by water loss, and that loss cannot be sustained. Starting in the second week, the rate of weight loss slows drastically, because the only way to lose weight is to expend more energy than we take in, and the Atkins diet is calorie-rich.

As Atkins's diet book sold millions of copies, it attracted a storm of criticism from researchers and organizations concerned with nutrition and obesity. One concern was safety. With heart disease still the nation's number one killer, did it make sense to promote eating fat, which gathers in the arteries and contributes to atherosclerosis? With the antioxidants in vegetables playing an increasingly evident role in good health, should dieters abandon antioxidant-laden broccoli for high-fat meat? Doctors also pointed to the known side effects of a high-protein, high-fat diet, including kidney failure, high blood cholesterol, osteoporosis, kidney stones, and cancer.

It's hard to know whether the Atkins diet failed under a shower of expert criticism, or through the simple fact that people could not stay with it. At any rate, the Atkins diet blazed bright and fizzled like a comet zooming across the night sky.

However, the death of the Atkins diet did not mark the death of the frenzy over fat. The national obesity epidemic continues, and it's safe to predict that another fad diet cannot be far off. We can only hope that your knowledge of human biology will protect you from being taken in by an unhealthy diet. In health, as in jobs, life partners, and promises in general, the same rule applies: If it sounds too good to be true, it probably is.

Our bodies can also make and store lipids.
Just as we can catabolize lipids for energy, we can also synthesize and store them. When we consume more calories than are needed to meet our ATP needs, the body converts excess glucose into lipids called **triglycerides**. These are commonly stored in our fat cells, also called *adipose cells*. We are all familiar with the result—fat deposits. **Figure 14.7** shows some samples.

Protein Metabolism Is Also Important to Good Health

Most of the protein we eat is broken down (catabolized) into its component amino acids. Unlike carbohydrates and lipids, proteins are not stored for future use. Instead, the body immediately breaks them apart and uses the released amino acids to create its own proteins. When cells wear out and die, their proteins can also be broken down into amino acids. These amino acids are often recycled to make other proteins. The ribosomes found in almost every cell in our body make proteins out of amino acids, directed by the cell's DNA and RNA. Because proteins are so crucial to everything we do, we need to make sure we get enough from our diet, especially during our growing years, during pregnancy, and at times when we have experienced severe tissue damage.

Once we have enough protein, eating more will not increase our bone or muscle mass. The excess is merely passed from the body. Body mass can be increased only through exercise!

Fat deposits • Figure 14.7

Fat is stored in basically two areas: just beneath the skin (subcutaneously) and deep in body cavities. Some research suggests that females have slightly more subcutaneous fat storage than males, while males have slightly more deep-cavity fat storage.

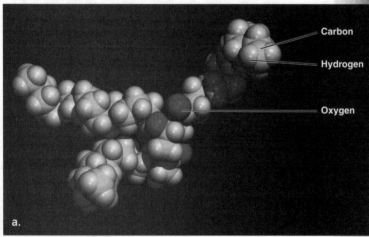

a.

Carbon

Hydrogen

Oxygen

b.

The caloric value of typical foods and the amount of energy used during moderate exercise • Figure 14.8

Food	Approximate calorie count	Approximate number of minutes of activity required to burn those calories (varies with body weight)
2 slices cheese pizza	800	86–92 minutes of playing basketball
Large blueberry muffin	465	47–57 minutes of mountain climbing
3 chicken wings	360	50–55 minutes of weightlifting
Candy bar	280	45–50 minutes of swimming
Breakfast pastry	170	25–30 minutes of playing Frisbee
Banana	112	30–35 minutes of windsurfing
Serving of strawberry yogurt	108	15–18 minutes of slow jogging
Orange	59	35–37 minutes canoeing

Energy Input Should Match Energy Output

When the amount of energy provided by all the nutrients taken in by the body matches the amount of energy it expends, body weight remains constant. This is known as *energy homeostasis*. When the two amounts don't match, we either gain or lose weight. We know that the amount of energy coming into our bodies is directly related to the food we eat. It is more difficult to calculate energy expenditure. Energy expenditure depends on our basal metabolic rate (the rate at which all our metabolic reactions use energy when we are resting and quiet), the amount of physical activity we engage in, and the heat given off by food being digested and stored.

The amount of energy we expend can fluctuate dramatically. During heavy exercise, we may use 15 times as much energy as we use when at rest. Children tend to expend more energy because of all the reactions in their bodies related to growth, and much older people often expend less energy than they did when they were young.

To maintain energy homeostasis, we need to regulate our energy intake and expenditure. **Figure 14.8** indicates the caloric value of some common foods, along with the amount of exercise needed to use that energy. In the next section we discuss what happens when we don't regulate our energy intake and output.

CONCEPT CHECK STOP

1. **Where** does each step in carbohydrate metabolism occur?

2. **Why** is protein metabolism more difficult for the body than lipid or carbohydrate metabolism?

3. **What** are the factors that determine how much energy our bodies expend?

14.3 Health Can Be Hurt by Nutritional Disorders

LEARNING OBJECTIVES

1. **Determine** how to calculate a healthy weight for your personal lifestyle and body size.
2. **List** and define the most common type of food poisoning.
3. **Describe** the world health issues surrounding nutrition.

Diet and nutrition are important aspects of overall health because most of the compounds that enter the body do so via the digestive system. If we put nothing useful into the digestive system, our bodies will not have a good source of raw material for the proteins, enzymes, and energy required for life. Conversely, if we fill the digestive system with foods that are high in necessary nutrients, our bodies will function at peak levels. Of course, we can get too much of a good thing. If we ingest more calories than we "spend," regardless of their quality, we will store the excess in adipose tissue as fat (triglycerides).

Much attention is given to our diet and its effect on the body, both in the media and in society at large. Our society is obsessed with being thin. For some, this obsession leads to one of two common eating disorders, **anorexia nervosa** and **bulimia nervosa**. Both disorders stem from the desire to be thin and, therefore, "beautiful." Eating disorders grow out of a culture that is obsessed with beauty, and it will be difficult to reduce their prevalence without changing societal attitudes about beauty. Hopefully, as we become more aware of health and nutritional issues, we will recognize the beauty of a healthy, well-proportioned body rather than a tall, rail-thin one. Interestingly, in other cultures of the world, being rail-thin is not at all desirable. Instead, that level of thinness indicates an inability to obtain proper nutrition, which is understandably not considered beautiful.

The opposite nutritional disorder is **obesity**. Some health professionals worry that obesity is becoming widespread. See *Ethics and Issues: How Far Should You Go to Look Skinny?* Obesity is usually defined in terms of **body mass index (BMI)**. You can calculate your BMI by dividing your weight in kilograms by the square of your height in meters. You can also consult a BMI chart like the one in **Figure 14.9**. Your BMI should give you an indication of how much of your weight is due to fat stored in adipose tissue. BMIs over 32 are generally considered to indicate obesity. However, if you are muscular or have denser or lighter bones than average, your BMI may not be an accurate indication of obesity.

BMI is a rough estimate of the amount of body fat present. To use this table, you find your height along the left column and your weight along the top row. Where these two meet is your BMI. A BMI between 18.5 and 24.9 is considered "normal and healthy," while those with BMI below 18.5 are labeled underweight and those above 30 are considered obese.

The body mass index • Figure 14.9

Weight in Pounds

Height	120	130	140	150	160	170	180	190	200	210	220	230	240	250
4'6"	29	31	34	36	39	41	43	46	48	51	53	56	58	60
4'8"	27	29	31	34	36	38	40	43	45	47	49	52	54	56
4'10"	25	27	29	31	34	36	38	40	42	44	46	48	50	52
5'0"	23	25	27	29	31	33	35	37	39	41	43	45	47	49
5'2"	22	24	26	27	29	31	33	35	37	38	40	42	44	46
5'4"	21	22	24	26	28	29	31	33	34	36	38	40	41	43
5'6"	19	21	23	24	26	27	29	31	32	34	36	37	39	40
5'8"	18	20	21	23	24	26	27	29	30	32	34	35	37	38
5'10"	17	19	20	22	23	24	26	27	29	30	32	33	35	36
6'0"	16	18	19	20	22	23	24	26	27	28	30	31	33	34
6'2"	15	17	18	19	21	22	23	24	26	27	28	30	31	32
6'4"	15	16	17	18	20	21	22	23	24	26	27	28	29	30
6'6"	14	15	16	17	19	20	21	22	23	24	25	27	28	29
6'8"	13	14	15	17	18	19	20	21	22	23	24	25	26	28

Height in Feet and Inches

☐ Underweight ■ Healthy weight ☐ Overweight ☐ Obese

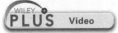

ETHICS AND ISSUES
How Far Should You Go to Look Skinny?

Obesity is quickly surpassing smoking as the number one preventable cause of death in the United States. Americans are literally killing themselves with their food choices—and they are not alone in this self-inflicted epidemic. World Health Organization reports that in 2008 there were over 1 billion overweight adults in the world, with a full 300 million of them classified as clinically obese. Although initially thought to be a problem of industrialized societies, the rate of obesity in developing countries is rising at an even faster rate.

Using body mass index (BMI) as a measure of obesity provides a good comparison for various countries. A BMI below 18.5 kg/m² is considered underweight, while a BMI of 25–29 kg/m² is considered overweight. A BMI over 30 kg/m² is obese. Adult BMI's range from 22–23 kg/m² in Africa and Asia, and to 25–27 kg/m² across North America, Europe, Latin America, North Africa, and most Pacific Island countries. Obesity rates range from below 5% in the developed areas of China, Japan, and some African nations to over 75% in relatively less developed urban Samoa.

Perhaps even more distressing than the worldwide explosion of obese adults is the increase in childhood obesity. WHO estimates that worldwide, over 22 million children under the age of five are obese. In the United States alone, the number of overweight adolescents has tripled in the past two decades. In Thailand, the obesity rate for 5–12 year olds jumped a full 4 percentage points in just two years!

Being obese takes a toll on the human body, causing health problems in just about every organ system. Blood pressure may rise uncontrollably; skeletal and muscular disorders are common in those carrying large amounts of additional weight; respiratory difficul-

ties can develop as the upper respiratory system carries more tissue; cardiovascular disease rates rise as weight increases; the risks of developing gallbladder disease or cancer rise with increasing weight; and the incidence of type 2 diabetes rises dramatically with excessive weight gain. All of these health concerns increase the cost of health care in developed nations.

Critical Reasoning Issues Recently in the United States, the television show *Dance Your *#@ Off* has become popular. During this reality show, obese contestants are brought together, taught proper nutrition and diet choices, given workout regimes, and taught to dance. They compete against one another in both dancing and weight loss. Those that score the highest marks on their dance and also lose the largest percentage of their body weight each week get to stay on the show, learning and losing even more.

NATIONAL GEOGRAPHIC

Daily energy allowance, 2001-2003
Kcal/person/day

- More than 3,500
- 3,000-3,500
- 2,500-2,999
- 2,000-2,499
- 1,550-1,999
- Less than 1,500
- No Data

Caloric extremes
Significant countries outlined

Obese population
30% or greater

Undernourished population
30% or greater

SOURCES: FOOD AND AGRICULTURE ORGANIZATION OF THE UNITED NATIONS; INTERNATIONAL OBESITY TASKFORCE

ISRAEL 46%
HAITI 47%
TAJIKISTAN 61%
ERITREA 73%
NAURU 79%
SAMOA 48%
NIUE
FR. POLYNESIA

Think Critically

1. What might be the emotional draw for this sort of reality TV? Can the lessons taught to these contestants be expected to spread through the viewing public? Is this a good way to teach healthy living without alienating anyone?

2. Some people feel that being overweight is not a problem, but rather a genetic predisposition or a lifestyle choice. Are overweight individuals right to defend their size? Is obesity a societal matter, or an individual choice?

The Digestive System

Many of us have seen some version of an eating contest, the most famous of which takes place every Fourth of July on Coney Island in New York. Nathan's Famous Fourth of July International Hot Dog Eating Contest began in 1916, and the winner gets the Mustard Belt, notoriety, and a dose of indigestion (or worse). Recent winners have consumed more than 60 hot dogs and buns in 12 minutes—that's nearly 20,000 calories and countless grams of fat in one sitting!

The strains put on the digestive system during such contests are explored in a National Geographic special called "The Science of Speed Eating," which follows a competitive eater who has trained his body to ignore the signals of fullness and to stretch his stomach to incredible proportions. Competitive eating is not for the weak. It has real dangers, including stomach perforations, esophageal tears, and an overwhelmed digestive system. There is also considerable question as to whether eating 44 lobsters or 552 Louisiana oysters in 10 minutes (done by speed eater Sonya Thomas, known as the "Black Widow") is an enjoyable experience.

Our digestive system is both simple and complicated. It is a series of closely related organs designed to extract from the food we eat every last gram of the nutrients studied in Chapter 14. In this task, the digestive organs are almost too good at what they do, but if and when they are abused or diseased, they can make our lives miserable.

CHAPTER OUTLINE

CHAPTER PLANNER ✔

- ❏ Study the picture and read the opening story.
- ❏ Scan the Learning Objectives in each section:
  p. 404 ❏   p. 410 ❏   p. 413 ❏   p. 422 ❏
- ❏ Read the text and study all figures and visuals. Answer any questions.

Analyze key features

- ❏ What a Scientist Sees, p. 408
- ❏ I Wonder..., p. 411
- ❏ Process Diagram, p. 412
- ❏ Biological InSight, p. 414
- ❏ Health, Wellness, and Disease, p. 419
- ❏ Ethics and Issues, p. 425
- ❏ Stop: Answer the Concept Checks before you go on:
  p. 409 ❏   p. 413 ❏   p. 421 ❏   p. 424 ❏

End of chapter

- ❏ Review the Summary and Key Terms.
- ❏ Answer the Critical and Creative Thinking Questions.
- ❏ Answer What is happening in this picture?
- ❏ Answer the Self-Test Questions.

15.1 Digestion Begins in the Oral Cavity

LEARNING OBJECTIVES

1. **Explain** the processes and functions of the digestive system.
2. **Describe** the general anatomy of the digestive tract.
3. **List** the digestive organs in order from mouth to anus.
4. **Discuss** the structure and function of the esophagus.

The digestive system is sometimes called a "tube within a tube," because it is basically a hollow structure with two openings that runs the length of your body. The digestive system has two major parts, the "gastrointestinal system," or **GI tract**, and a set of **accessory organs**. The GI tract begins at the oral cavity, winds through the abdominal cavity, and ends at the anus. The major accessory organs include the pancreas, the liver, and the gallbladder. Together, the GI tract and the accessory organs carry out five basic processes:

1. **Ingestion**. Foods and liquids are taken into the mouth and eaten.
2. **Mixing**. The smooth muscle in the walls of the GI tract mixes the food and sends it on its way through the tract.
3. **Digestion**. Food is broken down by both mechanical and chemical processes.
4. **Absorption**. The epithelial cells lining the GI tract absorb the digested food molecules and pass them to the blood or lymph.
5. **Defecation**. Any substance not digested or absorbed, for whatever reason, is passed along to the end of the GI tract, the anus, and leaves the body.

Figure 15.1 shows an overview of the digestive system.

The GI Tract Remains the Same Throughout Its Length

The structure of the GI tract is essentially the same along its entire length. It is composed of four layers:

- The innermost layer is composed of a mucous membrane, or **mucosa**. This slippery, smooth layer allows ingested food to move along the tract without tearing it.
- Under the mucosa, the **submucosa** includes the glands, nerves, and blood supply for the tract itself.

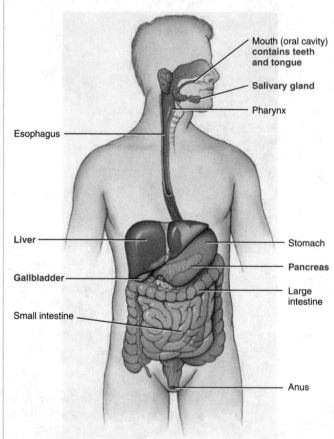

Mouth (oral cavity) contains teeth and tongue

Salivary gland

Pharynx

Esophagus

Liver

Stomach

Pancreas

Gallbladder

Large intestine

Small intestine

Anus

Right lateral view of head and neck and anterior view of trunk

Digestive system overview • Figure 15.1

The tubular structure of the GI tract is obvious when looking at it in its entirety. The tube begins at the esophagus and, with slight modifications, travels the length of the tract, ending at the anus. These modifications alter the function of the tract at various points, which we describe as different organs. Accessory organs aid in digestion, and are found along the length of the GI tract. Accessory organs are named in red above.

404 CHAPTER 15 The Digestive System

Layers of the GI tract • Figure 15.2

The serosa allows the GI tract to move as food passes within it. The muscularis is responsible for generating the movement of the tube, whereas the mucosa and submucosa come into contact with the food and provide the blood supply and innervation for the inner lining of the tract.

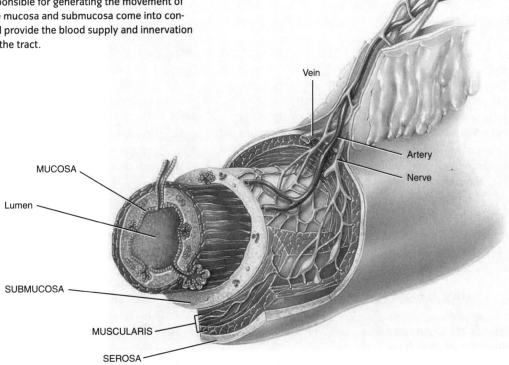

- The **muscularis** gives the tract the ability to move substances lengthwise. For most of the tract, the muscularis is composed of one layer of longitudinal muscle above another layer of circular muscle.
- The outer layer of the GI tract, the **serosa**, is a slippery membrane that permits the tract to move inside the abdominal cavity without catching or causing discomfort. Your digestive system is always active, as muscular contractions shift, lengthen, and shorten the tube. Although this movement is constant, you normally neither see nor feel it.

> **peristaltic wave**
> Rhythmic muscular contractions of a tube that force contents toward the open end.

These layers (**Figure 15.2**) work in unison to create the **peristaltic wave** that propels food through the tube, as seen in **Figure 15.3**.

The Mouth Starts It All

The best way to understand the actions of the digestive system is to follow some food through the GI tract, starting at the oral cavity, or mouth. Think about a hot slice

Peristaltic wave generation • Figure 15.3

The peristaltic wave is generated as you consciously swallow food. Movement of the tongue initiates the muscularis to begin a ring of contraction that is passed throughout the entire tract. Once you swallow food, the peristaltic wave travels the length of the tube; you no longer have conscious control over those smooth muscle contractions.

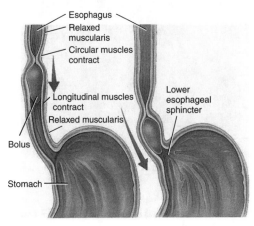

Anterior view of frontal sections of peristalsis in esophagus

of pizza. How does it provide energy and nutrients? Let's follow that slice along the digestive tract, and see how the body pulls nutrients from it and how its energy is used to create ATP for immediate use or adipose tissue for energy storage.

The pizza enters the digestive tract through the oral cavity. We tear off a bite of pizza with **incisors** and then crush it with the **molars** and **premolars**. Teeth and accessory organs then function as cutting tools (incisors), piercing and ripping utensils (canines), or grinding instruments (molars and premolars). Although we are not born with teeth extending through the gums, they erupt soon after birth in a predictable pattern. Incisors appear first, allowing food to be bitten off, often by 8 months of age. The premolars and molars appear last, with "wisdom teeth," our final set of grinding molars, appearing sometimes as late as our mid-twenties or early thirties.

Oral cavity • Figure 15.4 _____

The teeth and tongue in the oral cavity are ideal for mechanical digestion. The food is rolled around with the tongue and broken into smaller pieces with the teeth.

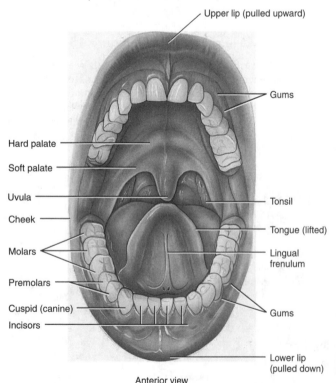

Upper lip (pulled upward)

Gums

Hard palate

Soft palate

Uvula

Cheek

Molars

Premolars

Cuspid (canine)

Incisors

Tonsil

Tongue (lifted)

Lingual frenulum

Gums

Lower lip (pulled down)

Anterior view

We first obtain 20 primary, deciduous, or baby teeth. These are replaced by our 32 permanent teeth, usually by age 21 (**Figure 15.4**).

The small bits of pizza are **macerated** with saliva. **Mechanical digestion** increases the efficiency of enzymes in the stomach and small intestine by creating small bits of food, still chemically identical to the original bite of pizza, with a great deal of surface area where enzymes can carry out the process of **chemical digestion**.

Most people try to take good care of their teeth, with regular brushing, flossing, and visits to the dentist. Why do we bother with such dental cleanliness? Our mouths contain hundreds of species of bacteria, which live on the oral surfaces and multiply rapidly when sugar is available. These bacteria excrete wastes as they grow and metabolize. The wastes are usually acidic, and if the acid remains on tooth surfaces, it can eat through the enamel to the softer **dentin** at the center of the tooth. **Plaque** is a combination of the bacterial colonies, their bacterial wastes, leftover sugars from chewed up food, epithelial cells from the host, and saliva. Plaque begins as a sticky substance on the surfaces of the teeth but can calcify with time into the tough layer of tartar your hygienist must scrape off.

macerated
Soaked until soft and separated into constituent parts.

mechanical digestion The physical crushing, chopping, and cutting of food.

chemical digestion The breaking down of food using enzymes that alter the chemical structure of the food.

The largest increase in bacterial growth occurs 20 minutes after eating.
The bacterial colonies are metabolizing the food from your last meal, growing and dividing at their highest rate roughly 20 minutes after you eat. As the bacteria are multiplying rapidly, they are digesting the sugar in your mouth and creating large quantities of acidic waste. Once the food is removed, the bacterial division slows. If you do not thoroughly and routinely remove this buildup of bacteria and acid, the acid may decay the enamel on the teeth, causing cavities. A cavity does not cause pain at first, but as the acids reach farther into the tooth, they eventually hit softer tissue near the tooth's nerve, called the **pulp**. By this time, the cavity is quite large and will require dental repair.

The recommended biannual dental cleaning is a great way to monitor plaque buildup and cavity formation. While removing plaque, the hygienist may spot any small cavities, which the dentist can repair before they destroy the pulp of the tooth. The repair process involves drilling out all rotten material and replacing it with an airtight seal made of gold, silver alloy, or composite resin.

The tongue balls things up.

The tongue, another accessory organ, manipulates the now-crushed pizza into a **bolus** and positions that bolus at the back of the oral cavity so it can be swallowed. The tongue is a muscle that can move in almost any direction in the oral cavity. On its surface, keratinized epithelium covers each **papilla**, creating a rough texture to help move the slippery food into position where the teeth can masticate it. Taste buds reside along the sides of the papillae. The tongue also secretes watery mucus containing a digestive enzyme, **lingual lipase**, from **sublingual salivary glands** on its undersurface. This enzyme begins the chemical digestion of lipids by breaking down triglycerides, such as those in the pizza's cheese.

> **bolus** A round, soft mass of chewed food within the digestive tract.
>
> **papilla** Any small, rounded projection extending above a surface.
>
> **lingual** Relating to speech or the tongue.

The tonsils are the first line of defense against microbes.

The **uvula** hangs from the top of the oral cavity at the back of the mouth. This structure functions as a trap door, swinging upward and closing the entrance to the nasal cavity when solid or liquid is forced to the back of the throat. If you try to talk or laugh while eating, the uvula may malfunction and allow food or drink into your nasal passages. The **tonsils**, at the back of the oral cavity, are your first line of defense against any microbes that may enter your mouth along with the pizza. When bacteria invade the oral cavity, the tonsils swell as they attempt to destroy the pathogen through the action of specific immune tissues.

MALT is a disease-prevention tissue.

Food is rarely sterile, and yet we almost never suffer disease from ingesting it. Starting with the tonsils, the mucosa of the GI tract contains a disease-prevention tissue called **MALT** (mucosa-associated lymphatic tissue). MALT is also prevalent in the small intestine, large intestine, and appendix. These nodules of lymphatic tissue prevent pathogens from taking over the **lumen** of the digestive tract and are important for preserving homeostasis. MALT tissues represent a large percentage of the entire immune system, including about half of the body's total lymphocytes and macrophages. Without MALT, pathogens could grow within the digestive tract, penetrate the epithelial lining, and cause serious internal infections.

Although MALT is effective, it can be overrun. Bacteria ingested with food suddenly enter a warm, moist, nutrient-rich environment where they can bloom and overwhelm the body's ability to combat them. Often, the acid environment of the stomach will kill these blooming bacteria, but sometimes even that is not enough. If the bacterial colony survives the stomach, the body may flush the entire tract via diarrhea or vomiting to help the immune system rid the body of the invading bacterium.

The salivary glands aid in digestion.

The **salivary glands** are accessory organs located within the oral cavity. They secrete watery saliva, normally in small quantities to moisten the oral mucosa. As soon as we smell food, the pizza in this instance, salivary production increases. Even the thought of food can increase saliva production. When food is in the mouth, excess saliva is needed to mix with the food and form the slippery bolus required for swallowing.

The major salivary glands are the **parotid** glands, located below and in front of the ears, and the **submandibular** glands under the tongue. A common childhood illness, mumps, is a disease of these glands. Learn more about this disease in *What a Scientist Sees: A Case of the Mumps* on the following page.

The parotid glands produce watery saliva that includes some ions (sodium, potassium, chloride, bicarbonate, and phosphate) and organic substances. The submandibular glands produce thicker, ropey saliva with similar ion content but a larger concentration of mucus. When the sympathetic nervous system is active, watery secretion from the parotid glands is inhibited, whereas the sticky submandibular secretion is not. The result is the familiar "cotton mouth" feeling that we associate with nervousness.

In addition to water and ions, saliva contains **lysozyme**, a **bacteriolytic** enzyme that helps destroy bacteria in the oral cavity. Another important component of saliva is **salivary amylase**, a digestive enzyme that breaks carbohydrate

> **bacteriolytic** Type of agent that lyses or destroys bacteria.

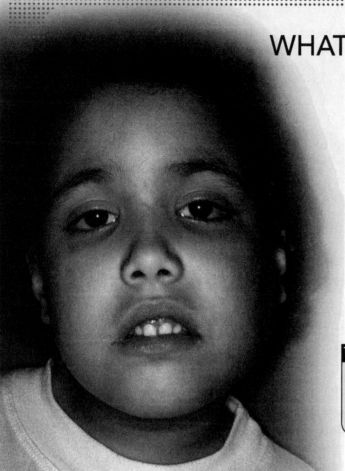

WHAT A SCIENTIST SEES

A Case of the Mumps

Mumps is a painful disease of the salivary glands, usually the parotid glands, causing swelling and a sore throat. The mumps virus is uncomfortable for young children but can cause an inflammation of the brain, pancreas, meninges, testes, or ovaries, especially in older children and adults. In very severe cases, mumps can cause infertility. As we vaccinate more infants, it could become a disease of the past. Mumps is already no longer the global threat it was in the 1950s. It is, however, still a very real problem in the developing world where vaccines are less available.

The largest U.S. outbreak of mumps in three years occurred in New Jersey and New York between August and October 2009. It began in a boys' camp in Sullivan County, New York.

Think Critically

1. How might this outbreak have started, and how did health officials trace it back to this particular camp? Review Chapter 10 for help with this question.
2. Using what you know of the anatomy of the mouth and ears (revisit Chapter 8), can you predict why mumps may lead to deafness?

polysaccharides into monosaccharides. Amylase occurs in low levels in saliva and in larger quantities in pancreatic secretions. As we chew the pizza crust, salivary amylase begins breaking the large carbohydrates down into the small monosaccharides that cells can absorb farther down the GI tract.

Deglutition occurs in stages. Swallowing, or **deglutition**, occurs as the bolus of macerated, saliva-mixed pizza is moved to the back of the throat. The tongue positions the bolus at the opening to the esophagus, where you consciously decide to swallow the pizza. This is the last muscular movement you control until the pizza has worked its way to the other end of your GI tract. The tongue is composed of voluntary, consciously controlled skeletal muscle. The muscularis of the GI tract is smooth muscle, controlled by the autonomic nervous system. At the very end of the tract, the anal sphincter is again skeletal muscle.

Swallowing has voluntary and involuntary stages. During the **voluntary stage**, you consciously swallow the pizza. During the **pharyngeal stage**, as seen in **Figure 15.5**, the bolus involuntarily passes through the pharynx. The epiglottis is closed against the larynx to allow the bolus to bypass the respiratory system and enter the esophagus. It is at this stage that the uvula covers the nasal opening and the larynx moves upward against the epiglottis. The epiglottis covers the opening to the respiratory system, and the bolus slides back toward the esophagus instead of dropping into the respiratory system. Talking while eating can cause the epiglottis to spasm, because it must be opened to allow air to escape in order to vocalize but must be closed to prevent the bolus from sliding into the respiratory tract. Because the epiglottis cannot be opened and closed at the same time, it spasms. Food may drop into the trachea, resulting in choking, and we may require assistance to remove the misplaced bolus.

Swallowing and the pharynx • Figure 15.5

As the bolus of food is swallowed, the larynx moves up, in turn shifting the position of the epiglottis. The bolus of food then slides past the larynx and on to the esophagus. the wave of contraction begun here continues through the entire system, pushing this mouthful into the stomach and eventually on to the remaining organs of the GI tract.

Nasopharynx
Hard palate
Soft palate
Uvula
Oropharynx
Epiglottis
Laryngopharynx
Larynx
Esophagus

Bolus
Tongue

a. Position of structures before swallowing

b. During the pharyngeal stage of swallowing, the tongue presses upward at the back of the mouth. This pulls the larynx up toward the epiglottis, closing the airway to passing food.

The Esophagus Connects the Oral Cavity with the Stomach

The esophagus is a collapsible 20- to 25-centimeter-long conduit that connects the oral cavity with the stomach. Once the bolus of pizza arrives at the top of the esophagus, a peristaltic wave begins. In this third stage of swallowing, the **esophageal stage**, food moves through the esophagus into the stomach via peristalsis. This wave will push the bolus along the esophagus in a controlled manner (neither food nor drink free-fall into the stomach). The esophagus terminates at its lower end with a sphincter muscle. A sphincter muscle is a circular muscle that closes off a tube, functioning like a rubber band pulled tightly around a flexible straw. These muscles appear many times along the GI tract, dividing one organ from the next. The **lower esophageal sphincter** (LES) at the base of the esophagus opens as the pizza bolus touches it, dropping the bolus into the upper portion of the stomach. You can listen to water traveling through the esophagus and hitting the LES if you have a stethoscope. Place the bell of the stethoscope near your xyphoid process, at the base of the sternum, and swallow a mouthful of water. You should be able to count to 10, then hear the water

splash against the lower esophageal sphincter. If you are lucky, you might hear the water splash again as it enters the stomach when the LES opens.

The esophagus runs right through the diaphragm at the **esophageal hiatus**. Occasionally, a portion of the upper stomach can protrude through this opening, resulting in a hiatal hernia. This condition can be painful and often requires medical intervention.

| CONCEPT CHECK | STOP |

1. **What** functions does the digestive system perform?
2. **What** are the four layers of the GI tract and the function of each?
3. **What** is the path of food through the organs of the digestive system?
4. **How** is the structure of the esophagus related to the general structure of the digestive tract?

15.2 The Stomach Puts Food to the Acid Test

LEARNING OBJECTIVES

1. **Describe** the modifications of the GI tract at the stomach.
2. **List** the phases of digestion in the stomach.

The next organ the pizza encounters in the digestive system is the **stomach**, a J-shaped organ that lies beneath the esophagus. The stomach is separated from the esophagus and the small intestine by two sphincter muscles. The lower esophageal sphincter is the upper boundary of the stomach, and the **pyloric sphincter** marks the lower end of the stomach. The pyloric sphincter, the strongest sphincter muscle of the digestive tract, opens to allow **chyme** to enter the small intestine only when chemically ready. This sphincter is so powerful that it can cause projectile vomiting in infants. The stomach contracts forcefully to push the food into the small intestine, but the pyloric sphincter remains closed until the chyme is fluid enough to be passed on. If the pyloric sphincter refuses to open, the contents of the stomach are instead ejected through the weaker lower esophageal sphincter, leaving the body at impressive speed.

> **chyme** The thick, partially digested fluid in the stomach and small intestine.

The GI Tract Has Major Modifications at the Stomach

The typical structure of the gastrointestinal tract undergoes modification at the stomach, as seen in **Figure 15.6**. The muscularis is usually composed of two layers of muscle, one longitudinal and one circular. The stomach has a third layer of muscle, called the **oblique** layer. The function of the stomach is to churn and mix the bolus of pizza with the acid environment of the stomach and begin protein digestion. The oblique layer helps this churning and mixing. Because the stomach is a holding area for ingested food, it must be able to expand. The walls of the stomach contain folds, or **rugae**, that permit expansion somewhat like a deflated punching ball. Reducing the capacity of the stomach is the subject of *I Wonder… How Does Gastric Bypass Surgery Work?*

The stomach must be protected from itself. A final modification of the stomach is due to the chemical environment in the organ, where the pH is only 2. Such high acidity breaks down large macromolecules and destroys many microbes, but it can also harm the stomach lining. Furthermore, the stomach also secretes enzymes that digest protein, the same compound that the stomach walls are composed of. Therefore, the stomach must be protected from its own contents. The stomach does this by producing a protective layer of thick, viscous, alkaline mucus. Nowhere else does the digestive tract need, or produce, such a mucus coating.

Histologically speaking, the stomach is "the pits." The walls of the stomach contain **gastric** pits, which secrete 2 to 3 quarts of **gastric juice** each day.

> **gastric** Related to the stomach.

See **Figure 15.7**. These pits are composed of **chief** cells and **parietal** cells. The chief cells secrete **pepsinogen** and **gastric lipase**. Pepsinogen is an inactive precursor of the enzyme **pepsin**, which digests proteins and therefore must be secreted in inactive form. (If pepsin itself were produced in stomach cells, it would digest the proteins of those cells.) Pepsinogen forms pepsin only under pH 2. The parietal cells produce **hydrochloric acid** and **intrinsic factor**. The hydrochlo-

The stomach • Figure 15.6

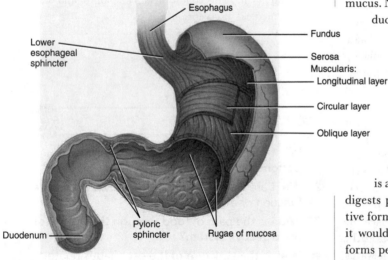

Anterior view of regions of stomach

Esophagus
Lower esophageal sphincter
Fundus
Serosa
Muscularis:
Longitudinal layer
Circular layer
Oblique layer
Duodenum
Pyloric sphincter
Rugae of mucosa

410 CHAPTER 15 The Digestive System

I WONDER...

How Does Gastric Bypass Surgery Work?

One of the functions of the stomach is to store the food we eat. Logically, the larger your stomach, the more food you can comfortably store in it. Equally, a smaller stomach would hold less, causing the owner of that stomach to eat smaller portions. Gastric bypass, or bariatric, surgery is a drastic attempt to reduce the stomach capacity of morbidly obese people. This surgery goes by many names stemming from the various methods used to surgically reduce the functional capacity of the stomach. In all cases, gastric bypass surgery results in the lumen of the stomach being divided into a small upper cavity and a larger "remnant" cavity that ingested food does not travel through. Both cavities remain attached to the small intestine, but food can only be stored in the smaller upper pouch.

The surgery itself is difficult, leading to complications within six months in 30% and death in 0.2% of patients. Getting through the surgery is just the first hurdle, as living with a diminished stomach requires a severe restructuring of behaviors and eating habits.

Because the stomach can no longer function normally, diet is strictly regulated, right down to the order in which foods are consumed. Proteins must be eaten first, because digesting them requires time in the stomach. Patients can eat only those foods prescribed by their physician and cannot snack between meals, because eating continuously throughout the day will "bypass the bypass"—no weight reduction will be seen if caloric intake remains high!

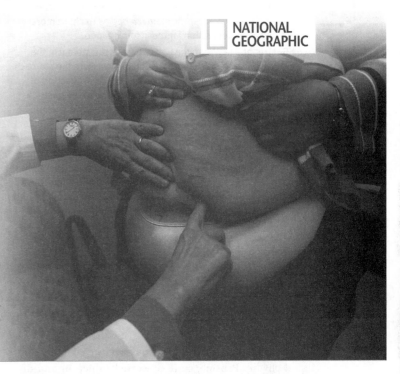

NATIONAL GEOGRAPHIC

ric acid is responsible for the acidic pH of the stomach, which activates pepsin, kills microbes, and denatures ingested proteins. Intrinsic factor is necessary for the absorption of vitamin B_{12}, a micronutrient that helps produce blood cells. Although intrinsic factor is produced in the stomach, it is active in the small intestine.

As the pizza is churned in the stomach, **gastric lipase** will continue the chemical breakdown of fats that began in the mouth. This enzyme specializes in digesting short-chain fatty acids, such as those found in milk, but works at an optimum pH of 5 or 6. In adults, both gastric lipase and lingual lipase have limited roles.

Gastric pits • Figure 15.7

Gastric pits are composed of chief cells and parietal cells. These cells are responsible for creating the specialized environment of the stomach.

Phases of gastric digestion • Figure 15.8

The activation of the stomach includes three phases.

❶ Cephalic phase. In the first phase, thoughts of food and the feel of food in the oral cavity stimulate increased secretion from the gastric pits. The stomach begins to churn more actively in preparation for the incoming food.

❷ Gastric phase. When the bolus reaches the stomach, the second phase of gastric digestion begins. Here the stomach produces gastrin as well as continuing the production of pepsin and HCl. Gastrin aids in stimulation of the gastric pits, providing a feedback system that speeds digestion. Impulses from the stomach also go back to the brain, maintaining contact with the nervous system.

❸ Intestinal phase. In the final phase of gastric digestion, the chyme begins to leave through the pyloric sphincter. As the chyme leaves the stomach, gastrin production decreases, the impulses to the brain indicate a lessening of chyme, and the brain begins to slow the stimulation of the gastric pits. At the same time, hormones from the beginning portion of the small intestine initiate activation of the small intestine.

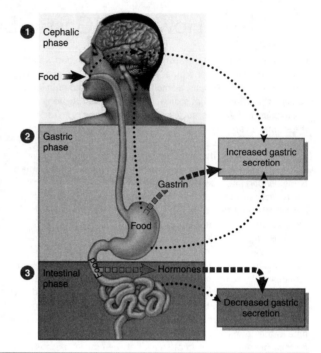

In the stomach, the pizza bolus is converted to a pasty, liquid chyme. Pepsinogen is converted to pepsin and digests the proteins of the tomato sauce and the cheese. The low pH assists in denaturing proteins and breaking down the remaining macromolecules, providing an easy substrate for digestion in the small intestine.

The stomach is an active organ. As the bolus of food reaches the stomach, small **mixing waves** are initiated. These waves occur every 15 seconds or so and help to break up the pizza. Even with these mixing waves, the pizza may stay in the **fundus** of the stomach for as long as an hour before being moved into the body of the stomach. There the pizza mixes with the gastric secretions and becomes soupy and thin. The mixing waves of the stomach become stronger, intensifying as they reach the pyloric sphincter. With each wave, a small portion of the chyme is forced through the pyloric sphincter and into the small intestine. The rest of the chyme washes back toward the body of the stomach to be churned further with the next mixing wave.

> **fundus** The portion of any hollow organ that extends above the opening of that organ.

Gastric Digestion Includes Three Phases

Digestion occurs in three phases in the stomach, as seen in **Figure 15.8**. During the **cephalic phase**, digestion consists of reflexes initiated by the senses. This phase started when you ordered the pizza, intensified as you got out the utensils to eat it, and peaked as you smelled the pizza after delivery. The scents and sounds associated with eating stimulate specific portions of the medulla oblongata, which in turn trigger secretion of the gastric pits. The parasympathetic nervous system is activated, increasing stomach movement. Interestingly, these reflexes can be dampened by stimulation of the sympathetic nervous system. Anger, fear, or anxiety opposes the parasympathetic nervous system, shutting down the cephalic phase and reducing your feelings of hunger.

Once food enters the stomach, stretch receptors and chemoreceptors are activated, initiating the **gastric phase**. Hormonal and neural pathways are set in motion, causing an increase in both gastric wave force and secretion from the gastric pits. As chyme is pushed past the pyloric sphincter, stomach volume decreases and stretch receptors begin to relax. The gastric phase then diminishes in intensity.

412 CHAPTER 15 The Digestive System

The final phase of gastric digestion is the **intestinal phase**. As chyme passes through the pyloric sphincter, intestinal receptors are stimulated. These receptors inhibit the actions of the stomach, causing it to return to rest. At the same time, these receptors stimulate digestion in the small intestine.

Once in the small intestine, the chyme itself stimulates the release of hormones.

Chyme containing glucose and fatty acids, such as the chyme from the pizza, causes the release of the hormones **cholecystokinin** (CCK) and **secretin**. CCK inhibits stomach emptying, whereas secretin decreases gastric secretions. Both of these also affect the **liver**, **pancreas**, and **gallbladder**, the accessory organs of the gastrointestinal tract. The combined action of these hormones holds the pizza in the stomach for a prolonged period, ensuring that the pizza is sufficiently broken down, despite its high level of hydrophobic fats.

After two to four hours, the stomach has emptied, and all the chyme has entered the small intestine. Because the pizza has a high fat concentration, it will move rather slowly through the stomach, taking closer to four hours. Had you eaten stir-fried vegetables with their much lower fat content, your stomach would have emptied much more quickly, leaving you feeling hungry again after just a few hours.

The peristaltic wave can be reversed.

Sometimes food in the stomach does not "agree" with the stomach because it contains bacteria or toxins that irritate the stomach lining. This situation may cause vomiting. Although not an easy task from a physiological standpoint, reversing the peristaltic wave and churning the stomach violently while holding the pyloric sphincter closed will expel the stomach contents. The esophageal sphincter is weaker than the pyloric sphincter and will open first when the stomach contents are under pressure. The entire contents of the stomach then return through the esophagus and the mouth. The acidity of the stomach is not buffered, causing some burning as the fluid passes the mucous membranes of the mouth and throat. Repeated vomiting can be detrimental to the lining of the mouth as well as the tooth enamel. In addition, replacing the hydrogen ion concentration in the stomach can deplete the hydrogen content of the blood, leading to electrolyte imbalances.

CONCEPT CHECK

1. **Why** is it important that the GI tract is modified at the stomach?
2. **What** are the phases of digestion in the stomach?

15.3 The Intestines and Accessory Organs Finish the Job

LEARNING OBJECTIVES

1. **List** the regions of the small intestine.
2. **Describe** what happens when chyme enters the duodenum.
3. **Explain** the roles of the three major accessory organs and the large intestine.
4. **Discuss** the structure and function of the large intestine.

The pizza's nutrients are now in the small intestine and finally ready for absorption. This organ is the only portion of the GI tube where nutrients are taken into the cells. Prior to reaching the small intestine, the food was cut up, broken down, and denatured. Some enzyme activity was initiated to break down large macromolecules. Here in the small intestine, the nutrients from the pizza are finally absorbed into the body. While the food is in the small intestine, digestion is completed by the accessory organs and is over as the nutrient-depleted chyme passes through the large intestine.

The cells of the small intestine are the only nutrient-absorbing structures in the digestive system. The larger their surface area, the greater the chances that nutrients taken in with food will be absorbed as they pass through the small intestine. The small intestinal wall has folds upon folds, increasing the surface area immensely.

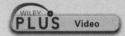

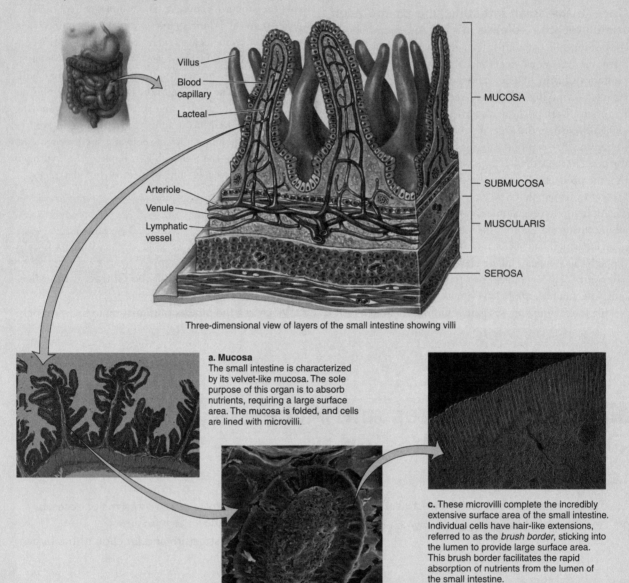

Villus
Blood capillary
Lacteal
Arteriole
Venule
Lymphatic vessel

MUCOSA
SUBMUCOSA
MUSCULARIS
SEROSA

Three-dimensional view of layers of the small intestine showing villi

a. Mucosa
The small intestine is characterized by its velvet-like mucosa. The sole purpose of this organ is to absorb nutrients, requiring a large surface area. The mucosa is folded, and cells are lined with microvilli.

c. These microvilli complete the incredibly extensive surface area of the small intestine. Individual cells have hair-like extensions, referred to as the *brush border*, sticking into the lumen to provide large surface area. This brush border facilitates the rapid absorption of nutrients from the lumen of the small intestine.

b. Nutrients absorbed by the inner core of the villus are passed into the capillary network or the lymphatic system of the villus' lacteal. Nutrients are often absorbed directly into this lacteal capillary system, which is part of the systemic circulatory system.

414

The Small Intestine Completes the Nutrition Extraction Phase

The small intestine has three regions: the **duodenum**, the **jejunum**, and the **ileum**. The duodenum is the shortest of the regions, extending approximately 25 cm from the pyloric sphincter. The name *duodenum* means 12, reflecting the fact that the region is approximately 12 fingers long. The jejunum encompasses the next 2 meters or so. *Jejunum* means "empty," and this region is characteristically empty during autopsy. The longest portion, the ileum, is about 3.5 in. long. The entire length of the small intestine is 6–7 m, making it the longest digestive organ. This structure is packed into the abdominal cavity by twisting and winding around the central **mesenteries**.

> **mesenteries** Folds in the lining of the abdominal cavity that help to secure the digestive organs.

How large is the surface of the small intestine?

Within the small intestine, the mucosa is shaped into permanent circular folds, which add important surface area to the organ. See **Figure 15.9**. Not only do these folds increase absorption, but they also force the chyme to move in spiral fashion, which creates a longer pathway through the intestine, allowing more time to absorb nutrients.

Because the whole point of this organ is to provide a surface area for absorption, the small intestine has many microscopic projections. The mucosa has finger-like extensions, or **villi**, each one approximately 0.5 to 1 mm long. These villi give the inner surface of the small intestine the look and feel of velvet. Areolar connective tissue is located at the center of each villus. This connective tissue supports an arteriole, a venule, a blood capillary network connecting the two, and a **lacteal**.

Beyond the villi, the small intestine also has **microvilli** on each **apical membrane** of the small intestinal mucosa. These hair-like projections of the cell membrane increase each individual cell's surface area. The microvilli are small and difficult to resolve under a light microscope, where they look like a fuzzy line, not individual structures. The entire surface of the cell is called a **brush border**. Through an electron microscope, scientists have discovered even smaller projections on the surface of these brush borders, which again increase surface area. The total surface area of the small intestine has been variously described as roughly the size of a small backyard or the size of a tennis court (about 260 m², or 2,800 ft²).

> **apical membrane** Membrane at the free end, or top, of the intestinal cells.

The small intestine has an abundance of MALT. The walls of the small intestine are dotted with intestinal glands, which secrete intestinal juice to help digestion. The small intestine also has an abundance of MALT, in the form of **Peyer's patches**. These nodules of lymphatic tissue are akin to tonsils embedded in the intestinal walls. Peyer's patches are an important part of the immune system, protecting the lumen of the digestive tract from bacterial invasion. If even one bacterium escaped the stomach, it could potentially cause serious problems here in the nutrient-rich, warm, moist environment of the small intestine. It is the job of these Peyer's patches to prevent such problems.

Digestion occurs in the small intestine. Both mechanical and chemical digestion occur in the small intestine. Mechanically, the peristaltic wave is modified into **segmentations** and **migrating motility complexes**. Segmentations are localized mixing contractions that swirl the chyme in one section of the intestine. They allow the chyme to interact with the walls of the small intestine but do not move it along the tract. Migrating motility complexes move the chyme along the length of the small intestine. These movements strengthen as the nutrient level in the chyme decreases.

When soupy chyme enters the duodenum, digestion of proteins, lipids, and carbohydrates has just begun. **Pancreatic juice** is added to the chyme as it enters the small intestine, adding a suite of digestive enzymes that are specific for different macromolecules. For example, **sucrase**, **lactase**, **maltase**, and **pancreatic amylase** all digest carbohydrates.

> **pancreatic juice** The fluid produced by the pancreas and released into the small intestine.

The pH buffers of the pancreatic juice immediately bring the pH of the chyme from 2 (as it was in the stomach) back to 7 in the small intestine, protecting the lining of the duodenum. Raising the pH up to 7 protects the walls of the small intestine; however, it renders pepsin

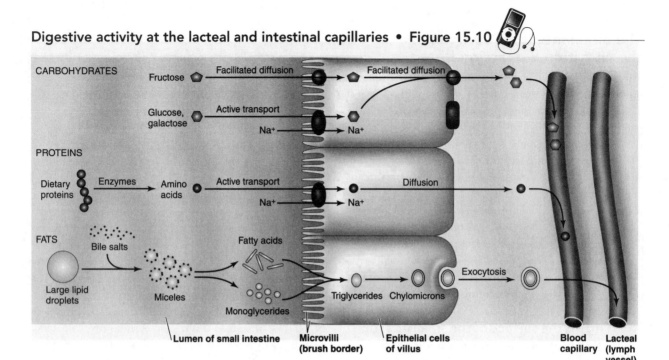

CARBOHYDRATES
Fructose — Facilitated diffusion — Facilitated diffusion
Glucose, galactose — Active transport
Na⁺ → Na⁺

PROTEINS
Dietary proteins — Enzymes — Amino acids — Active transport — Diffusion
Na⁺ → Na⁺

FATS
Bile salts
Large lipid droplets — Miceles — Fatty acids — Triglycerides — Chylomicrons — Exocytosis
Monoglycerides

Lumen of small intestine | Microvilli (brush border) | Epithelial cells of villus | Blood capillary | Lacteal (lymph vessel)

inactive. Protein digestion continues using **trypsin, chymotrypsin, carboxypeptidase**, and **elastase**, all secreted from the pancreas. Protein digestion is completed on the exposed edges of the intestinal cells themselves, using the enzymes **aminopeptidase** and **dipeptidase**.

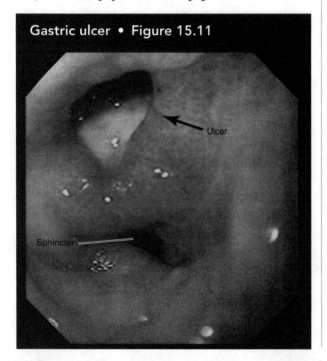

Gastric ulcer • Figure 15.11

Ulcer

Sphincter

In adults, most lipid digestion occurs in the small intestine, because lingual lipase and gastric lipase are barely effective past infancy. **Pancreatic lipase** is the main enzyme causing the breakdown of fats in adults, removing two of the three fatty acids from ingested triglycerides.

In the cells of the small intestine, carbohydrates, short-chain fatty acids, and amino acids are absorbed from the chyme and transported to the capillaries of the lacteal. This process is illustrated in **Figure 15.10**. Absorbed triglycerides are too large to pass directly into the bloodstream. They are converted to **chylomicrons** and transported in the lymphatic capillary of the lacteal. From here, the fats flow with lymph to the subclavian vein. Once in the bloodstream, **lipoprotein lipase** breaks down chylomicrons to short-chain fatty acids and glycerol.

> **chylomicrons** Small lipoproteins carrying ingested fat from the intestinal mucosa to the liver.

Ulcers are holes in the GI tract. **Ulcers** are open wounds that remain aggravated and painful instead of healing. A gastric or duodenal ulcer is such a wound in the lining of the GI tract, as seen in **Figure 15.11**. Gastric ulcers occur in the stomach, whereas duodenal ulcers are in the duodenum of the small intestine.

The mucous lining that normally protects the stomach from digestion must be compromised for an ulcer to develop. This can happen when alcohol or aspirin enters the stomach, because these compounds can degrade the mucous lining. Aspirin labels direct you to take the pills with a full glass of water so that they are washed through the stomach or dissolved rather than left sitting on the mucous layer. If the mucous layer is worn away, acidity in the lumen begins to burn the stomach lining, and pepsin will digest proteins of the stomach cells, creating an ulcer. Although in the past ulcers were commonly blamed on stress that caused the release of excess stomach acid, many gastric ulcers are actually caused by infection with *Helicobacter pylori*, a spiral bacterium that thrives in the highly acidic stomach. People who are susceptible to this bacterium often develop gastric ulcers due to bacterial colonies that live on the mucus. Rather than being counseled to reduce their stress level, the old-time ulcer treatment, these patients are given antibiotics to cure their ulcers.

Accessory Organs Help Finish the Job

Although the gastrointestinal tract provides both a location for nutrient digestion and the surface required to absorb those nutrients, it cannot complete the job alone. Along the length of the tract several accessory organs assist in digestion, including the pancreas, liver, and gallbladder. See **Figure 15.12**.

The pancreas is an enzyme factory. The pancreas functions as an exocrine gland in the digestive system, producing enzymes that are released via the **pancreatic duct**. Almost all of the enzymes that act in the small intestine are made in the pancreas. Pancreatic juice also buffers the acidity of the chyme as it leaves the stomach. The small intestine does not have the protective layer of mucus found in the stomach, so it has no protection from the corrosive pH 2 solution being released from the pyloric sphincter. The pancreas secretes pancreatic juice into chyme immediately as it enters the duodenum, largely neutralizing the chyme to safeguard the duodenum from acid burns.

In addition to secreting digestive enzymes into the digestive tract, the pancreas is also responsible for secreting hormones into the bloodstream. The pancreas makes insulin and glucagon, which are responsible for regulating glucose uptake by the cells. Insulin stimulates glucose uptake, whereas glucagon causes glucose to be released into the bloodstream by those muscle and liver cells sequestering it. The cells of the pancreas are described as either cells of the islets of Langerhans or acinar cells. Islet cells function as endocrine cells, secreting insulin and glucagon. Acinar cells produce digestive enzymes.

Major accessory organs • Figure 15.12

The accessory organs include the liver, gallbladder, and pancreas. The acinar cells of the pancreas secrete digestive enzymes into the small intestine via the pancreatic duct.

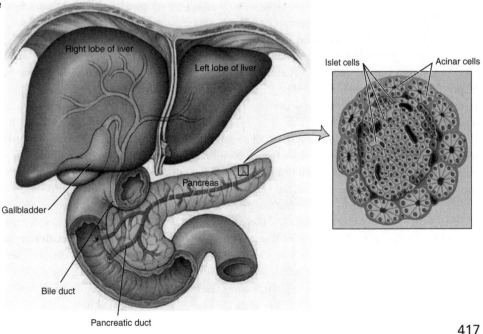

Right lobe of liver

Left lobe of liver

Islet cells

Acinar cells

Pancreas

Gallbladder

Bile duct

Pancreatic duct

417

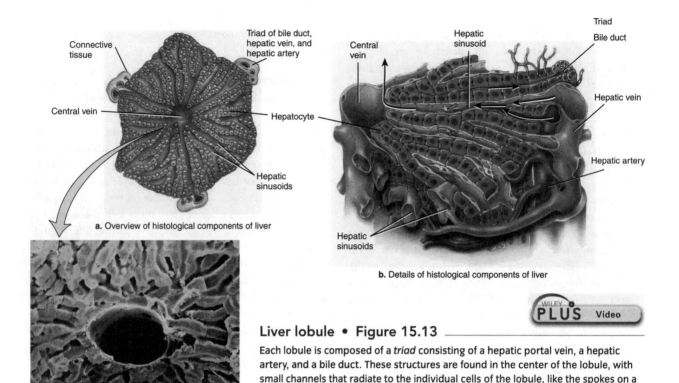

a. Overview of histological components of liver

b. Details of histological components of liver

Liver lobule • Figure 15.13

Each lobule is composed of a *triad* consisting of a hepatic portal vein, a hepatic artery, and a bile duct. These structures are found in the center of the lobule, with small channels that radiate to the individual cells of the lobule, like the spokes on a bicycle wheel. Fluid within the lobules is cleansed by the hepatocytes and sent on to the vena cavae.

The liver detoxifies what we add to the bloodstream. The liver is the largest organ of the body, aside from the skin, and usually weighs about 1,450 g. The liver has two lobes and sits mostly on the right side of the body. Within the lobes of the liver, the **hepatocytes** are arranged in **lobules**, as seen in **Figure 15.13**. The lobules are designed to allow maximum contact between hepatocytes and venous blood. The lobules monitor blood collected from the small intestine, adding and subtracting materials to maintain fluid homeostasis.

> **hepatocytes** Liver cells (*hepato* = liver; *cyte* = cell).

The liver is served by a **portal system**. The veins of the small intestine drain into the liver, where they break into capillaries again before being collected into a larger vein and returned to the heart. Blood flows through the digestive organs, travels from arteries to capillaries to veins, and proceeds on to the liver, where it moves back to capillaries, then to the veins that return to the heart. This portal system gives the individual hepatocytes access to the blood coming from the small intestine. This blood includes all absorbed compounds and nutrients, as well as toxins, from the small intestine. The hepatocytes must cleanse the blood before it reaches the heart,

removing toxins and storing excess nutrients, such as iron, and fat-soluble vitamins, such as A, D, and E.

Cholesterol, plasma proteins, and blood lipids are manufactured in the hepatocytes. The liver also monitors the glucose level in the blood; when it exceeds 0.1%, hepatocytes remove and store the excess as glycogen. When the glucose level drops, stored glycogen is broken down and released from the hepatocytes, and glucose again rises in the blood.

A diseased liver is a very serious health threat, and unfortunately quite common.

The gallbladder stores and releases bile. **Bile** is formed by the liver as a by-product of the breakdown of hemoglobin and cholesterol. It is stored in the gallbladder, under the right lobe of the liver. Bile salts from the gallbladder are released when fatty chyme is present in the duodenum, such as that from the greasy cheese pizza we have been following throughout this discussion. The concentrated bile salts act as an **emulsifier** or biological detergent, breaking larger fat globules into smaller ones. Bile aids in fat digestion by increasing the surface area on which the digestive activities of pancreatic lipase can act. Bile, therefore, is another form of mechanical digestion.

Stones can form in bile. A small, condensed crystal of cholesterol that forms in the gallbladder may attract calcium ions from the concentrated bile, resulting in the formation of a stone. Stones can grow big enough to get stuck in the bile duct when the gallbladder releases its contents. This causes pain and blocks the flow of bile. The gallbladder is often removed if stones are a chronic problem. After removal of the gallbladder, bile is still produced by the liver but not stored. The patient should not eat fatty meals, because there is no store of bile to aid in lipid digestion. See *Health, Wellness, and Disease: Gallbladder Removal Options* for more information.

The Large Intestine Absorbs and Reabsorbs

Once the pizza that we ate hours ago reaches the end of the small intestine, the body cannot pull any more nutrients from it. The chyme now passes from the small intestine into the next portion of the GI tract, the large intestine. See **Figure 15.14**. The overall function of the

Large intestine • Figure 15.14

The four parts of the colon can be easily seen in this image. A substance was given to the patient that reflects X-rays. Exposure to X-rays then provides a clear view of the colon. The ascending colon is on the left, the large horizontal loop is the transverse colon, and the very densely stained descending colon runs along the right side. The sigmoid colon makes its characteristic "S" turn at bottom center.

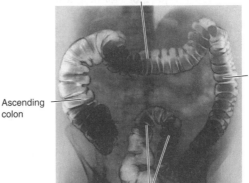

Transverse colon

Descending colon

Ascending colon

Sigmoid colon

HEALTH, WELLNESS, AND DISEASE
Gallbladder Removal Options

Occasionally the gallbladder will malfunction. It can become swollen and inflamed, or it may develop calcareous stones in the stored bile, or tumors or polyps may grow inside the walls of the gallbladder. In each case, bile will usually accumulate in the gallbladder, causing pressure and irritation. The gallbladder may also harbor a bacterial infection or burst as more and more bile is produced.

Removal of the gallbladder is the most common surgical solution to any gallbladder problem. There are two types of removal surgery, laparoscopic or open cholecystectomy. The Latin prefix for the gallbladder is *cholecyst-*, therefore a cholecystectomy is the removal (*-ectomy*) of the gallbladder. Laparoscopic surgery is far less invasive than open surgery. Small incisions are made in the skin, and a thin lighted laparoscope is inserted into the distended belly of the patient. The organs of the abdominal cavity are separated by filling the cavity with carbon dioxide. Small tools are inserted into the distended cavity, and using the light and camera of the laparoscope, the gallbladder is located. The blood vessels, nerves, and ducts attaching the gallbladder to the liver and duodenum are cut and sutured. The free organ is then removed from the body, along with any health problems it may carry. Open cholecystectomy is a more involved surgery, requiring a large incision in the skin and often

at least one overnight stay in the hospital. The abdominal cavity is opened, the lobes of the liver are pushed aside, and the gallbladder is exposed. Using scalpels, tissue clamps, retractors, sutures, and other common surgical tools, the gallbladder is removed. Open cholecystectomy is performed during emergency gallbladder removal, as it requires less patient preparation and less time to remove the diseased organ. As expected, recovery is more difficult from open surgery than from laparoscopy, and the scars are far larger.

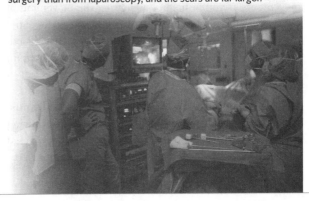

large intestine is to reabsorb the water that was added to the chyme to begin digestion. Along with the water, the large intestine absorbs many dissolved minerals and some vitamins. The valve that makes the transition from the ileum of the small intestine to the **cecum** of the large intestine is called the **ileocecal valve**. The ileum joins the large intestine a few centimeters from the bottom. The cecum hangs below the junction, forming a blind pouch that ends in the **vermiform appendix**.

The rest of the large intestine is the colon. The remainder of the large intestine is commonly called the **colon**. The four divisions of the colon describe the direction of flow within them:

- The **ascending colon** runs up the right side of the abdominal cavity.
- The **transverse colon** cuts across the top of the abdominal cavity, underneath the stomach.
- At the left side of the abdominal cavity, the colon turns back down, in the **descending colon**.
- At the lower left of the abdominal cavity, the colon makes an S turn to wind up in the center of the body. This turn is called the **sigmoid colon** and is the portion of the colon where feces may sit for long periods of time before moving out the rectum.

| polyp Growth protruding from a mucous membrane. |

Often, **polyps** can develop in the colon as feces rest against the mucosa.

The walls of the large intestine have **haustra**, pouches created by strands of muscle in the walls. These pouches fill with undigested material, which moves from pouch to pouch via **mass movements**.

Diarrhea results from an irritation of the colon. The chyme moves through the colon far too quickly for water or minerals to be absorbed. Medicines that prevent mass movements are often helpful in slowing the movement of chyme through the large intestine, giving the walls of the organ ample time to return the excess water to the bloodstream. To combat severe diarrhea, remedies that contain minerals and fluid are ingested to replace what is lost in the diarrhea.

The last 20 cm of the colon are the **rectum** and **anus**. Chyme remains in the colon for 3 to 10 hours, during which time it becomes progressively drier. Compacted chyme is called feces. When feces enter the upper portion of the rectum, they trigger the opening of the internal anal sphincter, a smooth muscle. The feces move into the rectum and press against the external anal sphincter. This pressure triggers **defecation**, a skeletal muscle action. As with all skeletal muscles, control over defecation is voluntary. On average, by age two and a half children are mature enough to control defecation.

Material moves through the large intestine in mass movements, created using a peristaltic wave. In the colon, water is reabsorbed from the soupy chyme, concentrating the waste material and conserving fluid. As the water is pulled back into the bloodstream across the lining of the colon, so too are minerals and vitamins. The removal of water leaves undigested remains of food and fiber in the colon, as well as bacteria, such as *E. coli* and other **obligate anaerobes** that naturally live in the large intestine. These colonies are necessary in the colon because they break down indigestible material and often produce essential vitamins. Sometimes these colonies can be embarrassing because they generate gas when fermenting solids.

| obligate anaerobes Bacteria that require an oxygen-free environment. |

The appendix may play a role in the immune system. Although the function of the appendix is unclear, it may play a role in the immune system. Some have suggested it is a structure that at some point in our evolution was used to store the "good" bacteria our bodies need along the length of the colon.

When the appendix acts up, we get **appendicitis**, which presents as pain near the belly button that migrates to the lower right side. Other symptoms include nausea, vomiting, low fever, constipation or diarrhea, inability to pass gas, and abdominal bloating. The abdomen becomes increasingly tender, and simple movements cause pain. These are all symptoms of a blockage in the appendix that prevents normal flow through the organ. Feces may be blocking the entrance, or lymph nodes in the surrounding walls may be swollen due to infection. In either instance, the contents of the appendix cannot move, leading to a buildup of pressure, decreased blood flow, and inflammation. If the pressure is not relieved quickly, the entire organ can rupture or suffer **gangrene**. For unknown

| gangrene Tissue death due to lack of blood flow. |

Summary of the functions of the digestive organs Table 15.1	
Organ	**Functions**
Mouth	See other listings in this table for the functions of the tongue, salivary glands, and teeth, all of which are in the mouth. Additionally, the lips and cheeks keep food between the teeth during mastication, and buccal glands lining the mouth produce saliva.
Tongue (accessory structure)	Maneuvers food for mastication, shapes food into a bolus, maneuvers food for deglutition, detects taste and touch sensations.
Salivary glands (accessory structure)	Produce saliva, which softens, moistens, and dissolves foods; cleanses mouth and teeth; and initiates the digestion of starch and lipids.
Teeth (accessory structure)	Cut, tear, and pulverize food to reduce solids to smaller particles for swallowing.
Pharynx	Receives a bolus from the oral cavity and passes it into the esophagus.
Esophagus	Receives a bolus from the pharynx and moves it into the stomach. This requires relaxation of the upper esophageal sphincter and secretion of mucus.
Stomach	Mixing waves macerate food, mix it with secretions of gastric glands (gastric juice), and reduce food to chyme. Gastric juice activates pepsin and kills many microbes in food. Intrinsic factor aids absorption of vitamin B_{12}. The stomach serves as a reservoir for food before releasing it into the small intestine.
Pancreas (accessory structure)	Pancreatic juice buffers acidic gastric juice in chyme (creating the proper pH for digestion in the small intestine), stops the action of pepsin from the stomach, and contains enzymes that digest carbohydrates, proteins, triglycerides, and nucleic acids.
Liver (accessory structure)	Produces bile, needed for emulsification and absorption of lipids in the small intestine; detoxifies blood containing absorbed nutrients and other substances.
Gallbladder (accessory structure)	Stores and concentrates bile and releases it into the small intestine.
Small intestine	Muscular contractions mix chyme with digestive juices; migrating motility complexes propel chyme toward the ileocecal sphincter; digestive secretions from the small intestine, pancreas, and liver complete the digestion of carbohydrates, proteins, lipids, and nucleic acids; circular folds, villi, and microvilli increase surface area for absorption; site where nutrients are absorbed.
Large intestine	Churning, peristalsis, and mass movements drive the contents of the colon into the rectum; bacteria produce some B vitamins and vitamin K; absorption of water, ions, and vitamins; defecation.

reasons, most cases of appendicitis occur in people ages 10 to 30. As soon as inflammation is diagnosed, the appendix is surgically removed to prevent it from rupturing and releasing pathogens into the intestine or the abdominal cavity.

See **Table 15.1** for a sunmary of the organs involved in digestion.

CONCEPT CHECK STOP

1. **What** are the regions of the small intestine?

2. **What** happens when chyme enters the duodenum?

3. **What** are the major functions of the pancreas, liver, and gallbladder?

4. **How** does the structure of the large intestine differ from that of the small intestine?

15.4 Digestion Is Both Mechanical and Chemical

LEARNING OBJECTIVES

1. **Define** mechanical and chemical digestion.
2. **List** the major enzymes of chemical digestion, and note their substrates.
3. **Discuss** the general role of the digestive system.
4. **Describe** the regulation of the digestive system.

Throughout this look at the digestive system, we have discussed various organs and their contribution to the process of digestion. Now it's time to summarize, so that we can view digestion as one continuous process.

Digestion is the breaking down of food into substances that can be absorbed and used by the body. This is accomplished through two processes: mechanical digestion and chemical (or enzymatic) digestion. **Mechanical digestion** refers to the chopping, cutting, and tearing of large pieces of food into smaller ones. Bites of apple, for example, are crushed and torn into pieces in your mouth, but these pieces are still recognizable as apple pieces, and no chemical alteration has occurred. The pieces have all the properties and chemical bonds of the original apple, but with a larger surface area needed for chemical digestion.

Mechanical digestion occurs mainly in the mouth. Once the bolus of food is passed to the esophagus, a small amount of mechanical digestion occurs in the stomach, as it rolls and churns the food into chyme. The chyme then moves through the pyloric sphincter into the duodenum, where large droplets of fat are emulsified via bile. The action of bile is a form of mechanical digestion, breaking larger fat droplets into smaller ones without altering the chemical structure of the fats. At this point, the chyme is ready for enzymatic degradation, and mechanical digestion is finished.

Unlike Mechanical Digestion, Chemical Digestion Alters Chemical Bonds

Most of the food we ingest is composed of **polymers**, long chains of repeating subunits, which our digestive enzymes must break into short chains, or monomers. It is these shorter units that are absorbed in the small intestine and used to produce the proteins and energy needed for survival.

In order to digest our myriad foodstuffs, we need several digestive enzymes. See **Figure 15.15**. As you know, enzymes are functional proteins that work best under a set of optimal conditions of pH, temperature, substrate, and product levels. (The substrate is the compound the enzyme acts upon, and the product is the result of that enzymatic

Hydrolase activity • Figure 15.15

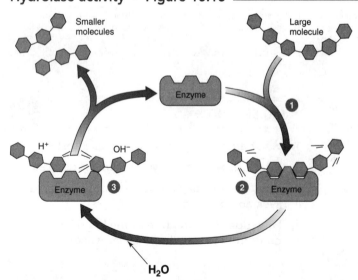

Most of our digestive enzymes are **hydrolases**, meaning that they catalyze the breakdown of large polymers by inserting water molecules between monomers. We unconsciously know that digesting requires water, because we find it uncomfortable to eat without drinking.

❶ Large molecule of food enters the digestive system.

❷ Enzyme binds to food (substrate) molecule.

❸ Enzyme uses H_2O to split the substrate molecule, leaving an OH^- on one product molecule and an H^+ on the other.

action.) All enzymes are specific for a particular substrate and catalyze only one reaction.

Enzyme names are usually built from the name of the substrate, followed by the suffix "-ase." It is easy to predict the function of an enzyme simply by evaluating its name. For example, lipase digests lipids, and nucleases digest nucleic acids. The major digestive enzymes, along with their substrates, products, and sources, are listed in **Table 15.2**.

Digestive enzymes Table 15.2			
Enzyme	**Source**	**Substrates**	**Products**
Saliva			
Salivary amylase	Salivary glands	Starches (polysaccharides)	Maltose (disaccharide), maltotriose (trisaccharide), and α-dextrins
Lingual lipase	Lingual glands in the tongue	Triglycerides (fats and oils) and other lipids	Fatty acids and diglycerides
Gastric Juice			
Pepsin	Stomach chief cells	Proteins	Peptides
Gastric lipase	Stomach chief cells	Triglycerides (fats and oils)	Fatty acids and monoglycerides
Pancreatic Juice			
Pancreatic amylase	Pancreatic acinar cells	Starches (polysaccharides)	Maltose (disaccharide), maltotriose (trisaccharide), and α-dextrins
Trypsin	Pancreatic acinar cells	Proteins	Peptides
Chymotrypsin	Pancreatic acinar cells	Proteins	Peptides
Elastase	Pancreatic acinar cells	Proteins	Peptides
Carboxypeptidase	Pancreatic acinar cells	Amino acid at carboxyl end of peptides	Amino acids and peptides
Pancreatic lipase	Pancreatic acinar cells	Triglycerides (fats and oils) that have been emulsified by bile salts	Fatty acids and monoglycerides
Nucleases			
Ribonuclease	Pancreatic acinar cells	Ribonucleic acid (RNA)	Nucleotides
Deoxyribonuclease	Pancreatic acinar cells	Deoxyribonucleic acid (DNA)	Nucleotides
Brush Border			
α-Dextrinase	Small intestine	α-dextrins	Glucose
Maltase	Small intestine	Maltose	Glucose
Sucrase	Small intestine	Sucrose	Glucose and fructose
Lactase	Small intestine	Lactose	Glucose and galactose
Enterokinase	Small intestine	Trypsinogen	Trypsin
Peptidases			
Aminopeptidase	Small intestine	Amino acid at amino end of peptides	Amino acids and peptides
Dipeptidase	Small intestine	Dipeptides	Amino acids
Nucleosidases and phosphatases	Small intestine	Nucleotides	Nitrogenous bases, pentoses, and phosphatases

All digestive enzymes, except for salivary amylase and pepsin, act in the small intestine. Salivary amylase begins to digest carbohydrates in the mouth and continues in the bolus of food entering the stomach. Pepsin, found in the stomach, works best at pH 2. The rest of the digestive enzymes operate best at pH 7 and are found inside the small intestine.

The Digestive System's Job Is to Prepare Nutrients

For some organisms, locating and ingesting nutrients is relatively simple. The single-celled **amoeba** oozes through the environment, constantly searching for nutrients. When it runs across a bit of organic material, the amoeba engulfs the particle and brings it into its body via **phagocytosis**. Once inside the amoeba, the particle is broken into its building blocks by digestive enzymes in the lysosome. Monosaccharides are released from carbohydrates, amino acids are released from proteins, and small carbon compounds are released from fatty acids. These small organic compounds are then used by the amoeba to generate essential enzymes, cellular structures, and energy. Micronutrients are obtained by the amoeba in a similar fashion, via **pinocytosis**. Often, micronutrients are released from larger compounds during lysosomal digestion.

> **amoeba** A single-celled organism that moves using pseudopods (false feet formed by oozing a portion of the body forward).

The human body is far more complex than the amoeba, but each cell still needs nutrients in order to survive. Interestingly, human cells absorb nutrients in exactly the same manner as the amoeba: through diffusion, osmosis, facilitated diffusion, and active transport (including both phagocytosis and receptor-mediated endocytosis). However, the cells cannot leave their positions in the tissues to ooze through the environment in search of nutrients. Although that would make a wonderful B-movie plot, our cells must remain organized and in position! Therefore, the digestive system's job is to prepare nutrients for circulation through the blood, which reaches every cell.

Those nutrients, of course, vary with the food the digestive system gets to work on. In addition, the food we eat has local and even global importance. See *Ethics and Issues: How Much Do We Help the World If We Go Vegan?*

Regulation of Our Digestive Activities Is Based on Blood Sugar Levels

Normally, blood sugar is kept at approximately 70 to 110 mg glucose per 100 ml of blood. This level is essential to keep neurons functioning. When blood glucose drops, we feel hungry. If we eat, blood sugar levels rise from the absorption of ingested glucose. If we do not eat, we begin to break down glycogen stores, where excess glucose has been stored in liver and skeletal muscles. Glycogen can break down to glucose relatively quickly. Fats and proteins can also be converted to glucose, but at a higher energy expense. During starvation, the protein of skeletal muscle, and even heart muscle, is broken down to provide glucose for the brain, as described in the coverage of the general adaptation syndrome in Chapter 9.

CONCEPT CHECK **STOP**

1. **How** does mechanical digestion differ from chemical digestion?
2. **What** are the major enzymes of chemical digestion and **what** molecules does each one digest?
3. **What** is the general role of the digestive system?
4. **What** happens when blood glucose drops? **What** happens to our blood sugar when we eat? **When** we don't eat?

ETHICS AND ISSUES
How Much Do We Help the World If We Go Vegan?

With the global population surging toward 7 billion, we have to wonder: Can the world feed itself? With food prices fluctuating (and usually rising), how many more hundreds of millions will be hungry if we don't solve inequities in both food production and food distribution?

It takes up to 10 calories of grain to produce 1 calorie of meat. Could it help to eat more grain directly instead of feeding it to animals? Yes, say vegetarians and vegans, who argue that eating meat is wrong on a number of levels. (Vegetarians eat no meat, but may use leather or eat dairy products, while vegans consume no animal products in any way.) Eating vegetable matter puts a person lower on the food chain and so uses available energy more efficiently. In theory, if people ate and digested the food needed to raise one cow to maturity, that food would satisfy many more people than could receive dietary satisfaction from the one cow.

However, the situation is more complicated than that. A large proportion of meat comes from animals that are raised partly or wholly on rangeland. Our digestive systems are not built to break down the cellulose in grasses, therefore grasses are not available to us as food. In this sense cattle expand, not contract, our food supply.

In any case, the trend in world food consumption is veering away from vegetarianism: More livestock and poultry are being eaten. Meat consumption is rising faster in the newly developing world, and in many cultures eating meat is a sign of wealth. In addition, meat does provide a source of protein and micronutrients, and our digestive systems are equipped to handle the full absorption of both.

Critical Reasoning Issues Some political leaders have derided energy conservation as only a sign of "personal virtue" and not a real force in the larger world. Vegetarianism is, as we have seen, a form of energy conservation—or is it?

NATIONAL GEOGRAPHIC

Think Critically

1. Do you see a strong or weak connection between your personal actions and their consequences for your community and larger society?
2. Explore the analogy between vegetarianism and energy conservation. How are they the same and how are they different?
3. According to recent studies of China's changing dietary demands with increasing cultural affluence, an affluent diet will use three times as much grain as a typical vegetarian diet. How might cultural practices affect the understanding of the "grain feeds more people" argument in other countries?

Neural Bases of Behaviour

Y our brain and the rest of your nervous system consist of billions of **neurons**. Each one is a tiny information-processing system with thousands of connections for receiving and sending electrochemical signals to other neurons. Each human body may have as many as one *trillion* neurons. (Be careful not to confuse the term *neuron* with the term *nerve*. Nerves are large bundles of axons—defined below—outside the brain and spinal cord.)

Neurons are held in place, supported, and nurtured by **glial cells**. Glial cells surround neurons and perform a variety of tasks, including cleaning up and insulating one neuron from another so their neural messages aren't scrambled. Glial cells also have a wide array of other duties, such as playing a direct role in nervous system communication and neural signalling (Arriagada et al., 2007; Wieseler-Frank, Maier, & Watkins, 2005; Zillmer, Spiers, & Culbertson, 2008).

No two neurons are identical, but most share three basic features: **dendrites**, the **cell body**, and an **axon** (FIGURE 2.6). To remember how information travels through the neuron, think of these three in reverse alphabetical order: *d*endrite → *c*ell *b*ody → *a*xon.

> ■ **neuron** A nervous system cell that receives and conducts electrochemical impulses.
>
> ■ **glial cell** A nervous system cell that supports, nourishes, insulates, and protects neurons.

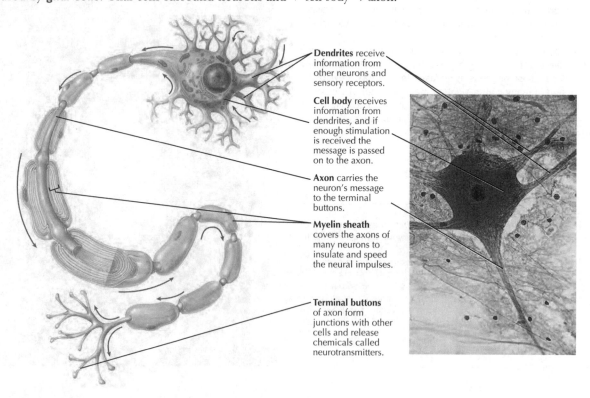

Dendrites receive information from other neurons and sensory receptors.

Cell body receives information from dendrites, and if enough stimulation is received the message is passed on to the axon.

Axon carries the neuron's message to the terminal buttons.

Myelin sheath covers the axons of many neurons to insulate and speed the neural impulses.

Terminal buttons of axon form junctions with other cells and release chemicals called neurotransmitters.

The structure of a neuron FIGURE 2.6

Arrows indicate direction of information flow: dendrites → cell body → axon → terminal buttons of axon.

42 **CHAPTER 2** Neuroscience and Biological Foundations

How Toxins and Drugs Affect Our Brain

Poisons, toxins, and mind-altering (psychoactive) drugs have their effect in the nervous system by interacting with neurotransmitter systems.

Normal neurotransmitter activation

Postsynaptic receptor site

Nerve impulse

A Like a key fitting into a lock, receptor sites on receiving neurons' dendrites and cell bodies recognize particular neurotransmitters by their distinctive shapes.

Blocked neurotransmitter activation

B Neurotransmitter and other molecules without the correct shape won't fit a particular receptor, so they cannot stimulate the receiving neuron.

Agonist drug "mimics" neurotransmitter

C Some *agonist drugs*, like the poison in the black widow spider or the nicotine in cigarettes, are similar enough in structure to a certain neurotransmitter (in this case, *acetylcholine*) that they can mimic its effects on the receiving neuron.

Antagonist drug fills receptor space and blocks neurotransmitter

D Some *antagonist drugs* block neurotransmitters like acetylcholine. Because acetylcholine is vital in muscle action, blocking it paralyzes muscles, including those involved in breathing, which can be fatal.

Examples of antagonists to acetylcholine include most snake venom and some poisons, like *botulinum toxin*. This is one of the most poisonous naturally occurring substances, but when used in tiny doses in the form of Botox®, it is effective in treating painful muscle contractions and excessive sweating. It is also used for cosmetic purposes to improve the appearance of frown lines and crow's feet wrinkles. Another example of an acetylcholine antagonist is curare, a plant toxin that has been widely used by South American hunter-gatherer peoples as an arrow poison. When the curare-tipped arrowhead breaks the skin it paralyzes the respiratory muscles and the animal quickly dies by asphyxiation.

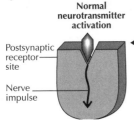

HOW DO NEURONS COMMUNICATE?

A neuron's basic function is to transmit information throughout the nervous system. Neurons communicate in a type of electrical and chemical language. The process of neural communication begins within the neuron itself, when the dendrites and cell body receive electrical messages. These messages move along the axon in the form of a neural impulse, or **action potential** (FIGURE 2.7 on pages 44–45).

A neural impulse travels along a bare axon at only about 10 metres per second. This is much slower than the speed at which electricity moves through a wire. Many mammalian axons, however, are enveloped in fatty insulation called a **myelin sheath**. This sheath blankets the axon, except in places called *nodes* where the myelin is very thin or absent. In a myelinated axon, the neural impulse moves about 10 times as fast as on a bare axon. This is because the action potential jumps from node to node rather than travelling along the entire length of the axon membrane.

Communication *within* the neuron (FIGURE 2.7A) is not the same as communication *between* neurons (FIGURE 2.7B). Within the neuron, messages travel electrically. But messages are transmitted chemically from

action potential
The voltage change across an axon membrane when an impulse is transmitted.

myelin sheath
The fatty insulation that segmentally wraps an axon and serves to speed neural transmission.

Neural Bases of Behaviour 43

Process Diagram

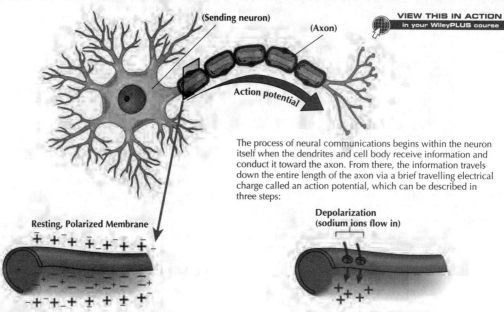

(Sending neuron)   (Axon)

Action potential

VIEW THIS IN ACTION
in your WileyPLUS course

The process of neural communications begins within the neuron itself when the dendrites and cell body receive information and conduct it toward the axon. From there, the information travels down the entire length of the axon via a brief travelling electrical charge called an action potential, which can be described in three steps:

Resting, Polarized Membrane

❶ Resting potential
When an axon is not stimulated, it is in a polarized state, called the *resting potential.* "At rest," the fluid inside the axon has more negatively charged ions than the fluid outside. This results from the selective permeability of the axon membrane and a series of mechanisms, called *sodium-potassium pumps,* that pull potassium ions in and pump sodium ions out of the axon.
The inside of the axon has a charge of about −70 millivolts relative to the outside.

**Depolarization
(sodium ions flow in)**

❷ Action potential initiation
When an "at rest" axon membrane is stimulated by a sufficiently strong signal, it produces an *action potential* (or depolarization). This action potential begins when the first part of the axon opens its "gates" and positively charged sodium ions rush through. The additional sodium ions change the previously negative charge inside the axon to a positive charge—thus depolarizing the axon.

(potassium ions flow out)

Depolarization

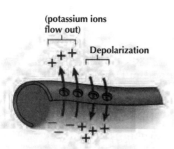

❸ Spreading of action potential and repolarization
The initial depolarization (or action potential) of Step 2 produces a subsequent imbalance of ions in the adjacent axon membrane. This imbalance thus causes the action potential to spread to the next section. Meanwhile, "gates" in the axon membrane of the initially depolarized section open and potassium ions flow out, thus allowing the first section to repolarize and return to its resting potential.

Flow of depolarization
Action potential

Action potential

Action potential

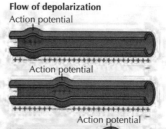

❹ Overall summary
As you can see in the figure above, this sequential process of depolarization, followed by repolarization, transmits the action potential along the entire length of the axon from the cell body to the terminal buttons. This is similar to an audience at an athletic event doing "the wave." One section of fans initially stands up for a brief time (action potential). This section then sits down (resting potential), and the "wave" then spreads to adjacent sections.

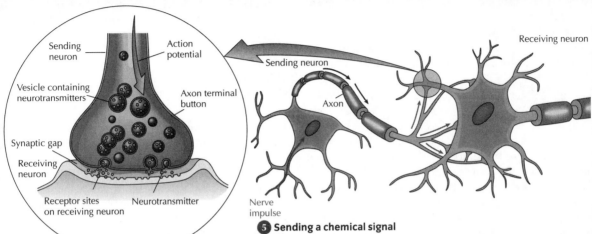

Sending neuron

Action potential

Vesicle containing neurotransmitters

Axon terminal button

Synaptic gap

Receiving neuron

Receptor sites on receiving neuron

Neurotransmitter

Sending neuron

Axon

Nerve impulse

Receiving neuron

6 **Receiving a chemical signal**

After neurotransmitters diffuse across the synaptic gap, they bind to the membrane of a specific receiving neuron. Each receiving neuron gets large numbers of neurotransmitter messages. As you can see in the photo, the axon terminals from thousands of other nearby neurons almost completely cover the cell body of the receiving neuron. Neurotransmitters deliver either excitatory or inhibitory messages, and the receiving neuron will produce an action potential and pass along the message only if the number of excitatory messages outweigh the number of inhibitory messages (in a process called *summation*). Why do we need competing messages? Like an accelerator and brake on a car, your body needs similar on (excitatory) and off (inhibitory) mechanisms. By using these two switches, your body manages an amazing balance between overexcitation, leading to seizures, and underexcitation, leading to unconsciousness and death.

5 **Sending a chemical signal**

When action potentials reach the branching axon terminals, they trigger the terminal buttons at the axon's end to release thousands of neurotransmitter molecules into the *synaptic gap,* the tiny space between the sending and receiving neuron. These chemicals then move across the synaptic gap and attach to receptors on the membranes of the receiving neuron. In this way, they carry the message from the sending neuron to the receiving neuron.

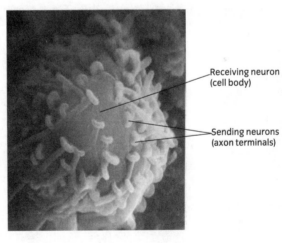

Receiving neuron (cell body)

Sending neurons (axon terminals)

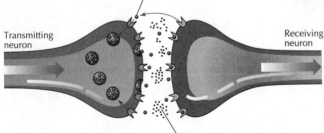

Reuptake

Transmitting neuron

Receiving neuron

Enzymatic breakdown

7 **Dealing with leftovers**

Neurotransmitters do not remain attached to their receptors forever—they bind and release. When unbound they are either taken back up into the terminal button of the sending neuron for breakdown and recycling in a process called "reuptake," or are destroyed right in the synapse by a variety of degradation enzymes.

neurotransmitters Chemicals that neurons release across the synapse in response to the arrival of an action potential, which affect other cells, including other neurons.

one neuron to the next. The chemicals that transmit these messages are called **neurotransmitters**.

Researchers have discovered hundreds of substances that function as neurotransmitters. These substances regulate a wide variety of physiological processes. See *What a Psychologist Sees* on page 43 for a description of some of these effects.

Studying the brain and its neurotransmitters will help you understand some common medical problems. (STUDY ORGANIZER 2.1 discusses some of the better understood neurotransmitters.) For example, we know that decreased levels of the neurotransmitter dopamine are associated with Parkinson's disease (PD), whereas excessively high levels of dopamine appear to contribute to some forms of schizophrenia.

One of the better-known brain chemicals are the endogenous opium-like peptides, commonly known as **endorphins** (a contraction of *endogenous*, meaning

"self-produced," and *morphine*). These nervous system chemicals mimic the effects of opium-like drugs, such as morphine: They elevate mood and reduce pain. They also affect memory, learning, blood pressure, appetite, and sexual activity.

HORMONES: A GLOBAL COMMUNICATION SYSTEM

We've just seen how the nervous system uses neurotransmitters to rapidly transmit messages across synapses to have widespread effects throughout the body. A second type of communication system exists. This second system is made up of a network of glands, called the **endocrine system** (FIGURE 2.8). Rather than neurotransmitters in synapses, this system uses **hormones** in blood to carry its messages (see FIGURE 2.9).

hormones Chemicals synthesized by endocrine glands that are released into the bloodstream to bind to target tissues and organs, producing bodily changes or maintaining normal function.

Study Organizer 2.1	How neurotransmitters affect us	
Neurotransmitter	**Behaviours and/or Mental Processes Affected**	
Serotonin	Sleep, mood, appetite, sensory perception, temperature regulation, sex drive, pain suppression, and impulsivity. Low levels associated with depression.	
Acetylcholine (ACh)	Muscle action, cognitive functioning, memory, rapid-eye-movement (REM) sleep, emotion. Suspected role in Alzheimer's disease.	
Dopamine (DA)	Movement, attention, memory, learning, and emotion. Excess DA associated with schizophrenia, too little with Parkinson's disease. Also plays a role in addiction and pleasure systems in the brain.	
Norepinephrine (NE) (or noradrenaline)	Learning, memory, dreaming, emotion, waking from sleep, eating, alertness, wakefulness, reactions to stress. Low levels of NE associated with depression, high levels with agitated, manic states.	
Epinephrine (or adrenaline)	Emotional arousal, memory storage, and metabolism of glucose necessary for energy release.	
Gamma aminobutyric acid (GABA)	Neural inhibition in the central nervous system. Tranquilizing drugs, like Ativan or Xanax, increase GABA's inhibitory effects and thereby decrease anxiety.	
Endorphins	Mood, pain, memory, and learning.	

The endocrine system
FIGURE 2.8

This figure shows the major endocrine glands, along with some internal organs to help you locate the glands.

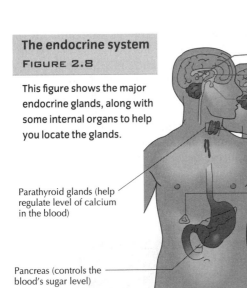

Pineal gland (helps regulate sleep cycle and body rhythms)

Hypothalamus (controls the pituitary gland)

Pituitary gland (influences growth and lactation; also secretes many hormones that affect other glands)

Thyroid gland (controls metabolism)

Parathyroid glands (help regulate level of calcium in the blood)

Adrenal gland (arouses the body, helps respond to stress, regulates salt balance and some sexual functioning)

Pancreas (controls the blood's sugar level)

Ovaries (secrete female sex hormones)

Testes (secrete male sex hormones)

Neurotransmitters send individual messages

To... Jean Bean
CC...
Subject: Lunch Tomorrow?
Attach...

Hi Jean,
Are you free for lunch tomorrow? If so, want to meet at noon at the Hong Kong Cafe? Hoping to see you then.

Hormones send global messages

To... Friends; family; co-workers
CC...
Subject: Party!
Attach...

Hi Everybody,
Jean Bean and I are hosting a party on Saturday night at 9 p.m. Please come, and tell your friends!

Why do we need two communication systems? FIGURE 2.9

You can think of neurotransmitters as individual e-mails, like those you send to particular people. Neurotransmitters deliver messages to specific receptors across specific synapses, which other neurons nearby probably don't "overhear." Hormones, in contrast, are like a global e-mail message that you send to everyone in your address book. Endocrine glands release hormones directly into the bloodstream. The hormones travel throughout the body, carrying messages to any cell that will accept them (that is, it has the appropriate hormone receptors). Hormones also function like your global e-mail recipients forwarding your message to yet more people. For example, a small part of the brain called the hypothalamus releases hormones that signal the pituitary gland, which then stimulates or inhibits the release of other downstream hormones.

Neural Bases of Behaviour   47

Your endocrine system has several important functions. It helps regulate long-term bodily processes, such as growth and sexual characteristics. For example, if testosterone were to be removed from a healthy young man, his genitals would get smaller and his sex drive would decrease (Brett et al., 2007). Hormones also maintain ongoing bodily processes (such as digestion and elimination), and they control the body's response to emergencies. In times of crisis and arousal, the hypothalamus sends messages through two pathways: the neural system and the endocrine system (primarily via the pituitary gland). The pituitary gland sends hormonal messages to the adrenal glands (which sit on top of each kidney, shaped similar to a Hershey's chocolate kiss). The adrenal glands then release three hormones: *cortisol,* a stress hormone that boosts energy and blood sugar levels; *epinephrine* (adrenaline); and *norepinephrine.* These last two hormones also serve as neurotransmitters, but, as you will see, they have different functions in the endocrine system.

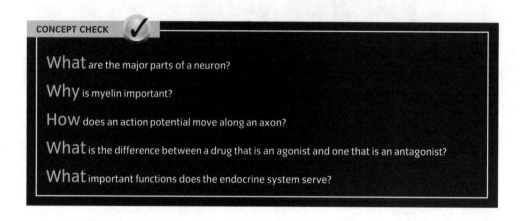

CONCEPT CHECK ✓

What are the major parts of a neuron?

Why is myelin important?

How does an action potential move along an axon?

What is the difference between a drug that is an agonist and one that is an antagonist?

What important functions does the endocrine system serve?

Nervous System Organization

LEARNING OBJECTIVES

Identify the major components of the nervous system.

Explain how the spinal cord initiates reflexes.

Explain why research investigating neuroplasticity and neurogenesis are important.

Describe the opposing roles of the sympathetic and parasympathetic nervous systems.

Have you heard the expression "Information is power"? Nowhere is this truer than in the human body. Without information, we could not survive. Neurons within our nervous system must take in sensory information from the outside world and then process and respond to it. Just as the circulatory system handles blood, which conveys chemicals and gases around the body, our nervous system uses electrical signals and chemicals to convey information.

The nervous system is divided and subdivided into several branches (**FIGURE 2.10**). One main part of our nervous system includes the brain and a large bundle of nerves that form the *spinal cord.* Because this system is located in the centre of your body (within your skull and spine), it is called the **central nervous system (CNS)**.

> **central nervous system (CNS)** The brain and spinal cord.

The second major part of your nervous system includes all the nerves outside the brain and spinal

The nervous system FIGURE 2.10

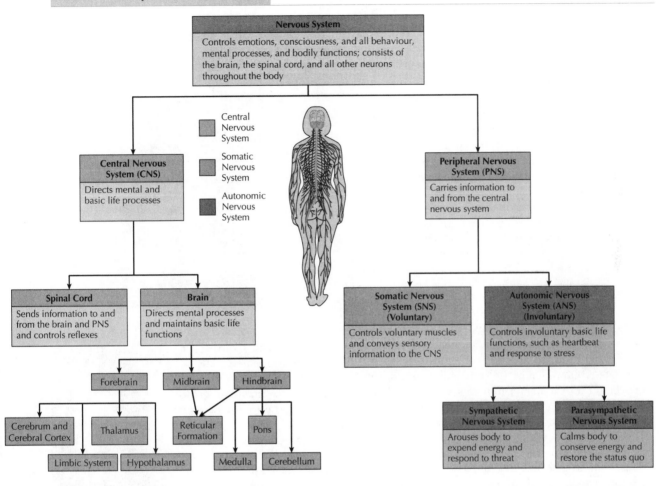

peripheral nervous system (PNS) All other nerves and neurons connecting the CNS to the rest of the body.

CENTRAL NERVOUS SYSTEM (CNS): THE BRAIN AND SPINAL CORD

Although the central nervous system (CNS) is incredibly versatile and remarkably powerful, it is also incredibly fragile. Unlike neurons in the PNS that can regenerate and require less protection, serious cord. This **peripheral nervous system (PNS)** carries messages (action potentials) to and from the central nervous system to the periphery of the body.

damage to neurons in the CNS is usually permanent. However, new research is revealing the brain is not as "hard wired" as we once thought. Scientists had long believed that after the first few years of life, humans and most animals are unable to repair or replace damaged neurons in the brain or spinal cord. We now know that the brain is capable of lifelong **neuroplasticity** and **neurogenesis**.

neuroplasticity The brain's remarkable malleability to reorganize and change its structure and function across the lifespan.

neurogenesis The division and differentiation of non-neuronal cells to produce neurons.

Nervous System Organization 49

Neuroplasticity: Changes in the Brain's Architecture

Rather than being a fixed, rigid organ, the brain is capable of changing its structure (anatomy) and function (physiology) through usage and experience (Deller et al., 2006; Kinsley & Lambert, 2008; Mateer & Kerns, 2000; Romero et al., 2008; Rossignol et al., 2008). It was once thought that this malleability occurred only during childhood and that by puberty the brain had its permanent adult form and function. Now, decades of research have shown the brain has the lifelong capacity to reorganize its neural pathways in response to new experiences and to compensate for lost function after damage. It is this dynamic rewiring that makes brains so wonderfully adaptive. For example, it makes it possible for us to learn a new sport, computer game, or foreign language. Moreover, neuroplasticity is the mechanism by which our brain can structurally and functionally modify itself following strokes and trauma (Taub, 2004; Whishaw et al., 2008; Wolf et al., 2008).

The idea that changes in neuronal architecture could account for changes in thinking and behaviour was first demonstrated in the 1940s by Dr. Donald Hebb (1904–1985) (**FIGURE 2.11**), a Canadian psychologist and the principal pioneer of neuropsychology. Hebb's description of how the brain and neural signals can account for the higher functions of the mind and consciousness was extremely influential. He believed the human conscious experience could be described in terms of patterns of neural signals (Hebb, 1949). Hebb suggested that neurons that are simultaneously active would tend to become associated with each other, such that activity in one would facilitate activity in the other (Hebb, 1949). Repeated stimulation ultimately strengthens the synapses, and associated neurons fire more readily, translating into some mental task. At the time, the idea was revolutionary; scientists had long wondered how the 1.5-kilogram gelatinous organ in our heads could initiate behaviour, interact with the environment, and form cohesive thoughts. Hebb's early work gave psychology the basic mechanism of synaptic plasticity. Many of Hebb's ideas have been subsequently supported by research findings.

Neurogenesis: The Making of New Neurons

The brain continually replaces lost cells with new cells. These cells originate deep within the brain and migrate to become parts of specific

Donald Hebb FIGURE 2.11

circuitries. The source of these newly created cells is neural **stem cells**—rare, immature cells that can grow and develop into any type of cell in the nervous system. Their fate depends on the chemical signals they receive (Abbott, 2004; Kim, 2004; Vaillend et al., 2008). Stem cell research has come a long way since the 1960s, when it was first described in transplanted mouse bone marrow cells by Canadian scientists Ernest McCulloch and James Edgar Till (Becker, McCulloch, & Till, 1963). These special cells are now used for a variety of purposes, such as bone marrow transplants. Clinical trials that have used transplanted stem cells to replace cells destroyed by strokes, Alzheimer's, Parkinson's, epilepsy, stress, and depression show their tremendous potential in treating neural injury and disease (Chang et al., 2005; Fleischmann & Welz, 2008; Hampton, 2006, 2007; Leri, Anversa, & Frishmann, 2007; Waldau & Shetty, 2008).

stem cells Precursor (immature) cells that can develop into any type of new specialized cells; a stem cell holds all the information it needs to make bone, blood, brain—any part of a human body—and can also copy itself to maintain a stock of stem cells.

Does this mean that people paralyzed from spinal cord injuries might be able to walk again? At this time, neurogenesis in the brain and spinal cord appears to be minimal. However, one possible option might be to transplant embryonic stem cells into the damaged area of the spinal cord. Researchers have transplanted mouse embryonic stem cells into a damaged rat spinal cord (Jones, Anderson, & Galvin, 2003; McDonald et al., 1999). When the damaged spinal cord was viewed several weeks later, the implanted cells had survived and spread throughout the injured cord area. More important, the rats also showed some movement in the previously paralyzed parts of their bodies. Similar findings have been reported by other research teams (Feng et al., 2008). Preliminary human clinical trials have shown that some spinal nerve regeneration can occur after a spinal cord injury has been treated with cell-growth-promoting substances (Wu et al., 2008).

The Spinal Cord

Beginning at the base of the brain and continuing down the back, the spinal cord carries vital information from the rest of the body to and from the brain. But the spinal cord doesn't just relay messages. It can also initiate some automatic behaviours on its own. We call these involuntary, automatic behaviours **reflexes** or **reflex arcs** because the response to the incoming stimuli is automatically "reflected" back (**Figure 2.12**).

reflexes or reflex arcs Involuntary, automatic behaviour initiated by the spinal cord in response to some stimulus.

We're all born with numerous reflexes, many of which fade over time. But even as adults, we still blink in response to a puff of air in our eyes, gag when something touches the back of the throat, and urinate and defecate in response to pressure in the bladder and rectum. Reflexes even influence our sexual responses. Certain stimuli, such as touching the genitals, can lead to clitoral and penile erection (see *Psychological Science*). However, to have the passion, sexual thoughts, and emotion, or to get aroused by sexy sights or sounds, the sensory information must ultimately include the brain.

The workings of the spinal cord   FIGURE 2.12

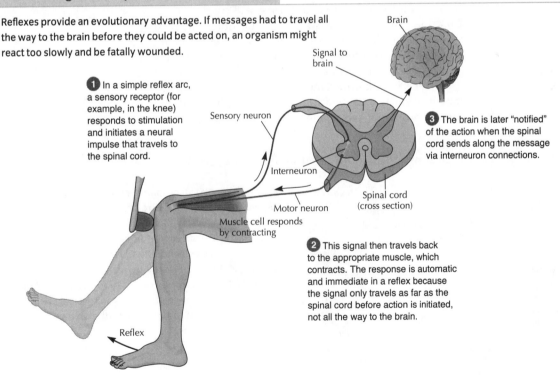

Reflexes provide an evolutionary advantage. If messages had to travel all the way to the brain before they could be acted on, an organism might react too slowly and be fatally wounded.

1 In a simple reflex arc, a sensory receptor (for example, in the knee) responds to stimulation and initiates a neural impulse that travels to the spinal cord.

3 The brain is later "notified" of the action when the spinal cord sends along the message via interneuron connections.

2 This signal then travels back to the appropriate muscle, which contracts. The response is automatic and immediate in a reflex because the signal only travels as far as the spinal cord before action is initiated, not all the way to the brain.

Brain

Signal to brain

Sensory neuron

Interneuron

Motor neuron

Spinal cord (cross section)

Muscle cell responds by contracting

Reflex

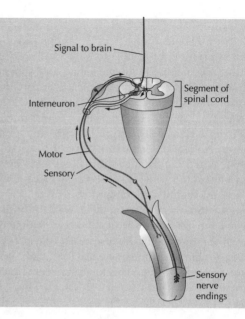

Psychological Science

The Brain Isn't Necessary for an Erection

Direct tactile (touch) stimulation of the penis or clitoris can trigger an erection. This occurs because of a spinal reflex that forms a loop from the genitals to the spinal cord and back. Sensory nerve endings in the genital area detect the tactile stimulation, and this information is then conveyed to the spinal cord. Nerves then transmit the output signal back to the penis or clitoris, and this signal causes the changes in blood flow in the genitals that account for an erection. Although the spinal cord does send sensory information onward to the brain, this role is not essential. People with spinal injuries that sever communication between the lower regions of the spinal cord and the brain can usually achieve erection with tactile stimulation alone.

PERIPHERAL NERVOUS SYSTEM (PNS): CONNECTING THE CNS TO THE REST OF THE BODY

somatic nervous system (SNS) Subdivision of the peripheral nervous system (PNS). The SNS receives incoming sensory information and controls the skeletal muscles.

The main function of the peripheral nervous system (PNS) is to carry information to and from the central nervous system. It links the brain and spinal cord to the body's senses, muscles, and glands.

The PNS is subdivided into the somatic nervous system and the autonomic nervous system.

In a kind of "two-way street," the **somatic nervous system (SNS)** first carries sensory information to the CNS and then carries messages from the CNS to skeletal muscles (**Figure 2.13**).

The other subdivision of the PNS is the **autonomic nervous system (ANS)**. The ANS is responsible for involuntary tasks, such as heart rate, digestion, pupil dilation, and breathing. Like an automatic

autonomic nervous system (ANS) Subdivision of the peripheral nervous system (PNS) that controls involuntary functions of tissues, organs, and glands. It is subdivided into the *sympathetic* nervous system and the *parasympathetic* nervous system.

The relationship between sensory and motor neurons FIGURE 2.13

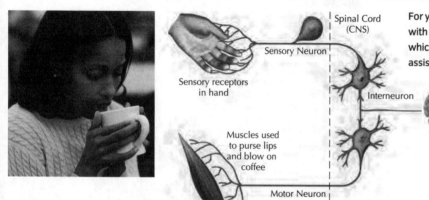

For you to be able to function, your brain must communicate with your body. This is the job of the *somatic nervous system*, which receives sensory information, sends it to the brain, and assists in the brain's response. *Sensory neurons* carry messages to the CNS. *Motor neurons* carry messages *away* from the CNS. *Interneurons* communicate within the CNS and link up the sensory inputs and the motor outputs. Most of the neurons in the brain are interneurons.

52 CHAPTER 2 Neuroscience and Biological Foundations

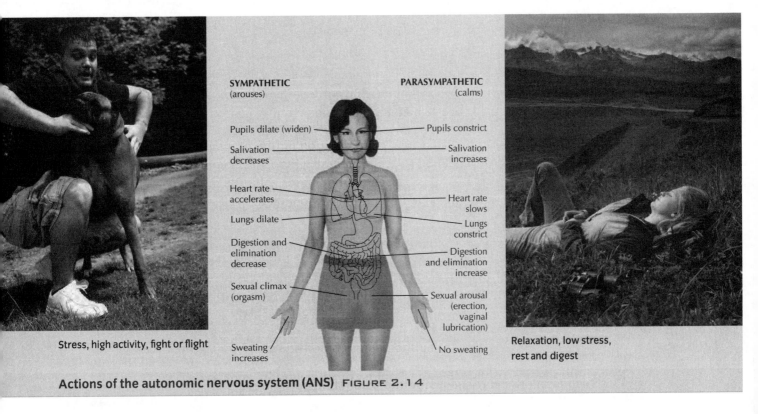

SYMPATHETIC
(arouses)

PARASYMPATHETIC
(calms)

Pupils dilate (widen)

Salivation
decreases

Heart rate
accelerates

Lungs dilate

Digestion and
elimination
decrease

Sexual climax
(orgasm)

Sweating
increases

Pupils constrict

Salivation
increases

Heart rate
slows

Lungs
constrict

Digestion
and elimination
increase

Sexual arousal
(erection,
vaginal
lubrication)

No sweating

Stress, high activity, fight or flight

Relaxation, low stress,
rest and digest

Actions of the autonomic nervous system (ANS) Figure 2.14

pilot, the ANS can sometimes be consciously overridden. But as its name implies, the autonomic system normally operates on its own without conscious effort (autonomously).

The autonomic nervous system is further divided into two branches: the sympathetic and parasympathetic, which tend to work in opposition to regulate the functioning of organs, like the heart, the intestines, and the lungs (**Figure 2.14**). Like two children playing on a teeter-totter, one branch will be up while the other is down, but they essentially balance each other.

During stressful times, either mental or physical, the **sympathetic nervous system** mobilizes bodily resources to respond to the stressor. This emergency response is often called the fight-or-flight response. If you saw a deadly snake coiled and ready to strike, your sympathetic nervous system would, among other things, increase your heart rate, respiration, and blood pressure; stop your digestive and eliminative processes; and release hormones, such as cortisol, into the bloodstream. The net result of sympathetic activation is to get more oxygenated blood and energy to the skeletal muscles and to prepare you to deal with the stressor—whether you defend yourself (fight) or escape (flight).

The sympathetic nervous system provides an adaptive, evolutionary advantage. Early in evolution, when an organism faced a dangerous predator or an aggressive intruder, there were only two reasonable responses: fight or flight.

This evolved automatic mobilization of bodily resources is still essential today. However, non-life-threatening events, such as traffic jams and pressing deadlines, also activate our sympathetic nervous system. Our bodies respond to these sources of stress with sympathetic arousal. As the next chapter discusses, ongoing sympathetic activation to such chronic stress can damage our health.

In contrast to the sympathetic nervous system and its fight or flight response, the **parasympathetic nervous system** functions to rest and digest. It is responsible for returning the body to its normal functioning by slowing heart rate, lowering blood pressure, and increasing digestive and eliminative processes. In non-arousing activities (such as reading or talking on the phone), this branch of the nervous system is involved in energy storage and conservation.

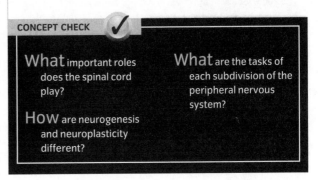

CONCEPT CHECK

What important roles does the spinal cord play?

How are neurogenesis and neuroplasticity different?

What are the tasks of each subdivision of the peripheral nervous system?

Nervous System Organization   53

A Tour Through the Brain

We begin our exploration of the brain at the lower end, where the spinal cord joins the base of the brain, and move upward toward the skull. As we move from bottom to top, vital reflexes, like breathing, generally give way to more complex mental processes, like making social judgements and planning (**FIGURE 2.15** and **FIGURE 2.16**).

Damage to the brain FIGURE 2.15

The 2005 debate over Terri Schiavo was largely about whether her husband should be allowed to remove her feeding tube. Although Terri was still able to move and breathe on her own, she had no higher-level brain functions. Terry's parents believed that the lower-level brain functions she exhibited were sufficient proof of life. Advocates on the other side felt that once the cerebral cortex ceases functioning, the "person" is gone and there is no reason to keep the body alive. What do you think? A lengthy court battle granted permission to remove her feeding tube. Terri Schiavo died on March 31, 2005, after nearly 14 days without food or water. She was 41 years old.

LOWER-LEVEL BRAIN STRUCTURES: THE HINDBRAIN, MIDBRAIN, AND PARTS OF THE FOREBRAIN

The billions of neurons that make up the human brain control most of what we think, feel, and do. Certain brain structures are specialized to perform certain tasks, a process known as **localization of function**. However, most parts of the brain perform integrative, interdependent functions.

> ■ **localization of function** Specialization of various parts of the brain for particular functions.

The Hindbrain

The **hindbrain** includes the medulla, pons, and cerebellum and functions collectively to generate most of your vital bodily processes.

The **medulla** is effectively an extension of the top of the spinal cord, carrying information to and from the brain. It also controls many essential automatic bodily functions, such as respiration and heart rate, so damage to this brain region is often fatal. But for your medulla you would also not be able to swallow, vomit, or defecate—all clearly essential functions.

The **pons** is involved in respiration, movement, sleeping, waking, and dreaming (among other things). The pons also has a role in relaying sensory information from the periphery to higher brain structures. For example, auditory information first enters the brain at the level of the pons.

The cauliflower-shaped **cerebellum** at the back of the brain ("little brain" in Latin) is, evolutionarily, a very old structure. It coordinates fine muscle movement and balance. The cerebellum also has the rather interesting task of taking a sequence of movements that always runs in the same order and packages them as a single automatic output. While executing complex martial arts moves or acrobatic movements nicely illustrate

The human brain FIGURE 2.16

This drawing summarizes key functions of some of the brain's major structures. The brainstem, which includes parts of the hindbrain, midbrain, and forebrain, provides a handy geographical landmark.

VIEW THIS IN ACTION
in your WileyPLUS course

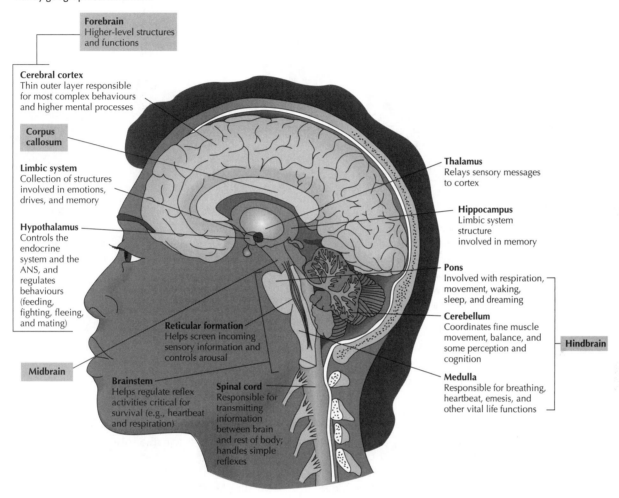

Forebrain
Higher-level structures and functions

Cerebral cortex
Thin outer layer responsible for most complex behaviours and higher mental processes

Corpus callosum

Limbic system
Collection of structures involved in emotions, drives, and memory

Hypothalamus
Controls the endocrine system and the ANS, and regulates behaviours (feeding, fighting, fleeing, and mating)

Midbrain

Reticular formation
Helps screen incoming sensory information and controls arousal

Brainstem
Helps regulate reflex activities critical for survival (e.g., heartbeat and respiration)

Spinal cord
Responsible for transmitting information between brain and rest of body; handles simple reflexes

Thalamus
Relays sensory messages to cortex

Hippocampus
Limbic system structure involved in memory

Pons
Involved with respiration, movement, waking, sleep, and dreaming

Cerebellum
Coordinates fine muscle movement, balance, and some perception and cognition

Medulla
Responsible for breathing, heartbeat, emesis, and other vital life functions

Hindbrain

the cerebellum at work, it is best demonstrated when a person is learning to drive a standard transmission car. For most, this process is initially very difficult, requiring tremendous concentration to get the clutch, gas, and gear change in the correct order. After a bit of practice, however, the driver is able to change gears effortlessly, without being distracted by music, conversation, or other variables: the cerebellum has tuned into the repetitive behaviours involved in the gear changing process and runs them as a single smooth behaviour.

This ability then frees up higher brain regions to do more complex tasks, like concentrating on road conditions and other drivers (and not changing radio stations, searching for music, or texting friends!).

The Midbrain   The **midbrain** helps us orient our eye and body movements to visual and auditory stimuli, and works with the pons to help control sleep and level of arousal. When you are visually tracking a moving object, it is the midbrain—among other regions—that is active.

A Tour Through the Brain   55

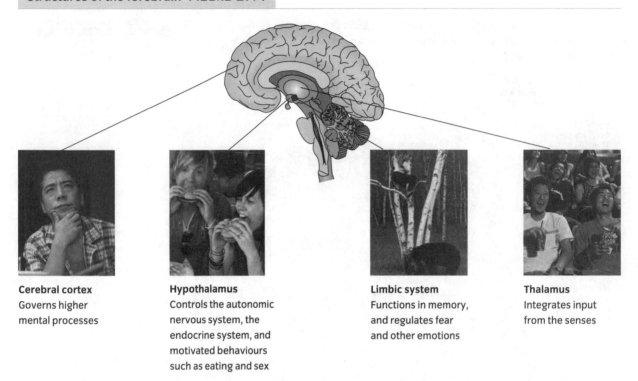

Cerebral cortex
Governs higher
mental processes

Hypothalamus
Controls the autonomic
nervous system, the
endocrine system, and
motivated behaviours
such as eating and sex

Limbic system
Functions in memory,
and regulates fear
and other emotions

Thalamus
Integrates input
from the senses

Running through the core of the hindbrain, midbrain, and brainstem is the **reticular formation** (RF). This diffuse, long, finger-shaped network of neurons filters incoming sensory information and alerts the higher brain centres to important events. Without your reticular formation, you would not be alert or attentive or perhaps even conscious.

The Forebrain

The **forebrain** is the largest and most prominent part of the human brain. It includes the thalamus, hypothalamus, limbic system, cerebrum, and cerebral cortex (**FIGURE 2.17**). The first three structures are located near the top of the brainstem. The cerebrum is wrapped above and completely around the other three structures, and the cerebral cortex (discussed separately in the next section) is the outermost layer of the cerebrum. (*Cerebrum* is Latin for "brain" and *cortex* is Latin for "covering" or "bark.")

The **thalamus** receives input from nearly all sensory systems and directs the information to the appropriate cortical areas. It may also have a role in learning and memory (Bailey & Mair, 2005; Ridley et al., 2005). Because the thalamus is the brain's major sensory relay centre to the cerebral cortex, damage or abnormalities can cause the cortex to misinterpret or not receive vital sensory information. Interestingly, brain-imaging research has linked thalamus abnormalities to schizophrenia, a serious psychological disorder involving problems with accurate sensory processing (such as hearing) and perception (Chapter 13) (Andreasen et al., 2008; Byne et al., 2008; Clinton & Meador-Woodruff, 2004; Preuss et al., 2005).

Beneath the thalamus lies the kidney-bean-sized **hypothalamus** (*hypo* means "under" or "below"). It is the control centre for many essential survival behaviours, such as hunger, thirst, sex, and aggression (Hinton et al., 2004; Williams et al., 2004; Zillmer, Spiers, & Culberton, 2008). It controls the autonomic nervous system and the body's internal environment, including temperature control, which it achieves by controlling the endocrine system. Looking as if it is dripping from the bottom of the hypothalamus is the *pituitary gland*. The pituitary is often wrongly referred to as the master endocrine gland, but this gland is actually a slave to the hypothalamus. After instruction from the hypothalamus, it releases hormones that activate the other endocrine glands in the body. The hypothalamus influences the pituitary in two ways: (1) through direct neural connections and (2) by releasing its own hormones into the blood supply of the pituitary.

An interconnected group of forebrain structures, known as the **limbic system**, is located roughly along the border between the cerebral cortex and the lower-level brain structures.

In general, the limbic system is responsible for emotions, learning, and memory and includes the *hippocampus* and the *amygdala* (some neuroanatomists also include parts of the thalamus, the hypothalamus, and the pituitary in the limbic system). The amygdala has been a major focus of research interest in the limbic system, particularly its involvement in aggression and fear (Asghar et al., 2008; Carlson, 2008; LeDoux, 1998, 2002, 2007). Another well-known function of the limbic system is its role in pleasure and reward (Dackis & O'Brien, 2001; Olds & Milner, 1954; Torta & Castelli, 2008). Even though limbic system structures and neurotransmitters are instrumental in emotional behaviour, the cerebral cortex also tempers and modulates emotion in humans.

The hippocampus is important in long-term memory and spatial navigation. It is one of the first brain regions to be affected in Alzheimer's patients, and this is probably why early symptoms of the disease involve memory loss and disorientation, which progressively worsen.

THE CEREBRAL CORTEX: THE CENTRE OF OUR HIGHER PROCESSING

cerebral cortex
Thin surface layer on the cerebral hemispheres that regulates most complex behaviour, including processing sensations, motor control, and higher mental processes.

The grey, wrinkled **cerebral cortex** is responsible for most of our complex behaviours and higher mental processes. It plays such a vital role in our sense of self that many consider it the essence of our subjective experience of life and the embodiment of exactly who we are. In fact, physicians can declare a person legally dead when the cortex dies, even when the lower-level brain structures and the rest of the body are fully functioning.

Although the cerebral cortex is only about 3 millimetres thick, it's made up of approximately 30 billion neurons and nine times as many glial cells. It contains numerous wrinkles called *convolutions* (think of a crumpled-up newspaper), which allow it to maximize its surface area while still fitting into the restricted space of the skull.

The full cerebral cortex and the two cerebral hemispheres beneath it closely resemble an oversized walnut. The deep valley, or *fissure,* down the centre marks the left and right *hemispheres* of the brain. The hemispheres make up about 80 percent of the brain's weight. They are mostly filled with axon connections between the cortex and the other brain structures. Each hemisphere gets signals from and controls the opposite side of the body.

The cerebral hemispheres are divided into eight distinct areas or lobes, with four in each hemisphere (**FIGURE 2.18**). Like the lower-level brain structures, each lobe specializes in somewhat different tasks—another example of localization of function. However, some functions are shared between the lobes.

The Frontal Lobes
The large **frontal lobes** coordinate messages received from the other three lobes. An area at the very back of the frontal lobes, known as the *motor cortex,* initiates all voluntary movement (which is different from the largely automatic motor tasks performed by the cerebellum). In the lower left frontal lobe lies *Broca's area.* In 1865, French physician Paul Broca discovered that damage to this area causes difficulty in speech production but not language comprehension. This type of impaired language ability is known as *Broca's aphasia.* Finally, the frontal lobes control most of the higher functions that distinguish humans from other animals, such as thinking, personality, emotional judgements, and memory. Abnormalities in the frontal lobes are often observed in patients with schizophrenia (Chapter 13). As seen in the case of Phineas Gage (Chapter 1) and in other research, damage to the frontal lobe affects motivation, creativity, self-awareness, initiative, reasoning, and suitable emotional behaviour. Our ability to function normally and respond appropriately in social situations is also a function of the frontal lobes (**FIGURE 2.19**).

The Parietal Lobes, the Temporal Lobes, and the Occipital Lobes
The **parietal lobes** interpret bodily sensations including pressure, pain, touch, temperature, and location of body parts. A band of tissue on the front of the parietal lobe, called the *somatosensory cortex,* receives information about touch and other skin and visceral senses (**FIGURE 2.20**).

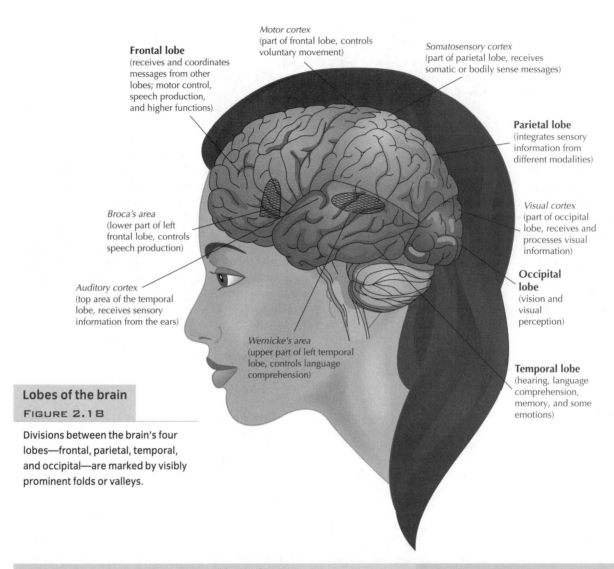

Motor cortex
(part of frontal lobe, controls voluntary movement)

Frontal lobe
(receives and coordinates messages from other lobes; motor control, speech production, and higher functions)

Somatosensory cortex
(part of parietal lobe, receives somatic or bodily sense messages)

Parietal lobe
(integrates sensory information from different modalities)

Broca's area
(lower part of left frontal lobe, controls speech production)

Visual cortex
(part of occipital lobe, receives and processes visual information)

Occipital lobe
(vision and visual perception)

Auditory cortex
(top area of the temporal lobe, receives sensory information from the ears)

Wernicke's area
(upper part of left temporal lobe, controls language comprehension)

Temporal lobe
(hearing, language comprehension, memory, and some emotions)

Lobes of the brain
FIGURE 2.18

Divisions between the brain's four lobes—frontal, parietal, temporal, and occipital—are marked by visibly prominent folds or valleys.

Accidental evidence of specialized brain functions? FIGURE 2.19

In 1998, construction worker Travis Bogumill was accidentally shot with a nail gun near the rear of his right frontal lobe. Remarkably, Bogumill experienced only an impaired ability to perform complex mathematical problems. This case study is consistent with experimental research showing that the frontal lobes and short-term memory are responsible for mathematical calculations, reasoning, problem solving, and thinking about future rewards or actions (Evans, 2003; Hill, 2004; Neubauer et al., 2004).

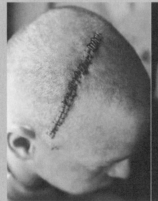
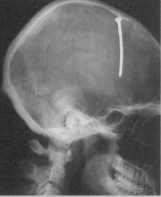

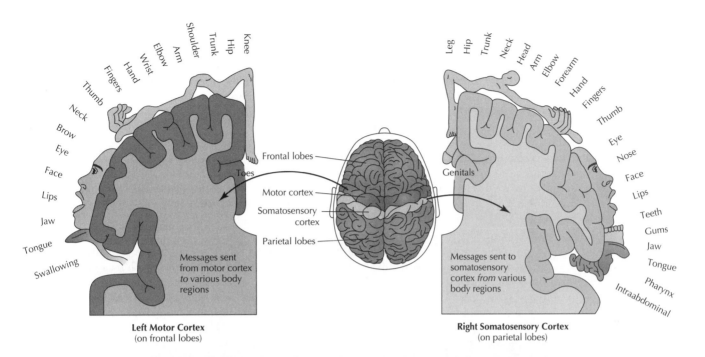

Messages sent from motor cortex *to* various body regions

Left Motor Cortex
(on frontal lobes)

Frontal lobes
Motor cortex
Somatosensory cortex
Parietal lobes

Messages sent to somatosensory cortex *from* various body regions

Right Somatosensory Cortex
(on parietal lobes)

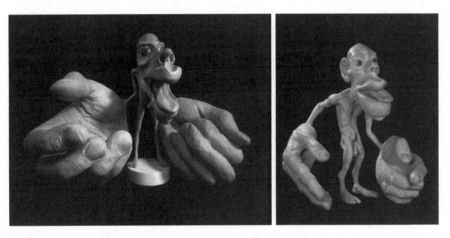

Body representation of the motor cortex and somatosensory cortex Figure 2.20

This drawing represents a vertical cross-section taken from the left hemisphere's motor cortex and right hemisphere's somatosensory cortex. If body areas were truly proportional to the amount of tissue on the motor and somatosensory cortices, our bodies would look like the oddly shaped human figures draped around the outside edge of the cortex. Notice that the most sensitive regions of the body and the regions of the body that have the greatest fine motor precision (such as the fingers and the lips) have the largest representations on the motor and somatosensory strip. This is superbly illustrated by clay homunculi ("little men") made to demonstrate the relative space body parts occupy on the motor and sensory strips. Newer research suggests the discrete mapping of the fingers onto the motor cortex may in fact be a bit of an oversimplification. It seems the representation of the fingers actually mingle and overlap suggesting a more accurate motor homunculus would look like a naked little man wearing mittens. Moreover, the body part position on the cortex appears to be organized according to the behaviours to be performed rather than simply a static map of the individual body parts (Graziano, 2006).

A Tour Through the Brain   59

The **temporal lobes** are responsible for hearing, language comprehension, memory, and some emotions. The *auditory cortex* (which processes sound) is located at the top front of each temporal lobe. This area processes incoming sensory information and sends it to the parietal lobes, where it is combined with other sensory information.

An area of the left temporal lobe, *Wernicke's area,* is involved in language comprehension. About a decade after Broca's discovery, German neurologist Carl Wernicke noted that patients with damage in this area could not understand what they read or heard. They could, however, speak quickly and easily. Their speech was often unintelligible because it contained made-up words, sound substitutions, and word substitutions. This syndrome is now referred to as *Wernicke's aphasia.*

The **occipital lobes** are responsible, among other things, for vision and visual perception. Damage to the occipital lobe can produce blindness, even though the eyes and their neural connection to the brain are perfectly functional.

The Association Areas   One of the most popular and enduring myths in psychology is that we use only 10 percent of our brain. This myth might have begun with early research showing that approximately three quarters of the cortex is *uncommitted* (that is, it had no precise, specific function responsive to electrical brain stimulation). Abundant research has shown these areas are not dormant, however. They are clearly involved in interpreting, integrating, and acting on information processed by other parts of the brain. They are called **association areas** because they associate, or connect, various areas and functions of the brain. The association areas in the frontal lobe, for example, help in decision-making and task planning. Similarly, the association area right in front of the motor cortex is involved in the planning of voluntary movement.

TWO BRAINS IN ONE? THE SPLIT SCREEN

We mentioned earlier that the brain's left and right cerebral hemispheres control opposite sides of the body. Each hemisphere also has separate areas of specialization.

(This is another example of *localization* of function, yet it is technically referred to as *lateralization.*)

Early researchers believed that the right hemisphere was subordinate to the left, or non-dominant, and had few special functions or abilities. In the 1960s, landmark research with *split-brain* patients began to change this view.

The primary connection between the two cerebral hemispheres is a thick, ribbon-like band of axons under the cortex called the **corpus callosum.** In some rare cases of severe epilepsy, when other forms of treatment have failed, surgeons cut the corpus callosum to stop the spread of epileptic seizures from one hemisphere to the other. Because this operation cuts the only direct communication link between the two hemispheres, it reveals what each half of the brain can do in isolation from the other. The resulting research with split-brain patients has profoundly improved our understanding of how the two halves of the brain function.

If you met and talked with a split-brain patient, you probably wouldn't even know he or she had had the operation. The subtle changes in split-brain patients normally appear only with specialized testing (FIGURE 2.21).

Dozens of studies on split-brain patients, and newer research on people whose brains are intact, have documented several differences between the two brain hemispheres (FIGURE 2.22 on page 62). Interestingly, left and right brain specialization is not usually reversed in left-handed people. About 68 percent of left-handers and 97 percent of right-handers have their major language areas on the left hemisphere. This suggests that even though the right side of the brain is dominant for movement in left-handers, other skills are often localized in the same brain areas as for right-handers.

What about the popular conception of the neglected right brain? Courses and books directed at "right-brain thinking" often promise to increase your intuition, creativity, and artistic abilities by waking up your "neglected" and "underused" right brain (e.g., Brady, 2004; Edwards, 1999). This myth of the neglected right brain arose from popularized accounts of split-brain patients and exaggerated claims and unwarranted conclusions about differences between the left and right hemispheres. Research has clearly shown that the two hemispheres work together in a coordinated, integrated way, with each making important contributions. Simply said, you cannot get by without your right or your left hemisphere.

Experiments on split-brain patients often present visual information to only the patient's left or right hemisphere, which leads to some intriguing results. For example,

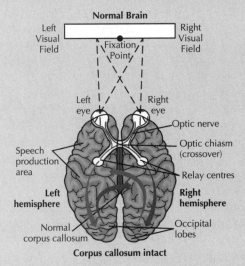

Verbal left hemisphere   Non-verbal right hemisphere

A When a split-brain patient is asked to stare straight ahead while a photo of a screwdriver is flashed only to the right hemisphere, he will report that he "saw nothing."

B However, when asked to pick up with his left hand what he saw, he can reach through and touch the items hidden behind the screen and easily pick up the screwdriver.

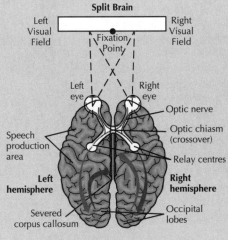

C When the left hemisphere receives an image of a baseball, the split-brain patient can easily name it.

Assuming you have an intact, unsevered corpus callosum, if the same photos were presented to you in the same way, you could easily name both the screwdriver and the baseball. Can you explain why? The answers lie in our somewhat confusing visual wiring system:

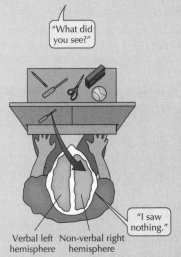

Normal Brain

Left Visual Field — Fixation Point — Right Visual Field

Left eye — Right eye

Speech production area

Optic nerve

Optic chiasm (crossover)

Relay centres

Left hemisphere   **Right hemisphere**

Normal corpus callosum   Occipital lobes

Corpus callosum intact

Split Brain

Left Visual Field — Fixation Point — Right Visual Field

Left eye — Right eye

Speech production area

Optic nerve

Optic chiasm (crossover)

Relay centres

Left hemisphere   **Right hemisphere**

Severed corpus callosum   Occipital lobes

Corpus callosum severed

D As you can see, our eyes connect to our brains in such a way that, when we look straight ahead, information from the left visual field (the blue line) travels to our right hemisphere, and information from the right visual field (the red line) travels to our left hemisphere. The messages received by either hemisphere are then quickly sent to the other across the corpus callosum.

E When the corpus callosum is severed, and information is presented only to the right hemisphere, a split-brain patient cannot verbalize what he sees because the information cannot travel to the opposite (verbal) hemisphere.

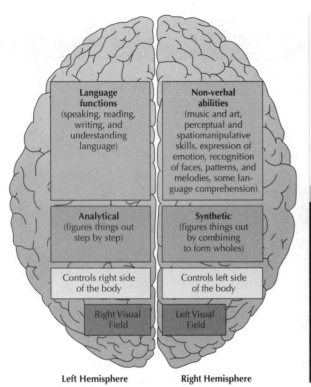

Language functions (speaking, reading, writing, and understanding language)	Non-verbal abilities (music and art, perceptual and spatiomanipulative skills, expression of emotion, recognition of faces, patterns, and melodies, some language comprehension)
Analytical (figures things out step by step)	Synthetic (figures things out by combining to form wholes)
Controls right side of the body	Controls left side of the body
Right Visual Field	Left Visual Field

Left Hemisphere   **Right Hemisphere**

Functions of the left and right hemispheres
FIGURE 2.22

In general, the left hemisphere specializes in verbal and analytical functions; the right hemisphere focuses on non-verbal abilities, such as spatiomanipulative skills (the ability to locate and manipulate objects in three-dimensional space), art and musical abilities, and visual recognition tasks. Keep in mind, however, that both hemispheres are activated when we perform almost any task or respond to any stimuli.

CONCEPT CHECK ✓

What are the main parts of the hindbrain, the midbrain, and the forebrain?

What are the primary functions of each of the four lobes of the cortex?

Why is the hypothalamus important?

How do Broca's aphasia and Wernicke's aphasia differ?

What are the findings of research with split-brain patients?

SUMMARY

1 Our Genetic Inheritance

1. **Neuroscience** studies how biological processes relate to behavioural and mental processes.

2. Genes (dominant or recessive) hold the code for inherited traits. Scientists use **behavioural genetics** methods to determine the relative influences of heredity and environment (heritability) on complex traits.

3. **Evolutionary psychology** suggests that many behavioural commonalities emerged and remain in human populations through natural selection because they were adaptive and improved survival and reproductive success.

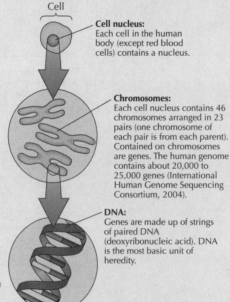

Cell

Cell nucleus:
Each cell in the human body (except red blood cells) contains a nucleus.

Chromosomes:
Each cell nucleus contains 46 chromosomes arranged in 23 pairs (one chromosome of each pair is from each parent). Contained on chromosomes are genes. The human genome contains about 20,000 to 25,000 genes (International Human Genome Sequencing Consortium, 2004).

DNA:
Genes are made up of strings of paired DNA (deoxyribonucleic acid). DNA is the most basic unit of heredity.

2 Neural Bases of Behaviour

1. **Neurons**, supported by **glial cells**, receive and send electrochemical signals to other neurons and to the rest of the body. Their major components are **dendrites**, a **cell body**, and an **axon**.

2. Within a neuron, a neural impulse, or **action potential**, moves along the axon.

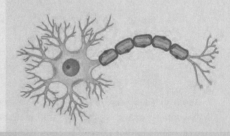

62   **CHAPTER 2**   Neuroscience and Biological Foundations

3. Neurons communicate with each other by using **neurotransmitters**, which are released at the synapse and bind to receptors on the receiving neuron. Neurons receive input from many synapses, some excitatory and some inhibitory. Hundreds of different neurotransmitters regulate a wide variety of physiological processes. Many poisons, toxins, and drugs act by mimicking or interfering with neurotransmitters.

4. The **endocrine system** uses **hormones** to broadcast messages throughout the body. The system regulates long-term bodily processes, maintains ongoing bodily processes, and controls the body's response to emergencies.

3 Nervous System Organization

1. The **central nervous system (CNS)** includes the brain and spinal cord. The CNS allows us to process information and adapt to our environment in unique and versatile ways. The spinal cord transmits information between the brain and the rest of the body, and initiates involuntary **reflexes**. Although the CNS is very fragile, recent research shows that the brain is capable of lifelong **neuroplasticity** and **neurogenesis**. Neurogenesis is made possible by **stem cells**.

2. The **peripheral nervous system (PNS)** includes all the nerves outside the brain and spinal cord. It links the brain and spinal cord to the body's senses, muscles, and glands. The PNS is subdivided into the **somatic nervous system (SNS)** and the **autonomic nervous system (ANS)**.

3. The ANS includes the **sympathetic nervous system** and the **parasympathetic nervous system**. The sympathetic nervous system mobilizes the body's fight-or-flight response. The parasympathetic nervous system returns the body to its normal functioning.

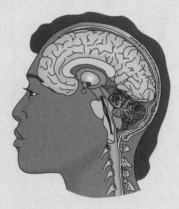

Central Nervous System

Somatic Nervous System

Autonomic Nervous System

4 A Tour Through the Brain

1. The brain is divided into the **hindbrain**, the **midbrain**, and the **forebrain**. The brainstem includes parts of each of these. Certain brain structures are specialized to perform certain tasks (**localization of function**).

2. The hindbrain (including the **medulla**, **pons**, and **cerebellum**) controls automatic behaviours and vital reflexes.

3. The midbrain helps us orient our eye and body movements, and helps control sleep and arousal. The **reticular formation** runs through the core of the hindbrain, midbrain, and brainstem.

4. Forebrain structures (including the **thalamus**, **hypothalamus**, and **limbic**

system) integrate input from the senses, control survival behaviours, and regulate the body's internal environment, emotions, learning, and memory.

5. The cerebrum and **cerebral cortex** are part of the forebrain and govern most higher processing and complex behaviours. It is divided into two hemispheres, each controlling the opposite side of the body. The **corpus callosum** links the hemispheres. Each hemisphere is divided into **frontal**, **parietal**, **temporal**, and **occipital lobes**. Each lobe specializes in somewhat different tasks, but a large part of the cortex is devoted to integrating actions performed by different brain regions.

6. Split-brain research shows that each hemisphere performs somewhat different functions, although they work closely together, communicating through the corpus callosum.

Learning

6

On November 14, 1997, 14-year-old Reena Virk was lured to a secluded area under a bridge in a waterfront park in a suburb of Victoria, British Columbia. There, she was viciously attacked and murdered by a group of eight of her peers, seven of whom were teenage girls. She was hit, kicked, and stomped on so severely that she experienced extensive internal injuries, finally drowning in the water under the bridge (Godfrey, 2005).

What caused this grisly murder? Despite media reports to the contrary, some have speculated that the attack was racially motivated. Reena Virk reportedly had difficulty fitting in. She was of South Asian descent, was slightly overweight, and was the child of immigrants who were not well-to-do (Batacharya, 2004). Whether or not these differences motivated the violence, hate crimes are a serious and growing problem around the world. People are ridiculed, attacked, and even murdered simply because of their ethnicity, sexual orientation, gender, or religious preference. Where does such hatred come from? Is prejudice learned?

We usually think of learning as classroom activities, such as math and reading, or as motor skills, like riding a bike or playing the piano. Psychologists define learning more broadly, as *a relatively permanent change in behaviour or mental processes because of practice or experience*. This relative permanence applies not only to useful behaviours (using a spoon or writing great novels) but also to bad habits, racism, and hatred. The good news is that what is learned can be unlearned, through retraining, counselling, and self-reflection. In this chapter, we discuss several types of conditioning, the most basic form of learning. Then we look at social-cognitive learning and the biological factors involved in learning. Finally, we explore how learning theories and concepts touch everyday life.

Suman Virk, mother of Reena Virk, speaks to reporters.

Classical Conditioning

LEARNING OBJECTIVES

Describe how a neutral stimulus can become a conditioned stimulus by being paired with an unconditioned stimulus.

Explain how stimulus generalization and discrimination affect learning.

Describe the processes of extinction and spontaneous recovery.

Identify an example of higher-order conditioning.

One of the earliest forms of learning to be studied scientifically was conditioning. We discuss classical conditioning, made famous by Pavlov's dogs, in this section and a different form of conditioning, known as operant conditioning, in the next section.

THE BEGINNINGS OF CLASSICAL CONDITIONING

Why does your mouth water when you see a large slice of chocolate cake or a hot pizza? The answer to this question was accidentally discovered in the laboratory of Russian physiologist Ivan Pavlov (1849–1936). Pavlov's early work focused on the role of saliva in digestion, and one of his experiments involved measuring salivary responses in dogs by using a tube attached to the dogs' salivary glands.

One of Pavlov's students noticed that many dogs began salivating at the sight of the food or the food dish, the smell of the food, or even the sight of the person who delivered the food long before receiving the actual food. This "unscheduled" salivation was intriguing. Pavlov recognized that an involuntary reflex (salivation) that occurred before the appropriate stimulus (food) was presented could not be inborn and biological. It had to have been acquired through experience—through **learning**.

Excited by their accidental discovery, Pavlov and his students conducted several experiments. Their most basic method involved sounding a tone on a tuning fork just before food was placed in the dogs' mouths. After several pairings of tone and food, the dogs would salivate on hearing the tone, even without receiving food. Pavlov and others went on to show that many things can become conditioned stimuli for salivation if they are paired with food: the ticking of a metronome, a buzzer, a light, and even the sight of a circle or triangle drawn on a card.

The type of learning that Pavlov described came to be known as **classical conditioning** (**FIGURE 6.1**). To understand classical conditioning, you first need to realize that **conditioning** is just another word for learning. You also need to know that some responses are inborn and don't require conditioning. For example, the inborn salivary reflex consists of an **unconditioned stimulus (UCS)** and an **unconditioned response (UCR)**. That is, the UCS (food) elicits the UCR (salivation) without previous conditioning (learning).

Before conditioning occurs, a **neutral stimulus (NS)** does not naturally elicit a relevant or consistent response. For example, as shown in Figure 6.1, Pavlov's dogs did not naturally salivate when a tone sounded. Similarly, as the figure shows, the sight of a cardboard box (neutral stimulus) doesn't naturally make a person hungry for a slice of pizza.

> **learning** A relatively permanent change in behaviour or mental processes because of practice or experience.

> **classical conditioning** Learning that occurs when a neutral stimulus (NS) becomes paired (associated) with an unconditioned stimulus (UCS) to elicit a conditioned response (CR).

> **conditioning** The process of learning associations between environmental stimuli and behavioural responses.

Process Diagram

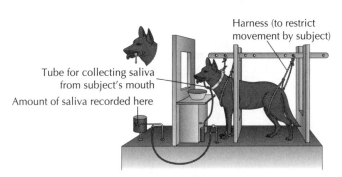

Harness (to restrict movement by subject)

Tube for collecting saliva from subject's mouth

Amount of saliva recorded here

	Pavlov's example	Modern-day example
Step 1 **Before conditioning** The neutral stimulus (NS) produces no relevant response. The unconditioned (unlearned) *stimulus* (UCS) elicits the unconditioned *response* (UCR).	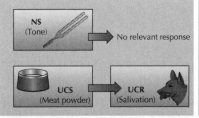	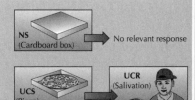
Step 2 **During conditioning** The neutral stimulus (NS) is repeatedly paired with the unconditioned (unlearned) *stimulus* (UCS) to produce the unconditioned *response* (UCR).	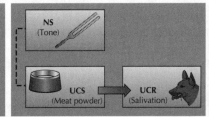	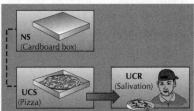
Step 3 **After conditioning** The neutral stimulus (NS) has become a conditioned (learned) stimulus (CS). This CS now produces a conditioned (learned) *response* (CR), which is usually similar to the previously unconditioned (unlearned) response (UCR).	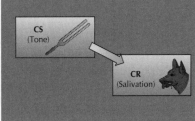	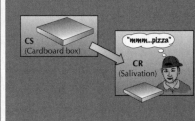
Summary An originally neutral stimulus (NS) becomes a conditioned stimulus (CS), which elicits a conditioned response (CR).	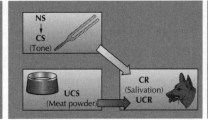	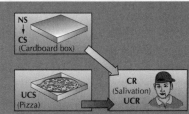

Classical Conditioning   153

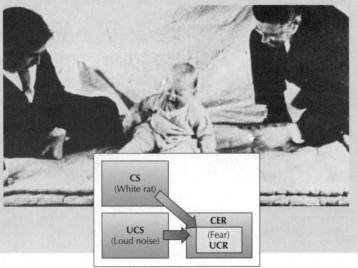

Conditioning and the case of Little Albert FIGURE 6.2

In the famous "Little Albert" study, a healthy 11-month-old child was first allowed to play with a white laboratory rat. Like most infants, Albert was curious and reached for the rat, showing no fear. Watson used the fact that infants are naturally frightened (UCR) by loud noises (UCS). Watson stood behind Albert and again put the rat (NS) near him. When the infant reached for the rat, Watson banged a steel bar with a hammer. The loud noise frightened Albert and made him cry. The white rat (NS) was paired with the loud noise (UCS) only seven times before the white rat alone produced a *conditioned emotional response* (CER) in Albert: fear of the rat.

CS
(White rat)

UCS
(Loud noise)

CER
(Fear)
UCR

Pavlov's discovery was that learning occurs when a neutral stimulus, such as a tone (or the cardboard box), is regularly paired with an unconditioned stimulus (food, or the smell of pizza in the cardboard box). The neutral stimulus (tone or the cardboard box) then becomes a **conditioned stimulus (CS)**, which elicits a **conditioned response (CR)**—salivation.

What does a salivating dog have to do with your life? Classical conditioning is the most fundamental way that all animals, including humans, learn many new responses, emotions, and attitudes. Your love for your parents (or boyfriend or girlfriend), your drooling at the sight of chocolate cake or pizza, and even negative reactions, like the hatred and racism that some people display, are largely the result of classical conditioning.

In a famous experiment, John Watson and Rosalie Rayner (1920) demonstrated that fear could also be classically conditioned (**FIGURE 6.2**).

Watson and Rayner's experiment could not be performed today because it violates several ethical guidelines for scientific research (Chapter 1). Moreover, Watson and Rayner ended their experiment without extinguishing (removing) Albert's fear, although they knew that it could endure for a long period. Watson and Rayner also have been criticized because they did not measure Albert's fear objectively. Their subjective evaluation raises doubt about the degree of fear they conditioned (Paul & Blumenthal, 1989).

Despite such criticisms, John Watson made important and lasting contributions to psychology. Unlike other psychologists of his time, Watson emphasized the study of strictly observable behaviours, and he founded the school of *behaviourism*, which explains behaviour as a result of observable stimuli and observable responses.

Watson's study of Little Albert has had legendary significance for many psychologists. Watson showed us that many of our likes, dislikes, prejudices, and fears are **conditioned emotional responses**—classically conditioned emotional responses to previously neutral stimuli. Watson's research in producing Little Albert's fears also led to powerful clinical tools for eliminating extreme, irrational fears known as *phobias* (Chapter 13).

FINE-TUNING CLASSICAL CONDITIONING

Now that you have an understanding of the key concepts of classical conditioning, we can discuss six important principles of classical conditioning: stimulus generalization, stimulus discrimination, extinction, spontaneous recovery, reconditioning, and higher-order conditioning (**FIGURE 6.3**).

Stimulus generalization occurs when an event similar to the original conditioned stimulus triggers the same conditioned response. The more the stimulus resembles the conditioned stimulus, the stronger the conditioned

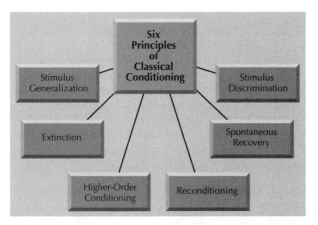

Six principles of classical conditioning **FIGURE 6.3**

"I don't care if she is a tape dispenser. I love her."

Which of the six basic principles of classical conditioning explain(s) this cartoon? Answer: Stimulus generalization

response (Hovland, 1937). For example, after first conditioning dogs to salivate at the sound of low-pitched tones, Pavlov later demonstrated that the dogs would also salivate in response to higher-pitched tones. Similarly, after conditioning, the infant in Watson and Rayner's experiment ("Little Albert") feared not only rats but also a rabbit, a dog, and a bearded Santa Claus mask.

Eventually, through the process of **stimulus discrimination** (a term that refers to a learned response to a specific stimulus but not to other similar stimuli), Albert presumably learned to recognize differences between rats and other stimuli. As a result, he probably overcame his fear of Santa Claus, even if he remained afraid of white rats. Similarly, Pavlov's dogs learned to distinguish between the tone that signalled food and those that did not.

Most behaviours that are learned through classical conditioning can be weakened or suppressed through **extinction**. Extinction occurs when the unconditioned stimulus (UCS) is repeatedly withheld whenever the conditioned stimulus (CS) is presented. This gradually weakens the previous association. When Pavlov repeatedly sounded the tone without presenting food, the dogs' salivation gradually declined. Similarly, if you have a classically conditioned fear of cats and later start to work as a veterinary assistant, your fear will gradually diminish.

However, extinction is not unlearning—it does not "erase" the learned connection between the stimulus and the response (Bouton, 1994). In fact, on occasion an extinguished response may spontaneously reappear (**FIGURE 6.4**). This **spontaneous recovery** helps

Extinction and spontaneous recovery FIGURE 6.4

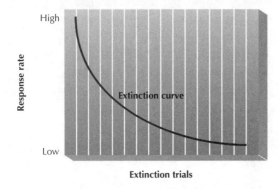

The more often the UCS is withheld whenever the CS is presented, the lower an individual's response rate to the UCS, until extinction occurs.

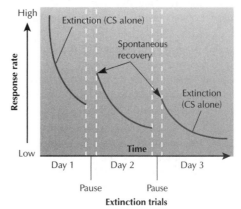

But an extinguished response may spontaneously reappear, which can trigger a rush of feelings and emotions as though the UCS were present.

Children are not born salivating upon seeing the McDonald's Golden Arches. So why do they beg their parents to stop at McDonald's after simply seeing a billboard for the restaurant? It is because of **higher-order conditioning**, which occurs when a neutral stimulus (NS) becomes a conditioned stimulus (CS) through repeated pairings with a previously conditioned stimulus (CS).

If you wanted to demonstrate higher-order conditioning in Pavlov's dogs, you would first condition the dogs to salivate in response to the sound of the tone (A). Then you would pair a flash of light with the tone (B). Eventually, the dogs would salivate in response to the flash of light alone (C). Similarly, children first learn to pair McDonald's restaurants with food and later learn that two Golden Arches are a symbol for McDonald's. Their salivation and begging to eat at the restaurant on seeing the arches are a classic case of higher-order conditioning (and successful advertising).

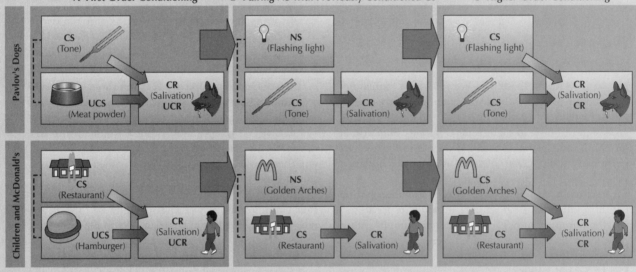

A First-Order Conditioning   **B Pairing NS with Previously Conditioned CS**   **C Higher-Order Conditioning**

explain why you might suddenly feel excited at seeing a former girlfriend or boyfriend, even though years have passed (and extinction has occurred). It also explains why couples who've recently broken up sometimes misinterpret a sudden flare-up of feelings and return to unhappy relationships. Furthermore, if a conditioned stimulus is reintroduced after extinction, the conditioning occurs much faster the second time around—a phenomenon known as **reconditioning**. Both spontaneous recovery and reconditioning help underscore why it can be so difficult for us to break bad habits (such as eating too many nachos) or internalize new beliefs (such as egalitarian racial beliefs). The phenomenon of **higher-order conditioning** (FIGURE 6.5) further expands and complicates our learned habits and associations.

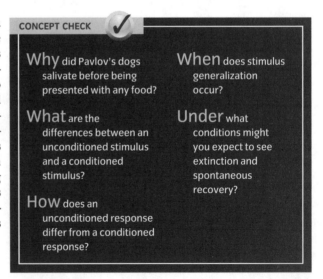

CONCEPT CHECK

Why did Pavlov's dogs salivate before being presented with any food?

What are the differences between an unconditioned stimulus and a conditioned stimulus?

How does an unconditioned response differ from a conditioned response?

When does stimulus generalization occur?

Under what conditions might you expect to see extinction and spontaneous recovery?

156   CHAPTER 6 Learning

Operant Conditioning

LEARNING OBJECTIVES

Explain how reinforcement and punishment influence behaviour.

Describe Thorndike's and Skinner's contributions to research on operant conditioning.

Identify examples of primary and secondary reinforcers.

Explain how different schedules of reinforcement affect behaviour.

Describe the negative side effects of punishment.

THE BEGINNINGS OF OPERANT CONDITIONING

Edward Thorndike (1874–1949), a pioneer of operant conditioning, determined that the frequency of a behaviour is modified by its consequences. He developed the **law of effect** (Thorndike, 1911), a first step in understanding how consequences can modify active, voluntary behaviours (**FIGURE 6.6**).

B. F. Skinner (1904–1990) extended Thorndike's law of effect to more complex behaviours. He emphasized that reinforcement and punishment always occur after the behaviour of interest has occurred. In addition, Skinner cautioned that the only way to know how we have influenced someone's behaviour is to check whether the behaviour increases or decreases.

Sometimes, he noted, we think we're reinforcing or we think we're punishing when we're actually doing the opposite. For example, a teacher may think she is encouraging shy students to talk by praising them each time they speak up in class. But what if shy students are embarrassed by this attention? If so, as Canadian researcher Mary Ann Evans (2001) points out, teachers may actually decrease the number of times the students talk in class.

> ■ **law of effect**
> Thorndike's rule that the probability of an action being repeated is strengthened when followed by a pleasant or satisfying consequence.

■ **operant conditioning**
Learning in which voluntary responses are controlled by their consequences (also known as instrumental or Skinnerian conditioning).

■ **reinforcement**
A consequence that strengthens a response and makes it more likely to recur.

■ **punishment**
A consequence that weakens a response and makes it less likely to recur.

onsequences are the heart of **operant conditioning**. In classical conditioning, consequences are irrelevant—Pavlov's dogs were still allowed to eat whether they salivated or not. But in operant conditioning, the organism performs a behaviour (an *operant*, as in "operation") that produces either reinforcement or punishment. **Reinforcement** strengthens the response, making it more likely to recur. **Punishment** weakens the response, making it less likely to recur.

Classical and operant conditioning also differ in another important way. In classical conditioning, the organism's response is generally passive and involuntary. In operant conditioning, the organism's response is generally active and voluntary. The learner "operates" on the environment and produces consequences that influence whether the behaviour will be repeated. For example, if your friends smile and laugh when you tell a joke, you are likely to joke more with them. If they frown, groan, or ridicule you, you are likely to joke less.

Thorndike box FIGURE 6.6

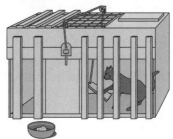

In one famous experiment, Thorndike put a cat inside a specially built puzzle box. When the cat stepped on a pedal inside the box (at first, through trial and error), the door opened and the cat could get out to eat. With each additional success, the cat's actions became more purposeful, and it soon learned to open the door immediately (from Thorndike, 1898).

Operant Conditioning   157

141

REINFORCEMENT: STRENGTHENING A RESPONSE

Reinforcers, which strengthen a response, can be grouped into two types: primary and secondary. Primary reinforcers satisfy an intrinsic, unlearned biological need (food, water, sex). Secondary reinforcers are not intrinsic; the value of this reinforcer is learned (money, praise, attention). Thus, when we were babies, we most likely found milk (a primary reinforcer) much more reinforcing than a $100 bill. By the time we reached adolescence, however, we most likely had learned to prefer the money (a secondary reinforcer).

Reinforcers can produce **positive reinforcement** or **negative reinforcement**, depending on whether certain stimuli are added or taken away (see **TABLE 6.1**). It's easy to confuse negative reinforcement with punishment, but the two concepts are actually completely opposite. Reinforcement (whether positive or negative) strengthens a behaviour, whereas punishment weakens a behaviour. If the terminology seems confusing, it may help to think of positive and negative reinforcement in the mathematical sense, that is, in terms of something being added (+) or taken away (−) rather than in terms of good and bad (Table 6.1).

Sometimes we use high-frequency behaviour to reinforce low-frequency responses: making yourself study before going to the movies is a good example. In this case, you are using what is called the **Premack principle**, named after psychologist David Premack. Recognizing that you love to go to movies, you intuitively tie your less-desirable low-frequency activities (making yourself study) to your high-frequency behaviour (going to the movies), thereby positively reinforcing the completion of the less desirable low-frequency behaviour.

Just as you saw in our discussion of classical conditioning, *extinction* can also occur in operant conditioning. In both classical and operant conditioning, removing the original source of learning causes extinction to occur. In classical conditioning, presenting the CS without the UCS eventually leads to extinction of the CR. In operant conditioning, if we remove the reinforcer that follows the response, the animal will eventually stop producing the response. How easy it is to extinguish a response depends on the rate with which we have been reinforcing that response.

What are the best circumstances for using reinforcement? It depends on the desired outcome. To make this decision, you need to understand various **schedules of reinforcement** (Terry, 2009): the rate or interval at which responses are reinforced. Although numerous schedules of reinforcement are possible, the most important distinction is whether they are continuous or partial. When Skinner was training his animals, he

How reinforcement strengthens and increases behaviours TABLE 6.1	Positive reinforcement *Adds to (+) and strengthens behaviour*	Negative reinforcement *Takes away (−) and strengthens behaviour*
Primary reinforcers Satisfy an unlearned biological need	You hug your baby and he smiles at you. The "addition" of his smile strengthens the likelihood that you will hug him again.	Your baby is crying, so you hug him and he stops crying. The "removal" of crying strengthens the likelihood that you will hug him again, which takes away the crying.
	You do a favour for a friend and she buys you lunch in return.	You take an aspirin for your headache, which takes away the pain.
Secondary reinforcers Value is learned, intrinsic	You increase profits and receive $200 as a bonus.	After high sales, your boss says you won't have to work on weekends.
	You study hard and receive a good grade on your psychology exam.	Your professor says you won't have to take the final exam because you did so well on your in-class tests.

found that learning was most rapid if the response was reinforced every time it occurred—a procedure called **continuous reinforcement**.

As you have probably noticed, real life seldom provides continuous reinforcement. Yet your behaviour persists because your efforts are occasionally rewarded. Most everyday behaviour is rewarded on a **partial (or intermittent) schedule of reinforcement**, which involves reinforcing only some responses, not all (Sangha, McComb, Scheibenstock, Johannes, & Lukowiak, 2002).

Once a task is well learned, it is important to move to a partial schedule of reinforcement. Why? Because under partial schedules, behaviour is more resistant to extinction. Four partial schedules of reinforcement are used: **fixed ratio** (FR), **variable ratio** (VR), **fixed interval** (FI), and **variable interval** (VI). The type of partial schedule selected depends on the type of behaviour being studied and on the speed of learning desired (Kazdin, 2008; Neuringer, Deiss, & Olson, 2000; Rothstein, Jensen, & Neuringer, 2008). A fixed ratio leads to the highest overall response rate, but each of the four types of partial schedules has different advantages and disadvantages (see STUDY ORGANIZER 6.1).

Partial reinforcement is described further in *What a Psychologist Sees*. Each of the four schedules of partial reinforcement is important for *maintaining* behaviour. But how would you teach someone to play the piano or to speak a foreign language? For new and complex behaviours, such as these, which aren't likely to occur naturally, **shaping** is an especially valuable tool. Skinner believed that shaping explains

■ **shaping** Reinforcing successively closer and closer approximations to the desired response.

Four schedules of reinforcement		Study Organizer 6.1		
		Definitions	**Response rates**	**Examples**
Ratio schedules (response based)	**Fixed ratio (FR)**	Reinforcement occurs after a predetermined set of responses; the ratio (number or amount) is fixed	Produces a high rate of response, but a brief drop-off or pause in responding just after reinforcement	A car wash employee receives $10 for every three cars washed. In a laboratory, a rat receives a food pellet every time it presses the bar seven times.
	Variable ratio (VR)	Reinforcement occurs unpredictably; the ratio (number or amount) varies	High response rates, no pause after reinforcement, and very resistant to extinction	Slot machines are designed to pay out after an average number of responses (maybe every 10 times), but any one machine may pay out on the first response, then seventh, then the twentieth.
Interval schedules (time based)	**Fixed interval (FI)**	Reinforcement occurs after a predetermined time has elapsed; the interval (time) is fixed	Responses tend to increase as the time for the next reinforcer is near, but drop off after reinforcement and during interval	You get a monthly paycheque. A rat's behaviour is reinforced with a food pellet when (or if) it presses a bar after 20 seconds have elapsed.
	Variable interval (VI)	Reinforcement occurs unpredictably; the interval (time) varies	Relatively low response rates, but they are steady because the receiver cannot predict when reward will come	In a class with pop quizzes, you study at a slow but steady rate because you can't anticipate the next quiz. A rat's behaviour is reinforced with a food pellet after a response and a variable, unpredictable interval of time.

Operant Conditioning 159

Partial Reinforcement Keeps 'Em Coming Back

Have you noticed that people spend long hours pushing buttons and pulling levers on slot machines in hopes of winning the jackpot? This compulsion to keep gambling in spite of significant losses is evidence of the strong resistance to extinction with partial (or intermittent) schedules of reinforcement. Machines in Ontario casinos and racetracks, for example, have payout rates of at least 85 percent—that is, for every dollar spent, a player "wins" $0.85. These are average payouts based on hundreds of thousands of games (Ontario Lottery and Gaming Corporation, 2007). Different machines are programmed in different ways. Some meet the percentage by giving very large but infrequent payouts to a few

lucky winners. Others give frequent smaller payouts to many players. In either case, people are reinforced just often enough to keep them coming back, always hoping the partial reinforcement will lead to more. The same compulsion leads people to go on buying lottery tickets even though the odds of winning are very low.

This type of partial reinforcement also helps parents maintain children's positive behaviours, such as tooth brushing and bed making. After the child has initially learned these behaviours with continuous reinforcement, occasional, partial reinforcement is the most efficient way to maintain the behaviour. (Chart adapted from Skinner, 1961.)

How does she do it? FIGURE 6.7

Momoko, a female monkey, is famous in Japan for her water-skiing, deep-sea diving, and other amazing abilities. Can you describe how her animal trainers used the successive steps of shaping to teach her these skills? First, they reinforced Momoko (with a small food treat) for standing or sitting on the water ski. Then they reinforced her each time she put her hands on the pole. Next, they slowly dragged the water ski on dry land and reinforced her for staying upright and holding the pole. Then they took Momoko to a shallow and calm part of the ocean and reinforced her for staying upright and holding the pole as the ski moved in the water. Finally, they took her into the deep part of the ocean.

a variety of abilities that we each possess, from eating with a fork, to playing a musical instrument, to driving a car with a stick shift. Parents, athletic coaches, teachers, and animal trainers all use shaping techniques, which involve successively reinforcing closer and closer approximations to the desired response (FIGURE 6.7).

PUNISHMENT: WEAKENING A RESPONSE

Unlike reinforcement, punishment *decreases* the strength of a response. As with reinforcement, punishment also has two forms: positive and negative (Miltenberger, 2008; Skinner, 1953).

Positive punishment is the addition (+) of a stimulus that decreases (or weakens) the likelihood of the response occurring again. **Negative punishment** is the taking away (−) of a reinforcing stimulus, which decreases (or weakens) the likelihood of the response occurring again (TABLE 6.2). (To check your understanding of the principles of reinforcement and punishment, see FIGURE 6.8.)

Punishment is a tricky business, and it isn't always intentional. Any process that adds or takes away something and causes a behaviour to decrease is punishment. Thus, if parents ignore all the A's on their child's report card ("taking away" encouraging comments) and ask repeated questions about the B's and C's, they may unintentionally be punishing the child's excellent grade achievement and weakening the likelihood of future A's. Similarly, dog owners who yell at or spank their dogs for finally coming to them ("adding" negative verbal or physical consequences) after being called several times are actually punishing the desired behaviour: coming when called.

How punishment weakens and decreases behaviours TABLE 6.2	
Positive punishment *adds stimulus (+) and weakens the behaviour*	**Negative punishment** *takes stimulus away (−) and weakens the behaviour*
You must run four extra laps in your gym class because you were late.	You're excluded from participating in gym class because you were late.
A parent adds chores following a child's poor report card.	A parent takes away a teen's cellphone following a poor report card.
Your boss chews you out about your performance.	Your boss reduces your pay after a poor performance.

The Skinner box application FIGURE 6.8

To test his behavioural theories, Skinner used an animal, usually a pigeon or a rat, and an apparatus that has come to be called a *Skinner box*. In Skinner's basic experimental design, an animal, such as a rat, received a food pellet each time it pushed a lever, and the number of responses was recorded. Note in this drawing that an electric grid on the cage floor could be used to deliver small electric shocks.

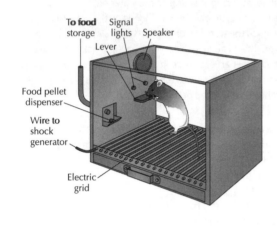

Test yourself

Is this positive reinforcement, negative reinforcement, positive punishment, or negative punishment? Fill in the name of the appropriate learning principle in the spaces provided in each box.

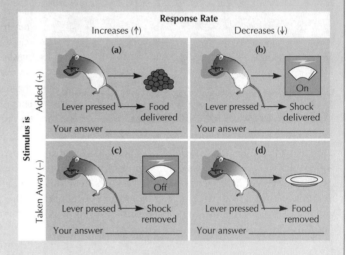

Answers: (a) positive reinforcement, (b) positive punishment, (c) negative reinforcement, (d) negative punishment

---

Punishment plays an unavoidable role in our social world. Dangerous criminals must be stopped and possibly removed from society. Parents must stop their teenagers from drinking and driving. Teachers must stop disruptive students in the classroom and bullies on the playground. Yet punishment can be problematic (Borrego et al., 2007; Leary et al., 2008; Loxton et al., 2008).

To be effective, punishment should be immediate and consistent. However, in the real world, this is extremely hard to do. Police officers cannot stop all drivers every time they speed. To make matters worse, when punishment is not immediate, the delay can cause the behaviour to be reinforced on a partial schedule, which makes it highly resistant to extinction. Think about gambling. It should be a punishing situation—gamblers usually lose far more than they win. However, the fact that they occasionally win keeps gamblers hanging in there.

Even if punishment immediately follows the misbehaviour, the recipient may learn what not to do but may not necessarily learn what he or she should do. It's much more effective to teach someone by giving a clear examples of correct behaviour than by simply punishing the incorrect behaviour. Finally, punishment can have serious side effects.

The Biology of Learning

LEARNING OBJECTIVES

Explain how an animal's environment can affect learning and behaviour.

Identify an example of biological preparedness.

Describe how instinctive drift constrains learning.

So far in this chapter, we have considered how external forces—from reinforcing events to our observations of others—affect learning. But we also know that for changes in behaviour to persist over time, lasting biological changes must occur within the organism. In this section, we will examine neurological and evolutionary influences on learning.

NEUROSCIENCE AND LEARNING: THE ADAPTIVE BRAIN

As Canadian psychologists Joe-Guillaume Pelletier and Denis Paré (2004) have suggested, each time we learn something, either consciously or unconsciously, that experience creates new synaptic connections and alterations in a wide network of brain structures, including the cortex, cerebellum, hypothalamus, thalamus, and amygdala (see also May et al., 2007; Möhler et al., 2008; Romero, et al., 2008).

Evidence that experience changes brain structure first emerged in the 1960s from studies of animals raised in enriched versus deprived environments. Compared with rats raised in a stimulus-poor environment, those raised in a colourful, stimulating "rat Disneyland" had a thicker cortex, increased nerve growth factor (NGF), more fully developed synapses, more dendritic branching, and improved performance on many tests of learning (Gresack, Kerr, & Frick, 2007; Lores-Arnaiz et al., 2007; Pham et al., 2002; Rosenzweig & Bennett, 1996).

Admittedly, it is a big leap from rats to humans, but research suggests that the human brain also responds to environmental conditions (**FIGURE 6.13**). For example, older adults who are exposed to stimulating environments generally perform better on intellectual and perceptual tasks than those who are in restricted environments (Schaie, 1994, 2008).

Daily enrichment FIGURE 6.13

For humans and non-human animals alike, environmental conditions play an important role in enabling learning. How might a classroom rich with stimulating toys, games, and books foster intellectual development in young children?

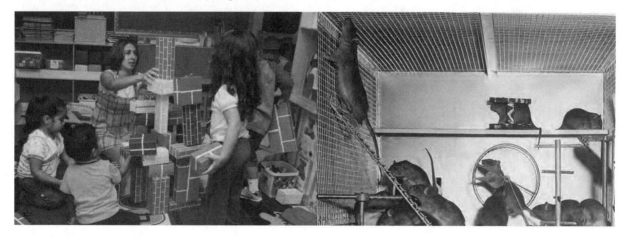

MIRROR NEURONS AND IMITATION

Recent research has identified another neurological influence on learning processes, particularly imitation. By using fMRIs and other brain-imaging techniques (Chapter 1), researchers have identified specific mirror neurons believed to be responsible for human empathy and imitation (Ahlsén, 2008; Fogassi et al., 2005; Hurley, 2008; Jacob, 2008). These neurons are found in several key areas of the brain, and they help us identify with what others are feeling and to imitate their actions. When we see another person in pain, one reason we empathize and "share their pain" is that our mirror neurons are firing. Similarly, if we watch others smile, our mirror neurons make it harder for us to frown.

Mirror neurons were first discovered by neuroscientists who implanted wires in the brains of monkeys to monitor areas involved in planning and carrying out movement (Ferrari, Rozzi, & Fogassi, 2005; Rizzolatti et al., 2002; Rizzolatti, Fogassi, & Gallese, 2006). When these monkeys moved and grasped an object, specific neurons fired, but they also fired when the monkeys simply observed another monkey performing the same or similar tasks.

Mirror neurons in humans also fire when we perform a movement or watch someone else perform it. Have you noticed how spectators at an athletic event sometimes slightly move their arms or legs in synchrony with the athletes, or how newborns tend to imitate adult facial expressions? Mirror neurons may be the underlying biological mechanism for this imitation and for an infant's copying of the lip and tongue movements necessary for speech. They also might help explain the emotional deficits of children and adults with autism or schizophrenia, who often misunderstand the verbal and non-verbal cues of others (Arbib & Mundhenk, 2005; Dapretto et al., 2006; Martineau et al., 2008).

EVOLUTION AND LEARNING: BIOLOGICAL PREPAREDNESS AND INSTINCTIVE DRIFT

Humans and other animals are born with various innate reflexes and instincts. Although these biological tendencies help ensure evolutionary survival, they are inherently inflexible. Only through learning are we able to react to important environmental cues—such as spoken words and written symbols—that our innate reflexes and instincts do not address. Thus, from an evolutionary perspective, learning is an adaptation that enables organisms to survive and prosper in a constantly changing world, or more simply to profit from experience.

Because animals can be operantly conditioned to perform a variety of novel behaviours (like water-skiing), learning theorists initially believed that the fundamental laws of conditioning would apply to almost all species and all behaviours. However, researchers have identified several biological constraints that limit the generality of conditioning principles. These include biological preparedness and instinctive drift.

Years ago, a young woman named Rebecca unsuspectingly bit into a Butterfinger candy bar filled with small, wiggling maggots. Horrified, she ran gagging and screaming to the bathroom. Many years later, Rebecca still feels nauseated when she sees a Butterfinger candy bar (but, fortunately, she doesn't feel similarly nauseated by the sight of her boyfriend, who bought her the candy).

Rebecca's graphic (and true!) story illustrates an important evolutionary process. When a food or drink is associated with nausea or vomiting, that particular food or drink can become a conditioned stimulus (CS) that triggers a conditioned **taste aversion**. Like other classically conditioned responses, taste aversions develop involuntarily (**FIGURE 6.14** on the next page).

Can you see why this automatic response would be adaptive? If one of our ancestral relatives became ill after eating a new plant, it would increase his or her chances for survival if he or she immediately developed an aversion to that plant, but not to other family members who might have been present at the time. Similarly, people tend to develop phobias of snakes, darkness, spiders, and heights more easily than of guns, knives, and electrical outlets presumably because the former were present in the ancestral environment, while the latter were not. We apparently inherit a built-in (innate) readiness to form associations between certain stimuli and responses known as **biological preparedness**.

Laboratory experiments have provided general support for both taste aversion and biological preparedness.

> **■ biological preparedness**
> Built-in (innate) readiness to form associations between certain stimuli and responses.

Taste aversion in the wild FIGURE 6.14

In applied research, Garcia and his colleagues used classical conditioning to teach coyotes not to eat sheep (Gustavson & Garcia, 1974). The researchers began by lacing freshly killed sheep with a chemical that caused extreme nausea and vomiting in the coyotes that ate the tainted meat. The conditioning worked so well that the coyotes would run away from the mere sight and smell of sheep. This taste aversion developed involuntarily. This research has since been applied many times in the wild and in the laboratory with coyotes and other animals (Aubert & Dantzer, 2005; Domjan, 2005; Workman & Reader, 2008).

For example, John Garcia and Robert Koelling (1966) produced taste aversion in lab rats by pairing flavoured water (NS) and a drug (UCS) that produced gastrointestinal distress (UCR). After being conditioned and then recovering from the illness, the rats refused to drink the flavoured water (CS) because of the conditioned taste aversion. Remarkably, however, Garcia discovered that only certain neutral stimuli could produce the nausea. Pairings of a noise (NS) or a shock (NS) with the nausea-producing drug (UCS) produced no taste aversion. Garcia suggested that when we are sick to our stomachs, we have a natural, evolutionary tendency to attribute it to food or drink. Being biologically prepared to quickly associate nausea with food or drink is adaptive because it helps us avoid that or similar food or drink in the future (Domjan, 2005; Garcia, 2003; Kardong, 2008).

Just as Garcia couldn't produce noise–nausea associations, other researchers have found that an animal's natural behaviour pattern can interfere with operant conditioning. For example, Keller Breland and Marian Breland (1961) tried to teach a chicken to play baseball. Through shaping and reinforcement, the chicken first learned to pull a loop that activated a swinging bat and then learned to actually hit the ball. But instead of running to first base, it would chase the ball as if it were food. Regardless of the lack of reinforcement for chasing the ball, the chicken's natural behaviour took precedence. This biological constraint is known as **instinctive drift**.

instinctive drift
The tendency of some conditioned responses to shift (or drift) back toward innate response pattern.

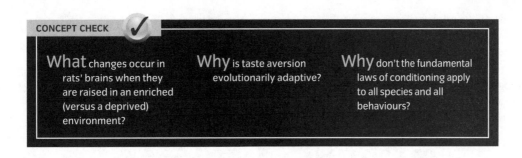

CONCEPT CHECK ✔

What changes occur in rats' brains when they are raised in an enriched (versus a deprived) environment?

Why is taste aversion evolutionarily adaptive?

Why don't the fundamental laws of conditioning apply to all species and all behaviours?

Memory

7

When Henry Molaison was 27 years old, portions of his temporal lobes and limbic system were removed as treatment for severe epilepsy. The surgery was successful—that is, his seizures could now be controlled, but something was clearly wrong with his memory. Two years after the surgery, he still believed he was 27. He had to be repeatedly reminded of events that had occurred after his surgery. As of 2008, more than 50 years later, Henry could not recognize the people who cared for his daily needs or the features of his own room. He would read the same magazines over and over again and laugh at the same old jokes he had been told dozens of times before. Right into his 80s, he still saw himself as a young man and had not recognized a photograph of his own face for decades (Corkin, 2002).

For more than three decades, Dr. Brenda Milner of the Montreal Neurological Institute worked with and studied Henry. Dr. Milner showed that while Henry could not remember one day from the next and could never remember her name, on some of the tasks she administered there were significant improvements in his performance. This occurred even though Henry had no memory of any prior exposure to the task.

Henry Molaison died at the age of 82 in December 2008. For more than 50 years he was recognized as the most important patient in the history of neuroscience. As a case study, he helped researchers and the medical community understand the biological basis of human learning and memory. Two generations of psychology students before you learned about this man, who was known to us only as H.M.

In December 2009, Henry Molaison's brain was sectioned into 2,401 paper-thin slices (see photo) to reveal the nature of the lesion.

CHAPTER OUTLINE

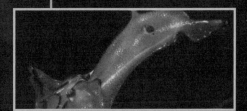

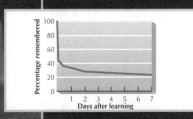

The Nature of Memory

Memory allows us to profit from our experiences and to adjust to ever-changing environments. Without memory we would not learn from past events or adapt to future situations. Consider Henry Molaison for a second as you read this paragraph; it is memory that makes the present meaningful and the future understandable. Yet our memories are also highly fallible. Although some people think of **memory** as a gigantic library or an automatic video recorder, our memories are never perfect records of events. Instead, memory is a *constructive and re-creative process* through which we actively organize and shape information. Memory is malleable. As you might expect, the belief that memory is accurate and precise often leads to serious errors and biases, which we'll discuss throughout this chapter.

> **memory**
> An internal record or representation of some prior event or experience.

HOW DOES MEMORY WORK?

Over the years, psychologists have developed numerous models (or representations) of how memory operates. As emerging research has provided insights into memory,

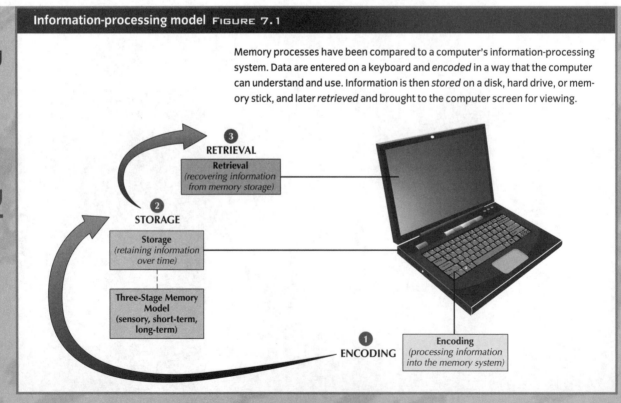

Process Diagram

Information-processing model FIGURE 7.1

Memory processes have been compared to a computer's information-processing system. Data are entered on a keyboard and *encoded* in a way that the computer can understand and use. Information is then *stored* on a disk, hard drive, or memory stick, and later *retrieved* and brought to the computer screen for viewing.

③ RETRIEVAL
Retrieval
(recovering information from memory storage)

② STORAGE
Storage
(retaining information over time)

Three-Stage Memory Model
(sensory, short-term, long-term)

① ENCODING
Encoding
(processing information into the memory system)

many of the older models have largely been abandoned. In this first section, we briefly discuss the two approaches that have the most empirical evidence and have withstood research scrutiny: the information-processing model and the three-stage model.

Information-Processing Model

According to the **information-processing model**, the barrage of information that we encounter every day goes through three basic levels of processing: **encoding**, **storage**, and **retrieval** (**FIGURE 7.1**).

With this information-processing model of memory, the brain encodes sensory information, such as sounds or visual images, into a neural code that it can understand; stores the information for later use; and retrieves information by searching for the appropriate stored "files" and bringing them back into short-term memory, where they can be worked with. These operations are analogous to incoming information being typed on a keyboard and translated into computer language, stored on a disk, and retrieved when brought to the computer screen to be viewed.

encoding Processing information into the memory system.

storage Retaining information over time.

retrieval Recovering information from memory storage.

The Three-Stage Model

Since the late 1960s, one of the most widely used models in memory research is called the **three-stage memory model** (Atkinson & Shiffrin, 1968). According to this model, memory comprises three different storage "boxes," or stages (sensory, short-term, and long-term), that each hold and process information in a specific way. Each stage has a different purpose, duration, and capacity (**FIGURE 7.2**). The three-stage memory model remains the leading paradigm in memory research because it offers a convenient way to organize the major research findings. Let's discuss this model in more detail.

The three-stage memory model FIGURE 7.2

Each "box" represents a separate memory system that differs in purpose, duration, and capacity. When information is not transferred from sensory memory or short-term memory, it is assumed to be lost. Information stored in long-term memory can be retrieved and sent back to short-term memory for use.

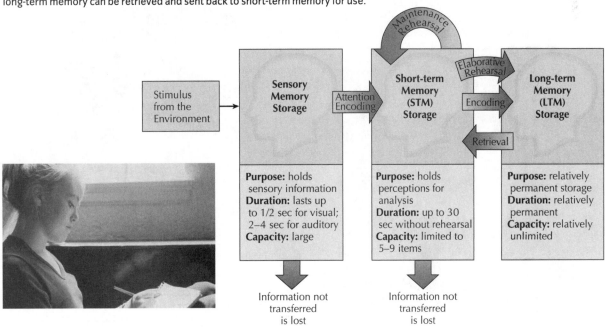

The Nature of Memory 183

SENSORY MEMORY: FIRST IMPRESSIONS

Everything we see, hear, touch, taste, and smell first enters our **sensory memory**. Information remains in sensory memory momentarily; if we attend to this new information, it is then transferred to the next stage of memory. For visual information, known as *iconic memory*, the visual image (icon) lasts about half a second (**FIGURE 7.3**). Auditory information (what we hear) is held in sensory memory for about the same time, but a weaker "echo," or *echoic memory*, of this auditory information can last up to four seconds (Lu, Williamson, & Kaufman, 1992; Neisser, 1967). Both iconic and sensory memory are demonstrated in *Applying Psychology*.

> **■ sensory memory**
> The first memory stage that holds sensory information and has a relatively large capacity but the duration of only a few seconds.

How do researchers test sensory memory?
FIGURE 7.3

In an early study of sensory memory, George Sperling (1960) flashed an arrangement of letters, like these, for 1/20th of a second. When told to recall the total arrangement in free recall, most people, he found, could recall only four or five letters. But when instructed to report just the top, middle, or bottom row, depending on whether they heard a randomly presented high, medium, or low tone after seeing the matrix, they reported almost all the letters correctly. It seems that all 12 letters are held in sensory memory right after they are viewed, but only those that are immediately attended to are noted and processed.

K Z R A
Q B T P
S G N Y

Applying Psychology

Demonstrating Iconic and Echoic Memory

As mentioned, visual and auditory information remains in sensory memory for a short time. For a simple demonstration of the duration of visual, or *iconic memory*, wave a lit sparkler when it is dark outside. Because the image, or icon, lingers for a fraction of a second after the sparkler is moved, you see the light as a continuous stream, similar to the image in this photo.

Auditory, or *echoic memory*, works similarly. Think back to a time when someone asked you a question while you were deeply absorbed in a task. Did you say "What?" and then immediately find you could answer them before they repeated the statement? Now you know why. A weaker "echo" (echoic memory) of auditory information can last up to four seconds.

Stop & Think
1. What do you think would happen if we did not possess iconic or echoic memory?
2. What might happen if visual or auditory sensations lingered not for seconds but for minutes?

Early researchers believed that sensory memory had an unlimited capacity. However, later research suggested that sensory memory does have limits and that stored images are fuzzier than once thought (Goldstein, 2008; Grondin, Ouellet, & Roussel, 2004).

■ **short-term memory (STM)** This second memory stage temporarily stores encoded sensory information and decides whether to send it on to long-term memory (LTM). Its capacity is limited to five to nine items, and its duration is about 30 seconds.

SHORT-TERM MEMORY: OUR "WORKING WITH" MEMORY

The second stage of memory processing, **short-term memory (STM)**, temporarily stores and processes sensory stimuli that has been encoded/attended to. If the information is meaningful, STM organizes and sends it along to relatively permanent storage, called long-term memory (LTM). Otherwise, it decays and is lost.

The *capacity* and *duration* of STM are limited (Best, 1999; Kareev, 2000). To extend the *capacity* of STM, you might use a memory technique called **chunking** (Boucher & Dienes, 2003; Miller, 1956). Have you noticed that credit card, social insurance, and telephone numbers are all grouped into three or four units separated by spaces? This is because it's easier to remember numbers in "chunks" rather than as a long string of single digits, as shown in *What a Psychologist Sees*.

You can extend the *duration* of your STM almost indefinitely by consciously repeating the information, a process called **maintenance rehearsal**. You are using maintenance rehearsal when you look up a

■ **chunking** The act of grouping separate pieces of information into a single unit (or chunk).

■ **maintenance rehearsal** Repeating information to keep it active in short-term memory.

Chunking in Chess

What do you see when you observe the arrangement of pieces on a chessboard? To the novice, a chess game in progress looks like little more than a random assembly of black and white game pieces. Accordingly, inexperienced chess players can remember the positions of only a few pieces when a chess game is underway. But expert players generally can easily remember all the positions. To the experts, the scattered pieces form meaningful patterns—classic arrangements that recur often. Just as you group the letters of this sentence into meaningful words and remember them long enough to understand the meaning of the entire sentence, expert chess players group the chess pieces into easily recalled patterns (or chunks) (Huffman, Matthews, & Gagne, 2001; Waters & Gobet, 2008).

What a Psychologist Sees

The Nature of Memory 185

phone number and say it over and over again in your head until you dial the number. People who are good at remembering names also know to take advantage of maintenance rehearsal. They repeat the name of each person they meet, aloud or silently, to keep it active in STM.

"Working with" Memory   Short-term memory is more than just a passive, temporary "holding area." Most current researchers (Baddeley, 1992; Baddeley & Jarrold, 2007; Jonides et al., 2008) realize that active processing of information occurs in STM. Because the short-term memory is active, and its contents are constantly being worked, we can think of STM as a three-part **working memory**. Let's look at each of these three parts (FIGURE 7.4).

Working memory as a central executive FIGURE 7.4

The *central executive* supervises and coordinates two subsystems, the *phonological rehearsal loop* and the *visuospatial sketchpad*, while also sending and retrieving information to and from LTM. Picture yourself as a food server in a busy restaurant, and a couple has just given you a complicated food order.

When you mentally rehearse the food order (the phonological loop) and combine it with a mental picture of the layout of plates on the customers' table (the visuospatial sketchpad), you're using your central executive.

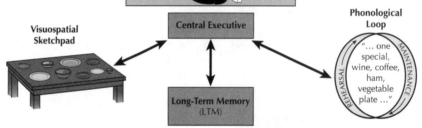

Central executive
(Coordinates material phonologically and visuospatially along with long-term memory)

Visuospatial Sketchpad

Central Executive

Long-Term Memory (LTM)

Phonological Loop

REHEARSAL — MAINTENANCE

"… one special, wine, coffee, ham, vegetable plate …"

Visuospatial sketchpad
(Mentally imagines visual and spatial material)

Phonological loop
(Rehearses through speech, words, numbers)

The *visuospatial sketchpad* holds and manipulates visual images and spatial information (Baddeley & Jarrold, 2007; Lehnert & Zimmer, 2008). Again, imagine yourself as the food server who's delivering the food to the same customers. Using your mind's visuospatial sketchpad, you can mentally visualize where to fit all the entrees, side dishes, and dinnerware on their table.

The working memory's *phonological rehearsal loop* holds and manipulates verbal (phonological) information (Dasi et al., 2008; Jonides et al., 2008). Your phonological loop allows you to subvocally repeat all your customers' specific requests while you write a brief description on your order pad.

LONG-TERM MEMORY: GIVING CONTEXT TO THE PRESENT

Think back to the opening story of Henry Molaison. Although his surgery was successful in stopping his severe seizures, it also destroyed the mechanism that transfers information from short-term to long-term memory. That was why he could not remember the people he saw every day and didn't recognize photos of his own aging face.

> **long-term memory (LTM)** This third memory stage stores information for long periods. Its capacity is limitless; its duration is relatively permanent.

Once information is transferred from STM, it is organized and integrated with other information in **long-term memory (LTM)**. LTM serves as a storehouse of information that must be kept for long periods. When we need the information—perhaps to remember something—it is sent back to STM for our use. Compared with sensory memory and short-term memory, long-term memory has relatively unlimited *capacity* and *duration* (Klatzky, 1984).

How do we store the vast amount of information that we collect over our lifetime? Several types of LTM exist (see STUDY ORGANIZER 7.1). The two major systems are explicit/declarative memory and implicit/nondeclarative memory.

Explicit/declarative memory refers to intentional learning or conscious knowledge. If asked to remember your cell phone number or your mother's name, you can state (declare) the answers directly (explicitly). Explicit/declarative memory can be further subdivided into two parts. *Semantic* memory is memory for general knowledge, rules, public events, facts, and specific information. It is our mental encyclopedia.

In contrast, *episodic* memory is like a mental journal into which personal experiences are written. This subsystem records the major events (episodes) in our lives. Some of our episodic memories are short lived, such as where you had coffee this morning, while others can last a lifetime, such as remembering your first elementary school crush or first passionate kiss.

Have you ever wondered why most preschoolers can remember events that happened to them in the previous

> **explicit/ declarative memory** The subsystem within long-term memory that consciously stores facts, information, and personal life experiences.

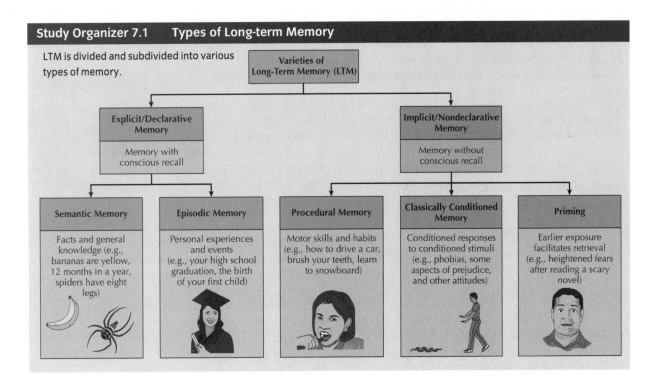

Study Organizer 7.1   Types of Long-term Memory

LTM is divided and subdivided into various types of memory.

Varieties of Long-Term Memory (LTM)

Explicit/Declarative Memory — Memory with conscious recall

Implicit/Nondeclarative Memory — Memory without conscious recall

Semantic Memory — Facts and general knowledge (e.g., bananas are yellow, 12 months in a year, spiders have eight legs)

Episodic Memory — Personal experiences and events (e.g., your high school graduation, the birth of your first child)

Procedural Memory — Motor skills and habits (e.g., how to drive a car, brush your teeth, learn to snowboard)

Classically Conditioned Memory — Conditioned responses to conditioned stimuli (e.g., phobias, some aspects of prejudice, and other attitudes)

Priming — Earlier exposure facilitates retrieval (e.g., heightened fears after reading a scary novel)

The Nature of Memory   187

few months, yet most of us adults can recall almost nothing of those years before age 3? Not that you would want to, but why don't we remember our own birth? Research suggests that for us to encode these early events and recall them much later, the frontal lobes—along with other neural structures—need to be sufficiently mature (Leichtman, 2006; Morris, 2007; Prigatano & Gray, 2008; Suzuki & Amaral, 2004; Wang, 2008).

Implicit/nondeclarative memory refers to non-conscious learning or acquiring knowledge unintentionally. Try telling someone else how you tie shoelaces without demonstrating the actual behaviour. Because your memory of this skill is non-conscious and hard to describe (declare) in words, this type of memory is sometimes referred to as *nondeclarative*.

> **implicit/ nondeclarative memory** The subsystem within long-term memory that consists of non-conscious procedural skills, simple classically conditioned responses (Chapter 6), and priming.

Implicit/nondeclarative memory consists of *procedural* motor skills, like skateboarding, as well as *classically conditioned memory* responses, such as fears and phobias or taste aversions.

Implicit/nondeclarative memory also includes *priming*, where prior exposure to a stimulus facilitates or inhibits (primes) the processing of new information (Amir et al., 2008; Becker, 2008; Tulving, 2000; Tulving & Schacter, 1990; Woollams et al., 2008). For example, you might feel a little edgy being home alone after seeing a scary movie, and watching a romantic movie might kindle your own romantic feelings. Priming can occur even when we do not consciously remember being exposed to the prime.

IMPROVING LONG-TERM MEMORY: PRACTICE MAKES PERMANENT

Several processes can be employed to improve long-term memory. These include organization, rehearsal or repetition, and effective retrieval.

Organization
To successfully encode information for LTM, we need to *organize* material into hierarchies. This involves arranging a number of related items into broad categories that are further divided and subdivided. (This organization strategy for LTM is similar to the strategy of chunking material in STM.) Many textbooks are laid out using organization principles in the hope of improving long-term retention of the contents. Grouping small subsets of ideas together, as subheadings under larger, main headings, and within diagrams, tables, and so on, helps to make the material in the text more understandable and memorable.

Admittedly, organization takes time and effort. But you'll be happy to know that a little memory organization and filing is done automatically while you sleep (Mograss et al., 2008; Siccoli et al., 2008). Unfortunately, despite claims to the contrary, research shows that we can't recruit our sleeping hours to memorize new material, such as a foreign language.

Rehearsal
Like organization, *rehearsal* also improves encoding for both STM and LTM. If you need to hold information in STM for longer than 30 seconds, you can simply keep repeating it (maintenance rehearsal). But storage in LTM requires *deeper levels of processing* called **elaborative rehearsal** (FIGURE 7.5A).

> **elaborative rehearsal** The process of linking new information to previously stored material.

The immediate goal of elaborative rehearsal is to *understand the information better* and not to simply memorize it. Understanding is one of the best ways to encode new information into long-term memory.

Retrieval
Finally, effective *retrieval* is critical to improving long-term memory. There are two types of **retrieval cues**. *Specific cues* require you only to recognize the correct response. *General cues* require you to recall previously learned material by searching through all possible matches in LTM—a much more difficult task (FIGURE 7.5B and FIGURE 7.5C).

> **retrieval cue** A clue or prompt that helps stimulate recall and retrieval of a stored piece of information from long-term memory.

Whether cues require recall or only recognition is not all that matters. Imagine that while apartment hunting, you walk into a stranger's kitchen and are greeted with the unmistakable smell of freshly baked chocolate chip cookies. Instantly, the aroma transports you to your grandmother's kitchen, where you spent many childhood afternoons doing your homework. You find yourself suddenly thinking of the mental

A Elaborative rehearsal

To improve elaborative rehearsal, you can expand (or elaborate on) the information to try to understand it better, actively explore and question new information, and search for meaningfulness. For example, a student might compare what she reads in an anthropology or history textbook with what she knows about world geography. Can you see how this might deepen her understanding and memory for the subject?

B Recall versus recognition memory

Can you *recall* from memory the names of the eight planets in our solar system? Why is it so much easier to *recognize* the names if you're provided with the first three letters of each planet's name: Mer-, Ven-, Ear-, Mar-, Jup-, Sat-, Ura-, Nep-? *Recall*, like an essay question, requires you to retrieve previously learned material with only general (often vague), nonspecific cues. In contrast, *recognition* tasks, as in a multiple-choice question, offer specific cues that only require you to identify (recognize) the correct response. (Note that in 2006, Pluto was officially declassified as a planet.)

C Longevity and recognition memory

Both name recognition and picture recognition for high school classmates remain high even many years after graduation, whereas recall memory would be expected to drop significantly over time.

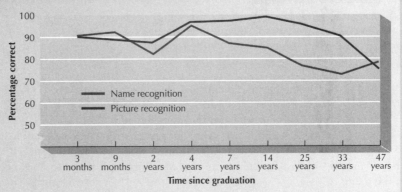

The Nature of Memory   189

shortcuts your grandmother taught you to help you learn your multiplication tables. You hadn't thought about these little tricks for years, but somehow a whiff of homemade cookies brought them back to you. Why?

In this imagined episode, you have stumbled on the **encoding specificity principle**, which states that retrieval of information will be better if conditions of recall are similar to conditions when encoded (Amir et al., 2008; Becker, 2008; Tulving & Thompson, 1973; Woollams et al., 2008). One important contextual cue for retrieval is *location*. In a clever, now classic study, Godden and Baddeley (1975) had underwater divers learn a list of 40 words either on land or underwater. The divers had better recall for lists that they had encoded underwater if they were also underwater at the time of retrieval; similarly, lists that were encoded above water were better recalled above water.

People also remember information better if their moods during learning and retrieval match (Kenealy, 1997; Nouchi & Hyodo, 2007). This phenomenon, called *mood congruence*, occurs because a given mood tends to evoke memories that are consistent with that mood. When you're sad (or happy or angry), you're more likely to remember events and circumstances from other times when you were also sad (or happy or angry).

Finally, as generations of coffee-devouring university students have discovered, if you learn something while under the influence of a drug, such as caffeine, you will remember it a little more easily when you take that drug again than during other times (Ahmadi et al., 2008; Baddeley, 1998; Zarrindast et al., 2005; Zarrindast et al., 2007). This is called *state-dependent retrieval*.

> ■ **encoding specificity principle** Retrieval of information is improved when the conditions of recovery are similar to the conditions that existed when the information was first encoded.

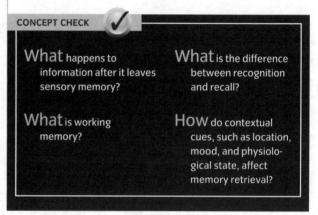

CONCEPT CHECK ✔

What happens to information after it leaves sensory memory?

What is working memory?

What is the difference between recognition and recall?

How do contextual cues, such as location, mood, and physiological state, affect memory retrieval?

Biological Bases of Memory

LEARNING OBJECTIVES

Describe two kinds of biological changes that occur when we learn something new.

Identify the primary brain areas involved in memory.

Explain how injury and disease can affect memory.

A large number of biological changes occur when we learn something new. Among them are neuronal and synaptic changes. In this section we will discuss these changes, along with the research surrounding where memories are located in the brain and what might cause memory loss.

NEURONAL AND SYNAPTIC CHANGES IN MEMORY

We know that learning and new experiences modify the brain's neural architecture (Chapters 2 and 6). As you learn to snowboard, for example, repeated practice builds specific neural pathways in your brain that make

Long-term potentiation (LTP)

Long-lasting increase in neural excitability caused by repeated neural input. Believed to be the biological basis of learning and memory.

it easier and easier for you to get down the mountain without falling over and breaking your neck. Research has shown this **long-term potentiation (LTP)** happens in at least two ways.

First, as early research with rats raised in "enriched" environments showed (Rosenzweig, Bennett, & Diamond, 1972; Chapter 6), repeated stimulation of a synapse strengthened the synapse by causing the dendrites to grow more spines. Spines are knobby outcroppings on dendrites and more of them mean more synapses, more receptor sites, and more sensitivity. The neuron is said to be more sensitive because the action potential can now affect a greater number of downstream neurons.

Second, learning affects a particular neuron's ability to release its neurotransmitters. This has been shown in research with *Aplysia*, a rather pretty looking sea slug that can be classically conditioned to reflexively withdraw its gills when squirted with water. This change in *Aplysia* is mediated by an increase in neurotransmitter release at specific synapses (**FIGURE 7.6**).

Further evidence comes from research with genetically engineered "smart mice," which have extra neural receptors for a neurotransmitter named NMDA (N-methyl-d-aspartate). These mice performed significantly better on memory tasks than did normal mice (Tang et al., 2001; Tsien, 2000). Evidence of long-term potentiation (LTP) has also been documented in humans (Berger et al., 2008; Tecchio et al., 2008).

HORMONAL CHANGES AND MEMORY

When stressed or excited, we naturally produce hormones, such as epinephrine and cortisol (Chapter 3), that arouse and energize the body. These hormones in turn affect the amygdala (a brain structure involved in emotion), which then signals the hippocampus and cerebral cortex (parts of the brain that are important for memory storage). Research has shown that direct injections of epinephrine or cortisol or electrical stimulation of the amygdala increases the encoding and storage of new information (Hamilton & Gotlib, 2008; Jackson, 2008;

How does a sea slug learn and remember?

FIGURE 7.6

After repeated squirting with water, followed by a mild shock, the sea slug, *Aplysia*, releases more neurotransmitters at certain synapses. These synapses then become more efficient at transmitting signals that allow the slug to withdraw its gills when squirted. Why might this ability be evolutionarily advantageous?

van Stegeren, 2008). Moreover, newer animal research has shown that a region of the amygdala can influence representations in the cortex, and this may be the mechanism by which long-term memories are strengthened (Chavez, McGaugh, & Weinberger, 2009). However, prolonged or excessive stress (and increased levels of cortisol) has been shown to interfere with memory (Al'absi, Hugdahl, & Lovallo, 2002; Heffelfinger & Newcomer, 2001; McAllister-Williams & Rugg, 2002).

The powerful effect of hormones on memory is evident in *flashbulb memories*—vivid images of circumstances associated with surprising or strongly emotional events (Brown & Kulik, 1977). In such situations, we secrete fight-or-flight hormones when the event occurs

Biological Bases of Memory   191

and then replay the event in our minds again and again, which makes for stronger memories. Despite their intensity, flashbulb memories are not as accurate as you might think (Cubelli & Della Sala, 2008; Talarico & Rubin, 2007). Even these types of memories, memories that feel crystal clear, are subject to errors; while we tend to remember the emotion and generalities of the event, many of the details are actually lost.

IT'S ALL IN YOUR HEAD: WHERE ARE MEMORIES LOCATED?

Early memory researchers believed that memory was localized, or stored in a particular discrete brain area. More recent research suggests that, in fact, memory tends not to be localized in a single region but stored in many separate areas throughout the brain.

Today, research techniques have advanced such that we can experimentally induce and measure memory-related brain changes as they occur. For example, James Brewer and his colleagues (1998) used functional magnetic resonance imaging (fMRI) to locate areas of the brain responsible for encoding memories of pictures. They showed 96 pictures of indoor and outdoor scenes to participants while scanning their brains, and then later tested participants' ability to recall the pictures. Brewer and his colleagues identified the *right prefrontal cortex* and the *parahippocampal cortex* as being the most active during the encoding of the pictures. These are only two of several brain regions involved in memory storage, however.

ψ Psychological Science

Brain and Memory Formation
Damage to any one of these areas can affect the encoding, storage, and retrieval of memories.

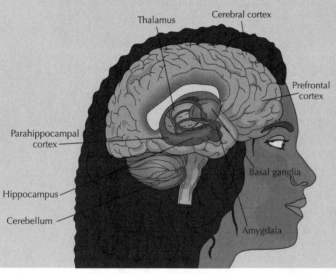

Amygdala	Emotional memory (Gerber et al., 2008; Hamilton & Gotlib, 2008; van Stegeren, 2008)
Basal Ganglia and Cerebellum	Creation and storage of the basic memory trace and implicit (nondeclarative) memories (such as skills, habits, and simple classically conditioned responses) (Chiricozzi et al., 2008; Gluck, 2008; Thompson, 2005)
Hippocampal Formation (hippocampus and surrounding area)	Memory recognition; implicit, explicit, spatial, episodic memory; declarative long-term memory; sequences of events (Hamilton & Gotlib, 2008; Yoo et al., 2007)
Thalamus	Formation of new memories and spatial and working memory (Hart & Kraut, 2007; Hofer et al., 2007; Ponzi, 2008)
Cortex	Encoding of explicit (declarative) memories; storage of episodic and semantic memories; skill learning; working memory (Davidson et al., 2008; Dougal et al., 2007; Thompson, 2005)

STOP

Stop & Think
1. What effect might damage to the amygdala have on a person's relationships with others?
2. What effect do you think damage to the thalamus might have on a person's day-to-day functioning?

192   CHAPTER 7   Memory

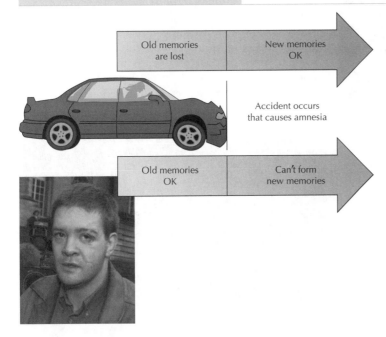

A In *retrograde amnesia*, the person loses memories of events that occurred *before* the accident yet has no trouble remembering things that happened afterward (old, "retro" memories are lost).

B In *anterograde amnesia*, the person cannot form new memories for events that occur *after* the accident. Anterograde amnesia also may result from a surgical injury (as in the case of Henry Molaison) or from diseases, such as chronic alcoholism.

Bodyguard Trevor Rees-Jones, the sole survivor of the car accident that killed Diana, Princess of Wales; Dodi Al-Fayed; and Henri Paul, experienced both anterograde and retrograde amnesia caused by his serious head injuries. He reports having no memory after getting into the black Mercedes and no memory of the accident or what happened soon after.

INJURY, DISEASE, AND MEMORY LOSS

Traumatic brain injury (TBI) occurs when the skull suddenly collides with another object. A closed TBI occurs when the skull is not penetrated and the brain is not exposed. A penetrating head injury damages or breaches the tough connective covering, which surrounds and protects the brain. Damage caused by compression, twisting, penetration, and distortion of the brain inside the skull all can cause serious and sometimes permanent damage to the brain. In an injury it is the frontal and temporal lobes that often take the heaviest hit because they directly collide with the bony ridges inside the skull.

Loss of memory as a result of brain injury is called *amnesia*. Two major types of amnesia are **retrograde amnesia** and **anterograde amnesia** (FIGURE 7.7). Usually, retrograde amnesia is temporary. Unfortunately, anterograde amnesia is usually permanent, but patients often show surprising abilities to learn and remember implicit/nondeclarative tasks (such as procedural motor skills). This type of memory was somewhat preserved for Henry Molaison.

Like traumatic brain injuries, disease can damage the physiology of the brain and nervous system and thereby affect memory processes. For example, **Alzheimer's disease (AD)** is a degenerative brain disease characterized by progressive mental deterioration that occurs most commonly in old age (FIGURE 7.8). The most noticeable early symptoms are minor disturbances in memory, which become progressively worse until in the final stages, the person fails to recognize loved ones, cannot take care of himself or herself, and needs total nursing care. The person ultimately dies from the advancing disease.

Alzheimer's does not attack all types of memory equally. A hallmark of the disease is an extreme decline in explicit/declarative memory (Haley, 2005; Libon et al., 2007; Salter et al., 2008). Alzheimer's patients fail to recall facts, information, and personal life experiences, yet they still retain some implicit/nondeclarative memories, such as simple classically conditioned responses and procedural tasks, like brushing their teeth and hair.

Brain autopsies of people with Alzheimer's show unusual tangles (structures formed from dead and dying

Alzheimer's disease (AD) Degenerative brain disease characterized by progressive mental deterioration and pathological memory loss.

Biological Bases of Memory 193

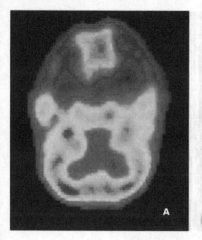
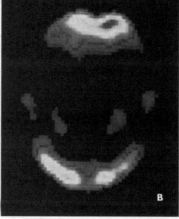

cell bodies) and plaques (structures formed from dead and dying axons and dendrites). Hereditary Alzheimer's generally strikes between the ages of 45 and 55. Some experts believe that the cause of Alzheimer's is primarily genetic, but others think that genetic makeup may make some people more susceptible to environmental influences (Diamond & Amso, 2008; Ertekin-Taner, 2007; Persson et al., 2008; Vickers et al., 2000; Weiner, 2008).

The effect of Alzheimer's disease on the brain
FIGURE 7.8

A **Normal brain** Note the large amount of red and yellow (signs of lots of brain activity) in the positron emission tomography (PET) scan of the normal brain.

B **Brain of a patient with Alzheimer's disease** The reduced activity in the brain of the Alzheimer's disease patient is evident. The loss is most significant in the temporal and parietal lobes. This suggests to researchers there is a strong link between these areas and memory storage.

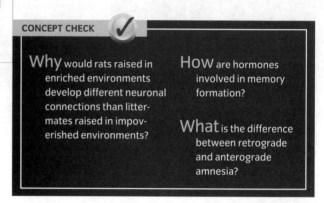

CONCEPT CHECK

Why would rats raised in enriched environments develop different neuronal connections than littermates raised in impoverished environments?

How are hormones involved in memory formation?

What is the difference between retrograde and anterograde amnesia?

Forgetting

LEARNING OBJECTIVES

Describe Ebbinghaus' research on learning and forgetting.

Outline the five key theories of why we forget.

Explain the factors that contribute to forgetting.

Psychologists have developed several theories to explain forgetting and have identified a number of factors that can interfere with the process of forming new memories. We examine these theories and factors in this section.

THEORIES OF FORGETTING

If you couldn't forget, your mind would be filled with meaningless data, such as every snack you've ever had in your life or every outfit you have ever worn. Similarly, think of the incredible pain you would continuously endure if memories of life's tragedies did not fade with time? The ability to forget is essential to the proper functioning of memory. Our annoyance with forgetting occurs

when we forget things we did not intend to forget. These are the times when forgetting is an inconvenience, and we might fail to recognize how adaptive and useful it really is.

Five major theories attempt to explain why forgetting occurs (FIGURE 7.9): decay, interference, encoding failure, retrieval failure, and motivated forgetting. Each theory focuses on a different stage of the memory process or a particular type of problem in processing neural information.

FACTORS INVOLVED IN FORGETTING

Since Ebbinghaus' original research, scientists have discovered numerous factors that contribute to forgetting. Five of the most important are the misinformation

194 **CHAPTER 7** Memory

Process Diagram

Sensory Memory	Short-term Memory (STM)	Long-term Memory (LTM)

Stimulus from Environment

INFORMATION → Encoding → INFORMATION ← Encoding / Retrieval → INFORMATION

A **Decay Theory.** Because memory is processed and stored in a physical form—for example, in a network of neurons—connections between neurons probably deteriorate over time. We know that skills and memory degrade if they go unused.

In other words, "use it or lose it." However, conclusive experimental support for decay theory is difficult to obtain. How can you prove that a previously stored memory does not exist?

Brittany Brianna → Encoding → Brittany Brianna Brittany ← Encoding / Brianna Retrieval → Brittany Brianna

B **Interference Theory.** Forgetting is caused by two competing memories. Interference is particularly strong among memories with similar qualities. **Retroactive interference** occurs when new information (such as one's new phone number) interferes

with old information (such as one's former number). In contrast, **proactive interference** occurs when old information interferes with new information. Calling a new girlfriend by an old girlfriend's name is proactive interference.

INFORMATION → Encoding → INFORMATION ← Encoding / Retrieval → [blank]

C **Encoding Failure Theory.** Our sensory memory receives the information and passes it to STM. But during STM, we may decide there is no need to remember the precise details, so we do not fully encode it and pass it on for proper storage in LTM.

For example, you are introduced to someone and a few seconds later you have no recollection of the person's name, as if the name "went in one ear and out the other."

Jason → Encoding → Jason ← Encoding / Retrieval → Jason

D **Retrieval Failure Theory.** Memories stored in LTM aren't forgotten. They're just momentarily inaccessible—perhaps because of interference, faulty cues, or emotional states. For example, the **tip-of-the-tongue phenomenon**—the feeling that you can almost remember a word or event that seems as if it is

on "the tip of your tongue." It then pops into your head and you can finally say it. Although it is difficult to distinguish retrieval failure from encoding failure, most memory failures probably stem from poor encoding, not retrieval failure.

Distressing Memory → Encoding → Distressing Memory ← Encoding / Retrieval → Distressing Memory

E **Motivated Forgetting Theory.** We forget some information—such as a dental appointment or an embarrassing remark we once made—for a reason. According to Freudian

theory, people forget unpleasant or anxiety-producing information either consciously (suppression) or unconsciously (repression). (See Chapter 13.)

Forgetting   195

165

Psychological Science

How Quickly We Forget

About a hundred and twenty years ago Hermann Ebbinghaus introduced the first experimental study on learning and forgetting. Using himself as a subject, he calculated how long it took to learn and remember a list of three-letter *nonsense syllables*, such as *SIB* and *RAL*. He then found that just one hour after learning a list perfectly, he remembered only 44 percent of the syllables. A day later, he recalled 35 percent, and a week later, only 21 percent. This figure shows his now famous "forgetting curve."

Depressing as these findings may seem (or the fact that Ebbinghaus had little else to do with his days), keep in mind that meaningful material is much more memorable than meaningless nonsense syllables. Even so, we all forget some of what we have learned.

On a more positive note, after some time passed and he believed he had forgotten the list, Ebbinghaus found that *relearning* a previously learned list took less time than the

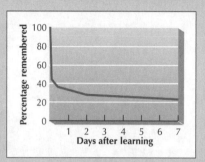

initial learning did. This research suggests that we retain some memory for things that we have learned, even when we seem to have forgotten them completely.

Most research based on Ebbinghaus' discoveries has found that there is an ideal time to practise something you have learned. Practising too soon is a waste of time, and if you practise too late, you will already have forgotten what you learned. The ideal time to practise is when you are about to forget.

Polish psychologist Piotr Wozniak used this insight to create a software program called SuperMemo. The program can be used to predict the future state of an individual's memory and help the person schedule reviews of learned information at the optimal time. So far the program has been applied mainly to language learning, helping users retain huge amounts of vocabulary. But Wozniak hopes that some day programs like SuperMemo will tell people when to wake and when to exercise, help them remember what they read and whom they have met, and remind them of their goals (Wolf, 2008).

STOP

Stop & Think
1. How do you think Ebbinghaus' findings might be applied to learning to play a musical instrument?
2. Can you think of any disadvantage of depending on a program like SuperMemo?

---

effect, the serial position effect, source amnesia, the sleeper effect, and spacing of practice.

Many people who haven't taken first-year psychology classes believe that when they are recalling an event, they're remembering it as if it were a video instant replay. However, as you know, our memories are re-creative and therefore highly fallible, filled with personal constructions and amendments that we create during encoding and storage. Research on the **misinformation effect** shows that information that occurs after an event may further alter and revise those constructions. Experimenters have created false memories in subjects by showing subjects doctored photos of themselves taking a fictitious hot-air balloon ride or by asking subjects to simply imagine an event, such as having a nurse remove

> **misinformation effect** Distortion of a memory by misleading post-event information.

a skin sample from their finger. In these and similar cases, a large number of subjects later believed that misleading information was correct and that fictitious or imagined events actually occurred (Allan & Gabbert, 2008; Garry & Gerrie, 2005; Mazzoni & Memon, 2003; Mazzoni & Vannucci, 2007; Pérez-Mata & Diges, 2007).

When research participants are given lists of words to learn and are allowed to recall them in any order they choose, they remember the words at the beginning (*primacy effect: STM is less crowded with information, so the words are more memorable*) and the end of the list (*recency effect: the most recent items put into STM and so are more memorable*) better than those in the middle, which are quite often forgotten (Azizian & Polich, 2007; Healy et al., 2008). This effect is known as the **serial position effect**.

The serial position effect has some interesting real-life implications. For example, a potential employer's memory for you might be enhanced if you are either the first or the last candidate interviewed.

Culture and memory FIGURE 7.10

In many societies, tribal leaders pass down important information by telling related stories. As a result, children living in these cultures have better memories for the information that is relayed to them through stories than do other children. Can you think of other ways in which culture might influence memory?

Each day we read, hear, and process an enormous amount of information, and it's easy to confuse who said what to whom, where, and in what context. Forgetting the true source of a memory is known as **source amnesia** (Kleider et al., 2008; Leichtman, 2006; Mitchell et al., 2005), and it has happened to all of us. While you know what city is Canada's capital, you probably don't remember where and when you learned it.

When we first hear something from an unreliable source, we tend to disregard the information in favour of a more reliable source. However, as the source of the information is forgotten (source amnesia), the unreliable information is less likely to be discounted. This is called the **sleeper effect** (Appel & Richter, 2007; Kumkale & Albarracín, 2004; Nabi, Moyer-Guse, & Byrne, 2007).

The sleeper effect can be a significant problem when reliable and unreliable information are intermixed—for example, when advertisements are disguised to look like more objective reports or newspaper articles. Can you see how, after a time, we may forget

the source and no longer discount the information in the ad?

If we try to memorize too much information at once (as when students stay up and pull an all nighter cramming before an exam), we learn and remember less than when study sessions are divided up (Donovan & Radosevich, 1999). *Distributed practice* refers to spacing your learning periods, with rest periods between sessions. Cramming is an example of *massed practice* because the time spent learning is massed into a long, unbroken bout.

Finally, as illustrated in FIGURE 7.10, cultural factors can play a role in how well people remember what they have learned.

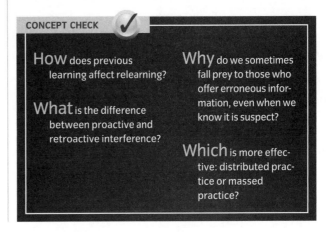

CONCEPT CHECK

How does previous learning affect relearning?

What is the difference between proactive and retroactive interference?

Why do we sometimes fall prey to those who offer erroneous information, even when we know it is suspect?

Which is more effective: distributed practice or massed practice?

Psychoactive Drugs

LEARNING OBJECTIVES

Explain the difference between dependence and addiction.

Summarize the differences among the four major types of psychoactive drugs.

Compare how the different psychoactive drugs affect the nervous system.

Psychoactive drugs influence the nervous system in a variety of ways. Alcohol, for example, has a diffuse effect on neural membranes throughout the nervous system. Most psychoactive drugs, however, act in a more specific way: by either enhancing or mimicking a particular neurotransmitter's effect (an **agonistic drug** action) or blocking or inhibiting it (an **antagonistic drug** action) (see FIGURE 5.9 on the next page).

In North America the most popular psychoactive drugs are caffeine, tobacco, and ethyl alcohol. Caffeine is the most widely used and is found in hot beverages, soft drinks, and energy drinks (see *Applying Psychology*). Because these drugs are legal drugs, do you think they are somehow better or safer than illegal drugs, such as Ecstasy, marijuana, and heroin? What about prescription drugs, such as antidepressants, or over-the-counter drugs, such as Aspirin and antacids? Because a pharmacist dispenses these drugs, are they "good" as opposed to "bad" drugs?

■ psychoactive drugs Chemicals that alter perception, conscious awareness, or mood.

■ agonistic drug A drug that mimics or enhances the activity of neurotransmitters.

■ antagonistic drug A drug that blocks or inhibits the activity of neurotransmitters.

Applying Psychology

Deja Brew: Energy Drinks Do Caffeine Differently

Since the introduction of Red Bull in North America in 1997, the energy drink market has grown exponentially. These soft drinks contain many different ingredients, such as vitamins and herbs, but their central ingredient is often caffeine. Of the hundreds of different brands marketed, the caffeine content ranges from 50 mg to 500 mg per container (Reissig et al., 2009). In Canada most of these drinks are classified as supplements; the current exception is Red Bull, which is regulated as a natural health product (Health Canada, 2006a). You can check to see whether the energy drink you are consuming is regulated as a natural health product or a supplement by looking on the side of the container for an eight-digit natural product number (NPN). Having an NPN does not necessarily mean a beverage is safe for all people to drink, however.

Although side effects from drinking energy drinks are possible (electrolyte disturbances, nausea, vomiting, and an

irregular heartbeat), moderate use by adults is generally considered to be safe. Side effects can occur when energy drinks are abused, such as when they are mixed with alcohol or consumed in large quantities (Health Canada, 2006a). Energy drinks have been aggressively marketed, especially to young men, for their performance-enhancing and stimulant effects. Do you drink energy drinks? Consider their effects on your body. Do you feel "recharged" after drinking them?

Adapted from EatRight Ontario. (2009). *Energy drink FAQs*. Retrieved from http://www.eatrightontario.ca/en/ViewDocument.aspx?id=196

Psychoactive Drugs   135

How agonistic and antagonistic drugs produce their psychoactive effect FIGURE 5.9

Most psychoactive drugs produce their mood-, energy-, and perception-altering effects by interacting with neurotransmitter systems. They can alter synthesis, storage, and release of neurotransmitters (Step 1). They can also alter the effect of neurotransmitters on the receiving site of the receptor neuron (Step 2). After neurotransmitters diffuse across the synapse, the sending neuron normally deactivates the unbound or excess neurotransmitter (Step 3).

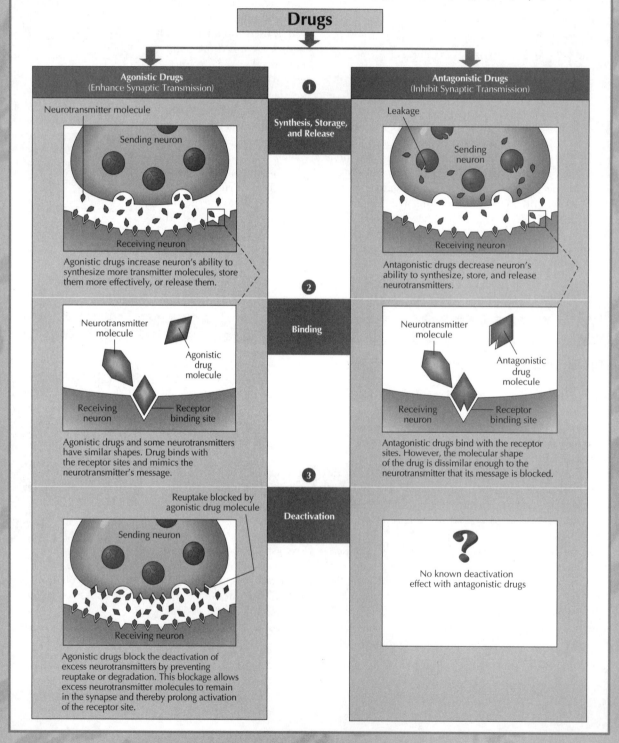

Drugs

Agonistic Drugs
(Enhance Synaptic Transmission)

Antagonistic Drugs
(Inhibit Synaptic Transmission)

❶ **Synthesis, Storage, and Release**

Neurotransmitter molecule
Sending neuron
Receiving neuron

Agonistic drugs increase neuron's ability to synthesize more transmitter molecules, store them more effectively, or release them.

Leakage
Sending neuron
Receiving neuron

Antagonistic drugs decrease neuron's ability to synthesize, store, and release neurotransmitters.

❷ **Binding**

Neurotransmitter molecule
Agonistic drug molecule
Receiving neuron
Receptor binding site

Agonistic drugs and some neurotransmitters have similar shapes. Drug binds with the receptor sites and mimics the neurotransmitter's message.

Neurotransmitter molecule
Antagonistic drug molecule
Receiving neuron
Receptor binding site

Antagonistic drugs bind with the receptor sites. However, the molecular shape of the drug is dissimilar enough to the neurotransmitter that its message is blocked.

❸ **Deactivation**

Reuptake blocked by agonistic drug molecule
Sending neuron
Receiving neuron

Agonistic drugs block the deactivation of excess neurotransmitters by preventing reuptake or degradation. This blockage allows excess neurotransmitter molecules to remain in the synapse and thereby prolong activation of the receptor site.

?
No known deactivation effect with antagonistic drugs

Most neuroscientists and biopsychologists believe that all drugs, regardless of their legal status, have good and bad uses. For example, the illegal drug Ecstasy (or MDMA, which stands for 3-4-methylene-dioxymethamphetamine) has potential uses in helping treat post-traumatic stress disorder (Winkelman & Roberts, 2007), and marijuana has many therapeutic applications in a variety of medical settings (see Köfalvi, 2008, for a review). Conversely, legal drugs, such as tobacco, can be very harmful to our health, and other legal drugs can be harmful to the safety of others (such as when alcohol is consumed before a person drives). So in general, it is not a useful dichotomy to lump illegal drugs into a "bad" drugs category and legal drugs into a "good" drugs category. A better way to think about psychoactive drugs is to appreciate that psychoactive substances can be both harmful and beneficial and that a drug's legal status can be unrelated to its usefulness. This distinction, along with how drug *use* differs from drug *abuse* and how chemical alterations in consciousness affect us, are important topics in psychology.

drug abuse Drug use that is necessary for feelings of continued well-being; use continues despite adverse consequences.

addiction A broad term referring to a condition in which a person has an overwhelming commitment to the drug of choice that supplants all other activities.

Is drug abuse the same as drug addiction? The term **drug abuse** generally refers to drug taking that is greater than simple recreational use, continues despite adverse consequences, and is necessary for feelings of continued well-being. **Addiction** is a broad term referring to a condition in which a person has an overwhelming commitment to their drug of choice that supplants all other activities. Addicted individuals feel compelled to use a specific drug to the detriment of all other aspects of their life, such as work, family, and school (Alexander, 1997).

Some researchers use the term **physical dependence** to refer to changes in physical or bodily processes that make a drug necessary for daily functioning. Physical dependence may be evident when the drug is withheld and the user undergoes **withdrawal** reactions, which are the unpleasant symptoms associated with drug cessation, such as discomfort and cravings. After repeated use of a drug, many of the body's physiological processes adjust, requiring more and more of the drug, producing a decreased sensitivity called **tolerance**.

Tolerance leads some users to escalate their drug use and to experiment with other drugs in an attempt to recreate the original pleasurable altered state. Sometimes, using one drug increases tolerance for another. This is known as **cross-tolerance**. For example, cross-tolerance is seen among LSD, mescaline, and psilocybin.

You may have heard of the term *psychological dependence* to refer to the "mental desire" for or craving to obtain a drug's effects. This is a vague and distracting phrase. Researchers have argued this description is not a diagnostic term and is somewhat arbitrary and misleading. Moreover, because "a mental desire"—or any mental desire—is produced by a physical brain, it is therefore not empirically separable from the concept of physical dependence (Alexander, 1997). We discuss substance abuse and substance dependence further in Chapter 13.

physical dependence Changes in physical or bodily processes that make the drug necessary for daily functioning.

withdrawal Characteristic signs that appear in a person when a drug is discontinued after prolonged use.

tolerance A state reached when the physiological reaction to the drug decreases, such that increasing doses are necessary for the same effect.

PSYCHOACTIVE DRUGS: FOUR CATEGORIES

Psychologists typically divide psychoactive drugs into four broad categories: depressants, stimulants, opiates, and hallucinogens. TABLE 5.1 provides examples of each and describes their effects.

Depressants (sometimes called "downers") act on the central nervous system to suppress or slow bodily processes and to reduce overall responsiveness.

depressants Drugs that slow or depress nervous system activity.

Effects of the major psychoactive drugs TABLE 5.1

	Category	Desired effects	Excessive use or overdose effects
	Depressants [slow nervous system activity]		
	Alcohol, barbiturates, anxiolytics, also known as antianxiety drugs or tranquilizers (Xanax), Rohypnol (roofies), Ketamine (special K), GHB	Tension reduction, euphoria, disinhibition, drowsiness, muscle relaxation	Anxiety, nausea, disorientation, impaired reflexes and motor functioning, amnesia, loss of consciousness, shallow respiration, convulsions, coma, death
	Stimulants [speed up nervous system activity]		
	Cocaine, amphetamine, methamphetamine (crystal meth), MDMA (Ecstasy)	Exhilaration, euphoria, high physical and mental energy, reduced appetite, perceptions of power, sociability	Irritability, anxiety, sleeplessness, paranoia, hallucinations, psychosis, elevated blood pressure and body temperature, convulsions, death
	Caffeine	Increased alertness	Insomnia, restlessness, increased pulse rate, mild delirium, ringing in the ears, rapid heartbeat
	Nicotine	Relaxation, increased alertness, sociability	Irritability, raised blood pressure, stomach pains, vomiting, dizziness, cancer, heart disease, emphysema
	Opiates (narcotics) [have sleep-inducing and pain-relieving properties]		
	Morphine, heroin, opium, codeine, OxyContin	Euphoria, pain relief, sleep, prevention of withdrawal discomfort	Nausea, vomiting, constipation, shallow respiration, convulsions, coma, death
	Hallucinogens (psychedelics) [alter consciousness and distort mood and perception]		
	LSD (lysergic acid diethylamide), mescaline (extract from the peyote cactus), psilocybin (magic mushrooms), *Salvia divinorum**	Heightened aesthetic responses, euphoria, mild delusions, hallucinations, distorted perceptions and sensations	Panic, nausea, headaches, longer and more extreme delusions, hallucinations, perceptual distortions ("bad trips"), psychosis * long-term effects of excessive *Salvia* use is currently unknown
	Marijuana	Relaxation, mild euphoria, increased appetite	Perceptual and sensory distortions, hallucinations, fatigue, lack of motivation, paranoia

138   CHAPTER 5   States of Consciousness

Alcohol's effect on the body and behaviour FIGURE 5.10

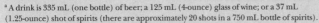

Number of drinks[a] in two hours	Blood alcohol (content (%)[b]	General effect[c]
(2)	0.05	Relaxed state; increased sociability
(3)	0.08	Everyday stress lessened
(4)	0.10	Movements and speech become clumsy
(7)	0.20	Very drunk; loud and difficult to understand; emotions unstable
(12)	0.40	Difficult to wake up; incapable of voluntary action
(15)	0.50	Coma and/or death

[a] A drink is 335 mL (one bottle) of beer; a 125 mL (4-ounce) glass of wine; or a 37 mL (1.25-ounce) shot of spirits (there are approximately 20 shots in a 750 mL bottle of spirits).

[b] In Canada, the legal blood alcohol level for drinking and driving is below 0.08.

[c] There is considerable variation among people.

Alcohol's effects are determined primarily by the amount that reaches the brain (FIGURE 5.10). Because the liver breaks down alcohol at the rate of about 30 mL per hour, the number of drinks and the speed of consumption are both very important. In addition, men's bodies are more efficient at breaking down alcohol. Even after accounting for differences in size and muscle-to-fat ratio, women have a higher blood alcohol level than men following equal doses of alcohol.

stimulants Drugs that speed up nervous system activity.

While depressants suppress central nervous system activity, **stimulants** (uppers) increase its overall activity and responsiveness. One of the more commonly used legal stimulants is nicotine, which despite its legal status causes serious health problems. Cigarette smoking is the most preventable cause of lung cancer, accounting for 85 percent of all new Canadian cases of this cancer. It has also been implicated in a variety of other cancers and in cardiovascular disease. The use of tobacco kills about 45,000 Canadians a year. That's more than the total number of deaths from AIDS, car accidents, suicide, murder, fires, and accidental poisonings combined (Canadian Lung Association, 2008). Nicotine's effects (relaxation, increased alertness, diminished pain and appetite) are so reinforcing that some people continue to smoke even after having a cancerous tumour removed. For example, psychology's own Sigmund Freud was one such person, continuing to smoke his trademark cigars even after

diagnosis and more than 30 surgeries for oral cancer and bone cancer of the jaw.

Opiates (or narcotics) are either derived from the opium poppy (opium, morphine, and heroin) or synthetically produced (Demerol, OxyContin). They are used to relieve severe pain (Kuhn, Swartzwelder, & Wilson, 2003), and are structurally similar to the brain's natural endorphins (Chapter 2), which decrease pain and elevate mood.

opiates Drugs derived from opium or synthetically derived and molecularly similar to opium that relieve pain and induce sleep.

Heroin first got its name from the German word for "heroic," because when heroin was first commercially introduced by Bayer and Co. in 1898, it was hailed as a drug with incredible potential. Not only was it highly effective in treating the coughing, chest pain, and discomfort associated with pneumonia and tuberculosis—two leading causes of death at that time—it also provided relief for severe pain (Alexander, 1997). Because of these tremendous benefits, and a lack of effective alternatives, it was widely prescribed. With its widespread use came the realization of its addictive properties.

Morphine, heroin, and many of the synthetic opiates are addictive because, after repeated flooding with these opiates, the brain eventually reduces the production of its own endorphins. If the user later attempts to stop, the brain lacks both the synthetic and the naturally occurring opiate chemicals, and withdrawal occurs

Psychoactive Drugs **139**

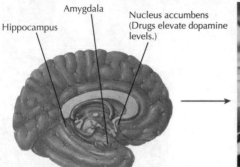

Hippocampus
Amygdala
Nucleus accumbens
(Drugs elevate dopamine levels.)

These key brain areas are associated with reward, pleasure, and addiction.

Opiates (e.g., heroin) mimic endorphins, which elicit euphoria and pain relief. Absence of the drugs triggers withdrawal symptoms (e.g., drug cravings).

(FIGURE 5.11). When opiates are used medically to relieve pain, they are generally not habit-forming, although this can happen. However, when repeatedly taken in other circumstances, such as for self-medication to dull the anguish of a marginalized life or dampen emotional pain, they can be extremely addictive (Alexander, 1997; Fields, 2007; Levinthal, 2008).

In the 2007 Ontario Student Drug Use and Health Survey (FIGURE 5.12), 21 percent of Ontario students in grades 7 to 12 report using opiate pain relievers, such as Tylenol 3, OxyContin, and Percocet, for non-medical purposes (Adlaf & Paglia-Boak, 2007). Of this group, 72 percent report obtaining the drugs from home.

One of the most intriguing alterations of consciousness comes from **hallucinogens**, drugs that produce sensory or perceptual distortions, including visual, auditory, and kinesthetic hallucinations. Some cultures use hallucinogens for spiritual purposes or as a way to experience "other realities." In Western societies, most people use hallucinogens for their reported "mind-expanding" potential.

Hallucinogens are commonly referred to as psychedelics (from the Greek for "mind manifesting"). They include mescaline (derived from the peyote cactus), psilocybin (derived from mushrooms), phencyclidine (synthetically derived), LSD (lysergic acid diethylamide, derived from ergot, a rye mould) and *Salvia* (*Salvia divinorum*, a herbaceous perennial of the mint family).

LSD, or acid, is a synthetic substance that produces dramatic alterations in sensation and perception. These alterations tend to primarily be visual, such as kaleidoscope-like images, vivid colours, and fantastic pictures. Generally

when on a "trip," users are aware that their altered perceptions are not real. LSD was first synthesized in 1943 by the Swiss chemist Albert Hofmann, who also took the first LSD trip after accidentally licking some of the drug off his finger.

LSD is a serotonin agonist and is usually not considered to be addictive, but it can still be a dangerous drug. Bad LSD trips, while uncommon, can be terrifying and may lead to accidents, deaths, or suicide. Flashbacks may unpredictably recur long after the initial ingestion (Abadinsky, 2008).

LSD use by high school and college students has been increasing (Connolly, 2000; Hedges & Burchfield, 2006; Yacoubian, Green, & Peters, 2003). Psychoactive drugs like Rohypnol (the date-rape drug) and MDMA (Ecstasy) are also increasing in popularity, especially at all-night rave parties. Other "club drugs," like GHB (gamma-hydroxybutyrate), ketamine (Special K), and methamphetamine (crystal meth), are also now more common (Abadinsky, 2008; Weaver & Scholl, 2008).

Although these drugs can produce desirable effects (e.g., Ecstasy's feeling of great empathy and connectedness with others), club drugs can be harmful. For example, they affect the motor coordination, perceptual skills, and reaction time necessary for safe driving. Their use may also lead to risky sexual behaviours. As with all illegal drugs, no quality of product laws protect buyers from unscrupulous practices. Sellers can substitute or cut the drugs with unknown, cheaper, and possibly even more dangerous substances. Some drugs, such as Rohypnol, are odourless, colourless, and tasteless, and they can easily be added to beverages without a person's knowledge (Fernández et al., 2005; National Institute on Drug Abuse, 2005).

Marijuana is also classified as a hallucinogen, even though it has some properties of a depressant (it induces drowsiness and lethargy) and some of an opiate (it acts as a weak painkiller). In low doses, marijuana produces mild euphoria; moderate doses lead to an intensification of sensory experiences and the illusion

140 **CHAPTER 5** States of Consciousness

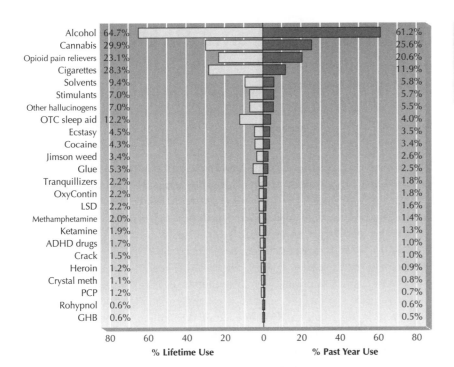

Psychoactive drug use among Ontario middle- and high-school students

FIGURE 5.12

The Ontario Student Drug Use and Health Survey, conducted by the Centre for Addiction and Mental Health (CAMH), began in 1977 and is a self-administered, anonymous survey of drug use, mental health, physical activity, and risk behaviour of approximately 6,200 students in grades 7 to 12. The 2007 drug-use results are shown here. By far the most commonly used drug is alcohol, followed by cannabis, and then non-medical use of opioid pain relievers.

Source: Adlaf & Paglia-Boak (2007).

that time is passing slowly. High doses may produce hallucinations, delusions, and distortions of body image (Kölfalvi, 2008; Ksir, Hart & Ray, 2008). The active ingredient in marijuana (cannabis) is THC, or tetrahydrocannabinol, which binds to receptors abundant throughout the brain.

Many researchers and clinicians have found marijuana to be extremely effective in the treatment of glaucoma (an eye disease), in alleviating the nausea and vomiting associated with chemotherapy, and with other health problems, such as chronic pain and the general wasting seen in advanced AIDS (Darmani & Crim, 2005; Fogarty et al., 2007; Health Canada, 2006b; Kölfalvi, 2008).

Medical use of marijuana is legal in Canada. Health Canada grants access to marijuana for patients suffering from the conditions listed above and for other diseases and disorders. It maintains its own supply of both dried marijuana and marijuana seeds via a contract with Prairie Plant Systems. A packet of 30 seeds costs $20 (plus tax) and the dried product costs patients $5.00/gram (Health Canada, 2006b).

As mentioned, a psychoactive drug can be helpful, but it can also be harmful. This is often unrelated to its legal status or its recreational use. While it is somewhat normal to experiment as a young adult, excessive use at the expense of other areas of life, such as friends, family, work, play, and school, signals a problem that needs to be addressed. The excessive drug use may be a visible sign but not necessarily the cause of the problem (Alexander, 1997). If a person is overwhelmingly involved with drugs, their life history and current situation might provide powerful insights into their addiction. Indeed, this might explain why many of Canada's at-risk youth are far more likely than stable teenagers to be involved with illegal psychoactive drugs (Pearce et al., 2008).

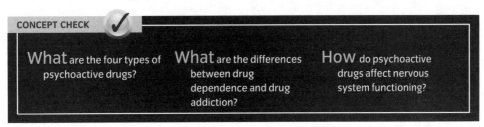

CONCEPT CHECK

What are the four types of psychoactive drugs?

What are the differences between drug dependence and drug addiction?

How do psychoactive drugs affect nervous system functioning?

20.1 Traits Are Inherited in Specific Patterns

LEARNING OBJECTIVES

1. **Explain** the origin of the 23 pairs of chromosomes in our body cells.
2. **Outline** Mendel's basic experimental plan.
3. **Describe** Mendel's two laws of inheritance.
4. **Describe** the difference between mitosis and meiosis.

W hat will my baby look like? Will it be intelligent? Short? Athletic? Oh my gosh, I hope it doesn't have my ridiculous ears or my horribly flat feet!" These common concerns reflect the fact that most of us are subtly aware that traits, appearances, and even intellect can be attributed to our **genes**. Genes, made of strings of DNA, contain the directions for making the millions of proteins that your body uses; we say that genes code for proteins. Genes and DNA are found in the nucleus of almost every cell in your body.

DNA Makes Up the Genes that Make Up the Chromosomes

If our genes are a way that DNA organizes itself, then our **chromosomes** are our genes' way of organizing themselves. Our chromosomes contain our genes, and our genes contain our DNA. It's a miraculous, multilevel information filing system, and more.

Only a few years ago, genetic researchers thought we must have over 100,000 different genes in our bodies, many more than a cat or mouse. We now know that isn't true. As of early 2008, the number of estimated genes in the human body is about 20,500. The problem for gene counters is that a long string of DNA (say, 300 nucleotides long) with a start and stop point looks like a gene, but it isn't one until we are sure it codes for proteins. If it doesn't have the instructions for making a protein, it isn't a gene. To complicate matters further, the same start and stop point may code for a few different proteins depending on how the intervening nucleotides are read.

We also now know that your genes are almost identical to the genes of any person next to you—more than 99% of our genetic material matches. Scientists refer to the exact sequence of nucleotides present on each individual's chromosomes as their **genotype**. We differ from each other in genotype by less than 1%, but that less than 1% makes all the difference in the world when discussing individuals.

Your DNA sequence codes for specific amino acids. DNA includes directions for making genes, so we say that DNA codes for them, as genes code for proteins. You may remember from Chapter 3 that DNA is composed of a four-base "alphabet," where three bases read as one "word." Your individual **DNA sequence** codes for the specific arrangement of amino acids in each of the millions of proteins in your body. The "genetic alphabet" of DNA may contain only four letters, but it is phenomenally sophisticated. The 3-billion-plus individual base pairs in the nucleus of the human cell spell out everything you need to become a human. Furthermore, this DNA exists in trillions of cells, and it can be copied thousands of times with little or no appreciable error. It's no wonder biologists are fond of saying that we have millions of miles of DNA in our bodies. Incredibly, the molecule is so durable that DNA found in fossils tens of thousands of years old can sometimes be analyzed! DNA is durable, but it is also easily lost in our shed cells, as more than one criminal has found.

> **DNA sequence** The sequence of bases (adenine, cytosine, thymine, and guanine) on a chromosome.

Our chromosomes come in pairs. Genes are located on chromosomes. Humans have 23 pairs of chromosomes, for a total of 46 individual units of organized DNA. Twenty-three chromosomes came from the egg, and the matching 23 were delivered via the sperm during fertilization. This means the egg and sperm do not have the usual **diploid** chromosome complement (23 pairs). Instead, they are **haploid**, carrying only 23 individual chromosomes, one from each pair.

Genetic factors are important in determining our individuality. Chromosome 11, for example, carries the same basic information in all of us. It contains genes that

> **diploid** Having the total number of chromosomes of the body cells, twice that of the gametes.
>
> **haploid** Having half the number of chromosomes of normal body cells, found in eggs and sperm.

code for some blood proteins, insulin, and the metabolic enzyme lactate dehydrogenase, as well as other proteins and regulating factors. The specifics of the information on your chromosome 11, however, are different from those found on the same chromosome in either of your parents. Think of building a planned neighborhood. Each house could have the same general blueprint and floor plan, but still look a bit different. Maybe the front doors are all centered, but with different arrangements of windows. On first glance, the neighborhood might look diverse, but with some study, you would notice important similarities among the houses. The same could be said about human beings. Hair can change. Facial proportions and muscular development can change. Deep within the cells, however, we are almost exactly the same.

Gregor Mendel Explained Patterns of Inheritance

Natural patterns seen in the inheritance of traits or characteristics were manipulated long before genes and chromosomes were discovered. For thousands of years, herders and breeders of animals have known they could develop better animals through selective breeding. Dog breeding, for example, is one of the oldest uses of genetics. Humans interbred those dogs with the traits they liked and could use: Some became hunting dogs (labs or pointers), some became sled dogs (huskies) or herders (border collies), and so on. Selective breeding also happened in the plant kingdom. Farming apparently developed as early farmers learned they could improve on food crops by wise choice of the parent plants.

Farmers and herders brought wild plants and animals into domestication and greatly improved their yields, but they had no scientific understanding of the mechanisms of the improvement. Only in the 19th century did a monk from Central Europe provide a plausible—and accurate—theory. His discoveries, along with those of Charles Darwin, gave rise to most of our understanding of modern biology.

Gregor Mendel was not only a monk—he was also a scientist able to use observation, experimentation, and the scientific method to help explain what he saw. He devoted years to studying the inheritance of traits in many plants, including garden peas.

The garden pea is an easy-to-grow plant with specific and definable traits, and it produces a simple flower. Left

The seven traits Mendel used to study genetic inheritance Table 20.1

TRAIT	DOMINANT	×	RECESSIVE
Flower color	Purple	×	White
Seed color	Yellow	×	Green
Seed shape	Round	×	Wrinkled
Pod color	Green	×	Yellow
Pod shape	Round	×	Constricted
Flower and pod position	Axial (along stem)	×	Terminal (at top of stem)
Plant height	Tall	×	Dwarf

alone, pea plants will produce mature pollen (the male gamete), which falls on the female reproductive parts of the plant—the stigma within the flower. Pollen tubes grow through the female stigma into the ovary. Once this pollen contacts the eggs, fertilization occurs and seeds develop.

Mendel realized he could control this process, and in doing so could gain an understanding of the processes of inheritance. He started by identifying traits in the pea plant that existed in only two forms and did not blend. For example, he noticed that pea flowers were purple or white, but never lavender, and the seeds were either yellow or green. In total, Mendel identified and studied seven nonblending traits: flower color, seed color, seed shape, pod color, pod shape, flower and pod position, and plant height, as shown in **Table 20.1**.

self-pollinating
Transferring the pollen of a flower directly to the stigma of the same flower.

cross-pollinating
Fertilizing the ovum of a flower with pollen from a different plant.

Using these traits, Mendel began his unparalleled experiments, **self-pollinating** and **cross-pollinating** his plants, then recording how the individual trait he was studying appeared in the offspring. In each test, Mendel observed hundreds of plants. As he followed these traits, he observed some surprising results—results that to this day accurately predict the outcome of genetic crosses. **Figure 20.1** shows an example of Mendel's experimental methods, breeding a purple plant with a white one.

Heritable units exist and randomly separate during gamete formation.
Mendel discovered that not only are traits inherited but also the propor-

Mendel's experiment for one trait • Figure 20.1
In the first generation, Mendel cross-pollinated two true breeding parents demonstrating opposite traits. In this example, he bred a purple flowered plant with a white flowered plant. He then recorded the flower colors of the first generation from this cross. He permitted the first generation to self-pollinate, and again recorded the results for every plant in the second generation.

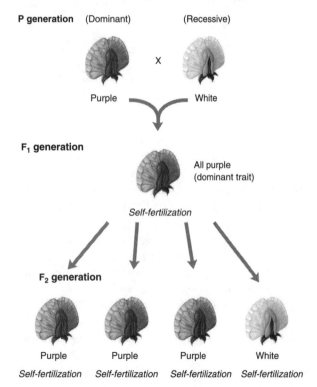

P generation (Dominant) (Recessive)

Purple X White

F₁ generation

All purple (dominant trait)

Self-fertilization

F₂ generation

Purple Purple Purple White

Self-fertilization Self-fertilization Self-fertilization Self-fertilization

tion of each trait in the next generation is fixed. If he began by crossing **true-breeding** parents displaying opposing traits (true-breeding plants produce the same traits in their descendants with every self-pollination), all the offspring in the first generation had only one of the parental traits. In experiments such as this, the first generation is referred to as the F_1 generation, short for first filial generation. For example, in crossing a purple-flowered plant with a white-flowered plant, the F_1 generation was 100% purple. It appeared that purple was **dominant** over white.

What had happened to the **recessive** (nondominant) white color? When Mendel self-pollinated the F_1 plants, the white flowers miraculously reappeared in the second generation, F_2. Oddly, flower color always had the same ratio: roughly one white-flowered plant for every three purple-flowered plants.

In seeking an explanation, Mendel decided there must be some "heritable unit," which we now understand as the various forms of genes. The term "genes" wasn't coined until 1913, well after Mendel died. Mendel hypothesized that these "heritable units" must exist in pairs in the parent and that these pairs separate as pollen and egg are formed. Each gamete would carry only one of the parent's "heritable units." Therefore, one of these "heritable units" from each parental plant is transferred to each offspring. Mendel called this the **law of segregation** and defined it as the random separation of parental "heritable units" during gamete formation. We now know this random separation is possible because of the special type of cell division called meiosis, which we will return to.

Mendel also formulated the law of independent assortment.
As Mendel's experiments got more sophisticated, he tracked several traits at once through dihybrid crosses (following the fate of two traits rather than just one), and again he saw a pattern. Mendel noticed that when a plant dominant for two traits is cross-pollinated with a plant recessive for both traits, the second, self-fertilized generation (F_2) will show a predictable 9:3:3:1 ratio of dominant and recessive traits. There seemed to be no connection between the expression of one trait and the expression of the other. The expression of each trait was independent from the expression of any other. In other words, even if a pea plant's flower color was dominant, he could not predict whether its seed color

558 CHAPTER 20 Inheritance, Genetics, and Molecular Biology

would also be dominant. Mendel's **law of independent assortment** states that each trait is carried in the egg and pollen as a separate entity, with no effect on any other trait. We now know that things are a bit more complicated than Mendel's law of independent assortment states, but he was on the right track. These crosses are depicted in **Figure 20.2**.

Cell Division Is a Key to Genetics

Mendel's extraordinary experiments and insights brought us the terms "dominant" and "recessive." However, Mendel didn't know about the existence of genes or chromosomes or the details of cell division. Our current understanding of the details of cell division has helped explain Mendel's early work in genetics.

Mendel's pea experiment for two traits • Figure 20.2

Mendel's second set of experiments traced the fate of two traits at once, resulting in a 9:3:3:1 ratio of dominant and recessive traits in the F_2 generation. The experiments led directly to his law of independent assortment.

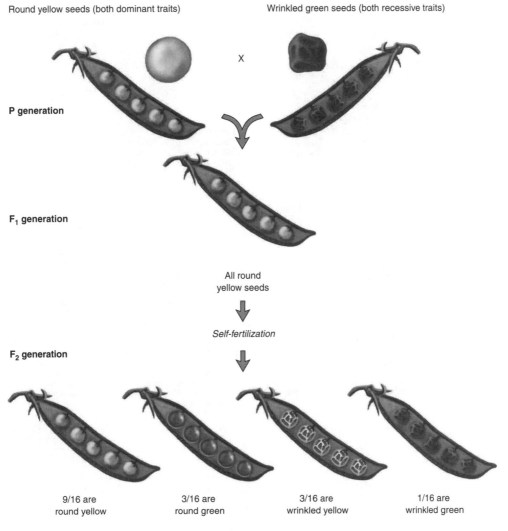

Round yellow seeds (both dominant traits)   Wrinkled green seeds (both recessive traits)

X

P generation

F₁ generation

All round
yellow seeds

Self-fertilization

F₂ generation

9/16 are
round yellow

3/16 are
round green

3/16 are
wrinkled yellow

1/16 are
wrinkled green

Ratio: 9:3:3:1

20.1 Traits Are Inherited in Specific Patterns **559**

PROCESS DIAGRAM

Mitosis • Figure 20.3

  ✓ THE PLANNER

INTERPHASE

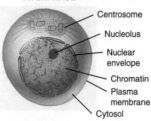

Centrosome
Nucleolus
Nuclear envelope
Chromatin
Plasma membrane
Cytosol

1 **Interphase** is the "resting" phase. The cell is not dividing, but rather carrying out its normal duties. The nuclear membrane is intact, the DNA is loose and unwound in chromatin threads, and nucleoli are present. In a cell that is destined to divide (some, like skeletal muscle and nerve cells, do not divide), the DNA and centrioles double during interphase, but interphase is not considered part of mitosis.

PROPHASE

Kinetochore

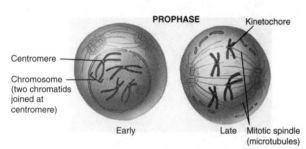

Centromere

Chromosome (two chromatids joined at centromere)

Early
Late — Mitotic spindle (microtubules)

2 In **prophase**, the nuclear membrane disappears; the chromatin condenses and becomes visible in the cell as chromosomes; the centrioles separate and migrate to opposite ends of the cell. As the centrioles migrate, the spindle apparatus is formed. This is a network of microtubules that attach to the middle of each chromosome. Prophase is the longest phase of mitosis.

METAPHASE

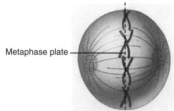

Metaphase plate

3 In **metaphase**, the middle phase of mitosis, the chromosomes are lined up on the central axis of the cell. As soon as the chromosomes are aligned, anaphase begins.

ANAPHASE

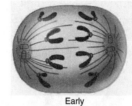

Early   Late

4 In **anaphase**, the spindle apparatus shortens, pulling the two arms of the chromosome in opposite directions. As the spindle fibers shorten, the chromosome separates at the middle, and the two arms are pulled away from each other. Anaphase is very quick, but it is here that the doubled genetic material separates into the exact amount of DNA needed for each daughter cell.

TELOPHASE Cleavage furrow

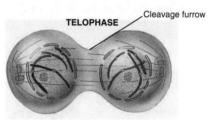

5 **Telophase** is the final phase of mitosis. The chromosomes, now separated into two equal groups, de-condense into chromatin, and the DNA returns to its original thread-like appearance. Nuclear envelopes form around these chromatin groups. The center of the cell pinches to form a cleavage furrow. The furrow deepens, eventually separating the cell into two separate cells, each with a nucleus containing the same amount of DNA as the parent cell.

IDENTICAL CELLS IN INTERPHASE

6 The two daughter cells contain identical genetic material, and are clones of the single parent cell. Once division is completed, the daughter cells are in interphase, meaning they have begun a new growth phase. Eventually they will each reach the size of the original cell. They may undergo mitosis as well, individually moving through the cycle again.

 WILEY PLUS Interactivity

The most well-coordinated, communication-rich event in a cell's life cycle is one kind of cell division called **mitosis**. Mitosis occurs constantly in the human body, with some cells dividing to form two daughter cells as often as every seven days. To carry out this complicated process, the cell must communicate with surrounding cells as well as its own organelles and biochemical pathways. During mitosis, DNA and organelles must be duplicated, and the DNA must then be condensed into manageable packets and sorted into separate nuclei. Once the DNA is separated into two nucleii, the original cell is divided and two separate, intact cells are formed, each containing all of the organelles and DNA of the parent cell. The stages of nuclear division, or mitosis, are described in **Figure 20.3**.

560 CHAPTER 20 Inheritance, Genetics, and Molecular Biology

Meiosis is the second kind of cell division. Meiosis is a second kind of cell division, but one that happens only in sex cells. Passing on your genes requires you to form haploid gametes. As we have seen, gamete is a general term for the reproductive cells that will form a new individual, in our case the egg and sperm. These are produced via meiosis, a specialized type of cell division that ensures the equal and orderly division of chromosomes. This process is shown in **Figure 20.4**. In order to form gametes properly, the normally **diploid** chromosome number must be cut in half, with the resulting gametes having exactly half the usual complement. This way, when two **haploid** gametes unite to form a **zygote**, the original diploid number is restored. The division must be accomplished

Meiosis • Figure 20.4   ✓ THE PLANNER

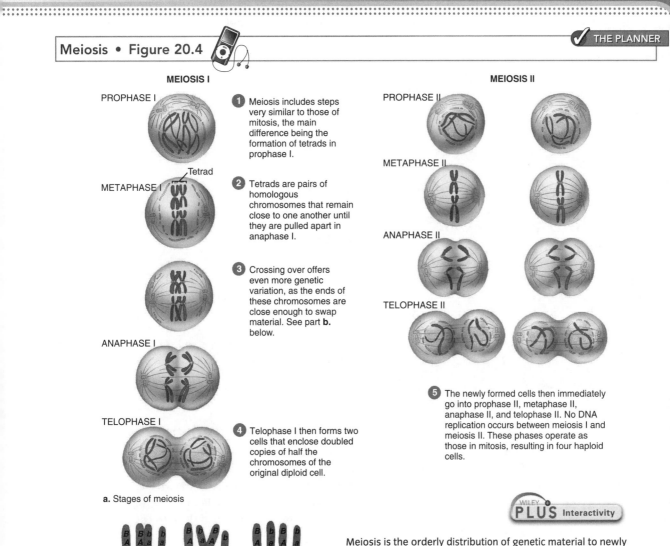

MEIOSIS I

PROPHASE I

1 Meiosis includes steps very similar to those of mitosis, the main difference being the formation of tetrads in prophase I.

METAPHASE I — Tetrad

2 Tetrads are pairs of homologous chromosomes that remain close to one another until they are pulled apart in anaphase I.

3 Crossing over offers even more genetic variation, as the ends of these chromosomes are close enough to swap material. See part **b.** below.

ANAPHASE I

TELOPHASE I

4 Telophase I then forms two cells that enclose doubled copies of half the chromosomes of the original diploid cell.

a. Stages of meiosis

MEIOSIS II

PROPHASE II

METAPHASE II

ANAPHASE II

TELOPHASE II

5 The newly formed cells then immediately go into prophase II, metaphase II, anaphase II, and telophase II. No DNA replication occurs between meiosis I and meiosis II. These phases operate as those in mitosis, resulting in four haploid cells.

WILEY PLUS Interactivity

Meiosis is the orderly distribution of genetic material to newly formed haploid gametes. It includes steps very similar to those of mitosis, the main difference being the formation of tetrads in prophase I. Crossing over at this stage offers even more genetic variation, as the ends of these chromosomes are close enough to exchange genetic material. Telophase I then forms two "cells" that immediately go into prophase II, metaphase II, anaphase II, and telophase II. These phases result in four haploid cells.

Tetrad of sister chromatids   Crossing-over between nonsister chromatids   Genetic recombination

b. Details of crossing-over during prophase I

561

so that each gamete has a predictable and reliable half of the chromosomes. Rather than being randomly split, **homologous** chromosomes come together and are then separated, one to each new gamete.

> **homologous**
> Similar in structure, function, or sequence of genetic information.

In the male, meiosis occurs exactly as depicted in Figure 20.3, and four sperm are produced from two divisions of a primary **spermatocyte**. Females produce only one egg from each round of meiosis, investing almost all of the cytoplasm and organelles in one gamete. The extra genetic material that is split out at anaphase I and anaphase II is ejected from the developing egg with very little associated cytoplasm. Regardless of whether an egg or four sperm are being produced, meiosis I separates homologous chromosomes by breaking apart tetrads, whereas meiosis II produces haploid gametes.

CONCEPT CHECK

1. **How** many chromosomes are carried in the egg? In the sperm?
2. **What** was Mendel's basic experimental plan?
3. **How** does Mendel's law of segregation differ from his law of independent assortment?
4. **What** is the main difference between mitosis and meiosis?

20.2 Modern Genetics Uncovers a Molecular Picture

LEARNING OBJECTIVES

1. **Explain** the interaction of dominant and recessive alleles.
2. **Describe** how alleles can also be multifactorial or codominant.
3. **Analyze** a Punnett square.

Mendel's experiments provided a great starting point for the science of genetics, although their significance was not recognized for almost 40 years. To understand inheritance as we now know it, we need more terms than "dominant" and "recessive." Let's run through some of those terms.

We all have the same basic arrangement of genes in our chromosomes, despite individual differences in **phenotype**. Your phenotype is all your observable traits or characteristics, including ones that are not easily seen, like blood type or color blindness. These phenotypic differences emerge from subtle differences in **genotype**—our complete set of genes—as well as environmental factors. Our phenotype is the result of our genotype and all the environmental influences on us, including the quality of our food, the type of shelter we live in, and even our financial "health."

> **phenotype** An organism's observable characteristics as a result of the genes and alleles being expressed.

> **genotype** The genes and alleles carried on the chromosomes.

Alleles Are Gene Variations

Genes are found in specific locations on their chromosomes. We know that chromosomes come in pairs, which means genes come in pairs as well. Each member of the gene pair is called an **allele**, and the members can be identical to each other or slightly different. An allele is an alternative form of a gene. It is the differences in alleles that give rise to different genotypes.

Alleles may have differences in the sequences of only one or a few DNA base pairs, but that small difference means they produce different proteins than their counterpart genes. That less-than-1% genotype difference between you and your neighbor or roommate is because of slightly different alleles, which combine to give rise to some very different phenotypes.

somatic Related to the body, in contrast to the gametes.

We have seen that each somatic cell contains two copies of every gene, one obtained from each parent. When the two alleles are identical, the genotype is **homozygous** for the trait that is controlled by those alleles. A homozygous gene is usually denoted by two identical letters, such as AA or aa. The capital **A** indicates dominance for that trait, and the small **a** indicates recessiveness. Homozygous individuals can be **homozygous dominant**, meaning both alleles code for the dominant trait (AA), or **homozygous recessive** (aa). If one allele codes for the dominant trait and the other codes for a recessive trait, the genotype is **heterozygous**. Heterozygotes are usually indicated with a capital and a lowercase letter (Aa).

We can see that sexual reproduction creates new mixtures of genes and alleles for each generation. The randomly created mixture that helps our survival and reproduction tends to get passed on and spread to others.

Complete Dominance Is a Small Part of Our Phenotype

Only homozygous recessive individuals express a recessive phenotype. If one allele is dominant, the dominant phenotype must be expressed. This means that if your appearance includes a recessive trait, all of your gametes carry only the recessive allele. You are homozygous recessive for that trait. If that trait is dominant in your phenotype, you could be homozygous dominant or heterozygous, and it is hard to predict which allele any one of your gametes will carry.

We all have traits that define our phenotype: hair that is brown, black, blonde, or red; eyes that are blue, green, brown, or hazel; hair that is straight or curly; skin that is dark or light. As it turns out, however, human inheritance is more complicated than that of Mendel's pea plants. Some of our phenotypic traits come from one allele completely dominating another, as in Mendel's plants. However, most alleles do not follow the simple dominance pattern, as we will see. In fact, only a few of our phenotypic traits demonstrate simple dominant–recessive interactions. These traits are listed in **Table 20.2.**

Dominant/recessive traits in humans	Dominant phenotype	Recessive phenotype
Cleft in chin	No cleft	Cleft present
Hairline	Widow's peak	Straight hairline
Eyebrow size	Broad	Slender
Eyebrow shape	Separated	Joined
Eyelash length	Long	Short
Dimples	Dimples	No dimples
Earlobes	Free lobe	Attached
Eye shape	Almond	Round
Freckles	Freckles	No freckles
Tongue rolling	Roller	Nonroller
Finger middigital hair	Hair	No hair
Hitchhiker's thumb	Straight thumb	Hitchhiker's thumb
Interlaced fingers	Left thumb over right	Right over left
Hair on back of hand	Hair	No hair

Table 20.2

We can predict the possibility of passing these traits on to our offspring just as Mendel did with his peas. The alleles exhibit **complete dominance**. Although these traits are not critical to our overall **fitness**, they do demonstrate that a few human genes follow the same rules as Mendel's pea plants.

fitness Ability to produce living offspring and pass on DNA.

Incomplete Dominance and Codominance Complicate the Picture

Many traits in humans, including hair color, eye color, and facial structure, exhibit **incomplete dominance** or **codominance** rather than the complete dominance that Mendel found. That is, the traits result not from one gene dominating another but from several genes affecting the phenotype simultaneously. How can this happen?

Incomplete dominance tends to produce different phenotypes based on the combination of alleles present in heterozygotes. The trait produced is an intermediate one: Instead of straight or curly hair, incomplete dominance leads to something in the middle—wavy hair.

Codominance occurs when the effect of both alleles appears in the heterozygote. We will see that blood types are good examples of codominance.

Many human traits are also **polygenic**, meaning the phenotype results from the interaction of many genes, not the expression of just one. Furthermore, many of our traits are **multifactorial traits**, meaning polygenic traits that are also influenced by environment. These traits express a continuum of phenotypes, usually producing a bell-shaped curve on a plot of their distribution in the population. Body type, muscular development, fat deposition, and height are all multifactorial traits.

Blood type is an example of codominance.

Blood type is an excellent example of codominance, as seen in **Figure 20.5**. There are three alleles for blood type: the A allele, the B allele, and the O allele. The A allele codes for a modification of the original precursor erythrocyte surface protein randomly designated "A." Similarly, the B allele codes for modifications that produce the marker protein B. The O allele codes for no modified marker protein, effectively a null allele. If one of your alleles is A and the other is A or O, you have type A blood. Similarly, if you have two B alleles or a B and an

O, your blood type is B. If one allele is A and the other B, however, you have type AB blood. If you are homozygous O, you have type O blood. In each case, both alleles are expressed in the phenotype, which is the meaning of codominant. The alleles do not blend to form an entirely new AO marker protein, nor do they form an AB protein that is different from the individual A or B modified markers. Instead, each allele codes for a separate protein, which is translated and added to the membrane of the red blood cells. Therefore, in type AB blood, the erythrocytes show both the A and the B protein, and with the genotype AO you will find both an A and an O marker on the red blood cells.

Incomplete dominance governs the human voice pitch, eye color, and hair curliness.

The lowest and highest pitches in male voices occur in men who are homozygous dominant (AA) or homozygous recessive (aa) for the trait that determines pitch. All intermediate-range (baritone) voices are heterozygous (Aa). We see the same blending of traits in eye color. If one parent has green eyes and the other has brown, there is a good chance the children will express a blended, dark blue eye color. Recently, scientists have discovered that eye color is determined via an interaction of at least three different genes, each affecting the phenotype of the other. Although this trait requires more than one gene, the interactions between them can be understood in light of incomplete dominance. In Caucasians, hair can be straight (H'H'),

Blood type inheritance • Figure 20.5

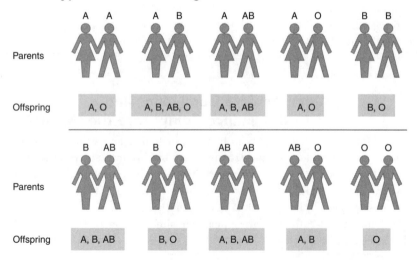

There are three different alleles for human blood type: A, B, and O. Each of us has two blood type alleles, one from our biological mother and one from our biological father. We all have one of the following allele combinations: AA, AO, AB, BB, BO, or OO. For an AA or AO combination, the blood type is group A. For BB and BO, the blood type is B. For OO, the blood type is O. The figure shows ten sets of parents with various blood types and their offspring's possible blood types.

Hair patterns • Figure 20.6

Note that the uppercase and lowercase conventions are not used here because one trait is not dominant over the other.

GENOTYPES	PHENOTYPES
HH (curly)	
HH' (wavy)	
H'H' (straight)	

wavy (HH'), or curly (HH). Wavy hair is an intermediate phenotype, indicating incomplete dominance of the curly trait, as seen in **Figure 20.6**.

Punnett Squares Show the Possibilities

The Punnett square, a tool used to determine the probability of genotypic combinations in offspring, works much like the multiplication tables you may remember from grade school. The alleles carried by one parent for the gene in question are listed across the top, representing that parent's potential gametes. The left side lists the other parent's alleles. In the center boxes of the table, the allele at the top and the one to the left are "multiplied" or combined, resulting in one possible allelic combination from these two parents.

Sex chromosomes carry different traits, and Punnett squares help us figure them out. Further complicating the inheritance pattern of humans, the sex chromosomes (X and Y) carry different traits. There are more alleles on the X chromosome than on the Y, meaning that there are not matching alleles on these two chromosomes. Males (XY) have only one copy of the alleles found only on the X chromosome. The gene that codes for color vision is one such allele. The gene for color discrimination is on the X chromosome but not the Y. If a female XX carries the gene for color blindness on only one of her two X chromosomes, she will not express the defect, but half of her eggs will carry the defective gene. However, her sons are in danger of being color-blind. Because the fertilizing sperm carries a Y chromosome, it cannot provide a second copy of that allele to overcome the defect with a correct copy of the gene, resulting in a color-blind male child. Despite these differences, inheritance patterns for these so-called sex-linked traits, which we will cover later in this chapter, can be predicted using a simple Punnett square (named after a fascinating British biologist who wrote one of the first texts on genetics). See **Figure 20.7** for an example of a Punnett square.

Punnett square for the inheritance of red-green color blindness • Figure 20.7

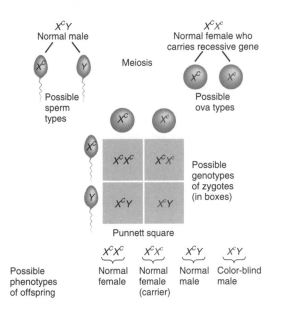

Punnett squares predict phenotypic ratios. Punnett squares predict the phenotypic ratios that Mendel observed in his pea plant experiments. Crossing a homozygous dominant individual and a homozygous recessive individual yields 100% heterozygous offspring, regardless of the trait. All of the offspring will express the dominant trait. Self-pollinating these heterozygotes yields three phenotypically dominant offspring and one phenotypically recessive individual (who has a homozygous recessive genotype). The same Punnett square can be used to represent flower color in peas or attached earlobes in humans. It is amazing that Mendel accurately explained this using his "heritable unit" theory without any knowledge of genes or chromosomes. Even with inheritance patterns of codominance or incomplete dominance, Punnett squares predict the proportions of potential genotypes of the offspring. The phenotypic expression of those genes may not yield the typical 3:1 or 9:3:3:1 ratios expected by Mendel, but the genotype ratios remain the same.

CONCEPT CHECK   **STOP**

1. How do dominant and recessive alleles interact?
2. What are multifactorial traits? Codominant traits?
3. What can be learned from a Punnett square?

20.3 The Central Dogma: Genes Direct the Formation of Proteins

LEARNING OBJECTIVES

1. **Summarize** the steps in transcription and translation.

How do we know that alleles are the heritable units of Mendel's observations? Although this seems obvious now, considerable time and several breakthroughs were required to identify the "heritable unit" and then to find out where it existed in the cell and to determine how it worked. In 1941, two scientists demonstrated that DNA was the chemical in Mendel's "heritable unit." George Beadle and Edward Tatum, using cultures of the fungus *Neurospora*, showed that one sequence of DNA coded for one protein. This **one gene codes for one enzyme** idea marked the beginning of our understanding of how DNA produces proteins. Before this, it was thought that proteins might contain the unit of heredity because they occur in such enormous variety. Early scientists thought that since 20 amino acids make up the myriad proteins in the body, but only four nucleotides comprise DNA, surely the amino acids were the key to inheritance. This line of thought suggested that proteins were the basis of heredity.

Although proteins seemed a logical candidate as the genetic material, many scientists had begun to question this theory. Beadle and Tatum began looking for a way to conclusively identify the heritable unit. They understood that X-rays caused inheritable mutations that could prevent proper functioning of some pathways in organisms. They reasoned that if they could "knock out" and then restore a function, they could learn what molecule was carrying the information that the radiation destroyed. Beadle and Tatum demonstrated that knocking out one gene inhibits the function of one protein. This was good evidence that DNA controls protein production. Their experiment is summarized in **Figure 20.8**.

Transcription and Translation Convert DNA into Protein

The next step was to determine how DNA controls the production of proteins. This mechanism has two steps: **transcription** and **translation**. These paired processes convert the information carried on DNA into proteins for the cell. Transcription is copying information from one

The one gene, one protein theory • Figure 20.8

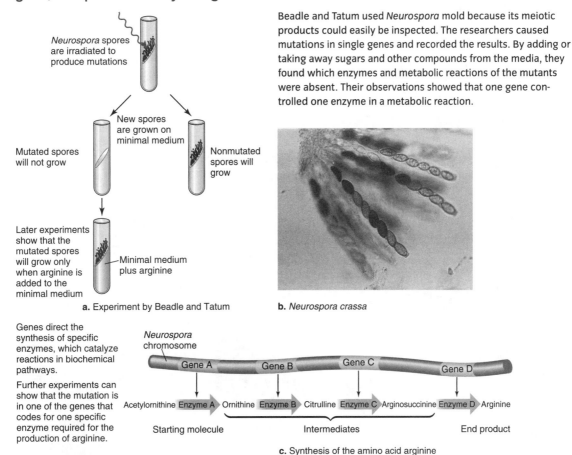

Beadle and Tatum used *Neurospora* mold because its meiotic products could easily be inspected. The researchers caused mutations in single genes and recorded the results. By adding or taking away sugars and other compounds from the media, they found which enzymes and metabolic reactions of the mutants were absent. Their observations showed that one gene controlled one enzyme in a metabolic reaction.

Neurospora spores are irradiated to produce mutations

New spores are grown on minimal medium

Mutated spores will not grow

Nonmutated spores will grow

Later experiments show that the mutated spores will grow only when arginine is added to the minimal medium

Minimal medium plus arginine

a. Experiment by Beadle and Tatum

b. *Neurospora crassa*

Genes direct the synthesis of specific enzymes, which catalyze reactions in biochemical pathways.

Further experiments can show that the mutation is in one of the genes that codes for one specific enzyme required for the production of arginine.

Neurospora chromosome

Gene A | Gene B | Gene C | Gene D

Acetylornithine → Enzyme A → Ornithine → Enzyme B → Citrulline → Enzyme C → Arginosuccinine → Enzyme D → Arginine

Starting molecule | Intermediates | End product

c. Synthesis of the amino acid arginine

---

medium to another using the same language or alphabet. As you hear a lecture and take notes, you transcribe the information you hear into written form. Translation is converting information from one language to another. If English is not your native tongue, you may be translating the words on the page into a more familiar language as you read them. In the formation of proteins, the meanings of transcription and translation are similar.

Transcription is a change in medium.
The information for new proteins is encoded in DNA that is stored in your cell nuclei, but the machinery for making proteins resides in the cytoplasm. Transcription is the copying of a sequence of nucleotide bases in DNA to **messenger RNA (mRNA).** Unlike DNA, mRNA can leave the nucleus and carry information from the DNA to the cell's protein-producing machinery.

As discussed in Chapter 3, there are structural differences between DNA and RNA. RNA is a single-stranded molecule, composed of individual nitrogenous bases arranged along a sugar phosphate backbone. Although this backbone is similar to that in DNA, the sugar in RNA is ribose, not the deoxyribose of DNA. The nitrogenous base thymine found in DNA is replaced by **uracil** during RNA synthesis. The usual base-pairing rule of DNA (A to T and C to G) is altered in RNA because of this substitution. Here the bases pair up A to U and C to G.

Translation makes the proteins.
After the DNA code is transcribed to mRNA, it must be converted (translated) from nucleic acid "language" to amino acid "language." This occurs at the ribosomes, using **transfer RNA (tRNA)** to match up amino acids with mRNA bases.

PROCESS DIAGRAM

Transcription and translation • Figure 20.9

THE PLANNER

WILEY PLUS Interactivity

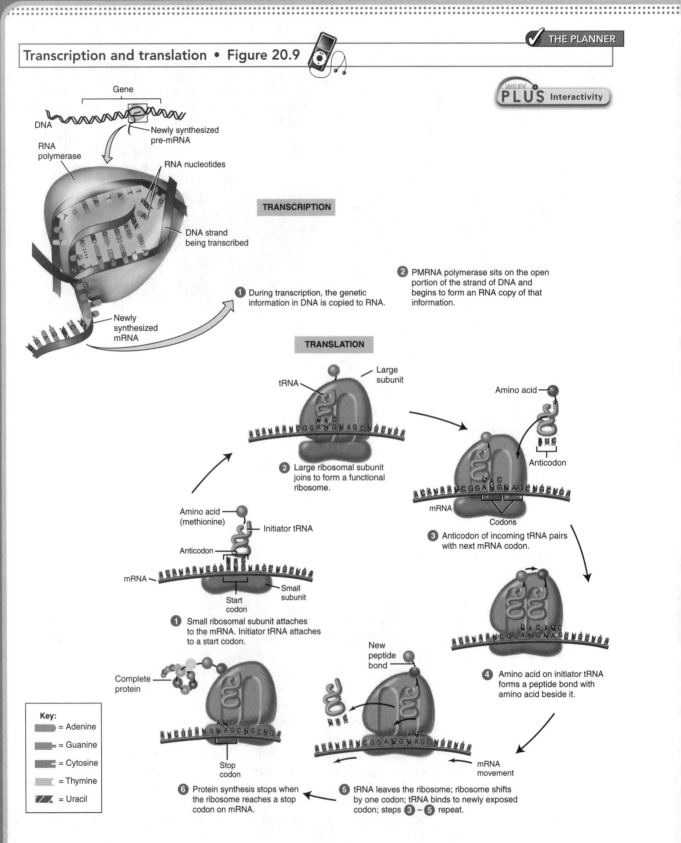

TRANSCRIPTION

1 During transcription, the genetic information in DNA is copied to RNA.

2 PMRNA polymerase sits on the open portion of the strand of DNA and begins to form an RNA copy of that information.

TRANSLATION

2 Large ribosomal subunit joins to form a functional ribosome.

3 Anticodon of incoming tRNA pairs with next mRNA codon.

1 Small ribosomal subunit attaches to the mRNA. Initiator tRNA attaches to a start codon.

4 Amino acid on initiator tRNA forms a peptide bond with amino acid beside it.

5 tRNA leaves the ribosome; ribosome shifts by one codon; tRNA binds to newly exposed codon; steps 3 – 5 repeat.

6 Protein synthesis stops when the ribosome reaches a stop codon on mRNA.

Key:
- = Adenine
- = Guanine
- = Cytosine
- = Thymine
- = Uracil

568 CHAPTER 20   Inheritance, Genetics, and Molecular Biology

Messenger RNA is "decoded" by tRNA three bases at a time. These three bases on mRNA are called a **codon**. The matching three bases on the tRNA molecule are the **anticodon**. When codon and anticodon meet at the ribosome, the amino acid carried by the tRNA is incorporated into the growing polypeptide chain. Each codon indicates 1 of the 20 amino acids.

Biologists call the mechanism of transcription and translation the "central dogma of biology" because it has relevance to all aspects of their science. We now know that the "central dogma" is not quite "one gene, one protein." In some cases, one gene makes just a part of a protein rather than a whole protein. **Figure 20.9** outlines these important biological processes.

CONCEPT CHECK

1. **What** are the steps of transcription? The steps of translation?

20.4 Genetic Theory Is Put to Practical Use

LEARNING OBJECTIVES

1. **Explain** the information in a pedigree chart.
2. **Define** sex-linked traits.
3. **Describe** chromosomal disorders and genetic counseling.
4. **Compare** the values and costs associated with prenatal testing.

Couples often request genetic counseling before they choose to conceive. Genetic counseling is the practice of predicting the potential combinations of alleles two individuals may produce. If there is a family history of congenital disease, or if the potential parents feel they are at risk of carrying a detrimental recessive allele, genetic counseling can help alleviate their fears. Knowing the probability of having a child with a genetic anomaly can help couples decide whether to conceive.

Pedigree Charts Trace Traits Through Families

Pedigree charts are symbolic representations of genetic transmission of phenotypic traits through families. Using a pedigree chart like the one shown in **Figure 20.10**,

> **autosomal** Any chromosome other than the sex chromosomes, X and Y.

researchers can trace the pathway of a disease through families, and characteristics of its transmission can be deduced. If, for example, the disease is **autosomal** dominant, anyone with alleles Aa or AA will be afflicted. If the disease shows up sporadically or appears in a child of two **asymptomatic** parents, the disease is probably autosomal recessive, and both parents are heterozygous carriers for the dysfunctional allele.

> **asymptomatic** Without symptoms.

Pedigrees of autosomal dominant and autosomal recessive diseases • Figure 20.10

A pedigree chart can show the frequency of a phenotypic trait in successive generations. Pedigree charts can also simply show ancestry—a family tree is a kind of pedigree chart. These kinds of pedigree charts are most commonly used when studying the ancestry of humans, horses, and show dogs.

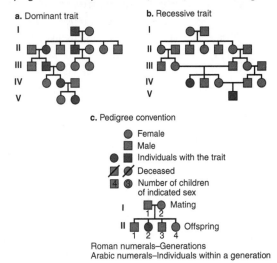

a. Dominant trait
b. Recessive trait
c. Pedigree convention

- ○ Female
- ■ Male
- ● ■ Individuals with the trait
- Deceased
- Number of children of indicated sex
- Mating
- Offspring

Roman numerals—Generations
Arabic numerals—Individuals within a generation

Some Traits Are Sex-Linked

Humans have one pair of chromosomes, called the sex chromosomes, that do not match in terms of size or content. The sex chromosomes include the large X chromosome and the smaller Y. These two determine gender. If a Y chromosome is present during development (XY), the fetus will become a male. If there is no Y present (XX), the fetus becomes female.

Females have two copies of every gene on the X chromosome.

Since only one copy of each allele is needed during normal growth and development, one X chromosome is randomly shut down. This shutdown occurs during development, leaving one condensed X chromosome as a **Barr body** within the nucleus. All the cloned progeny of this cell get the same functional X and the same Barr body. Thus, human females consist of patches of genetically distinct tissues, based on which X is inactivated. This patterning is called mosaicism. During development, the alleles on the active X chromosome are expressed and those on the inactivated X are repressed. Differences in the alleles carried on the two X chromosomes are markers for these cloned cell populations. In some organisms, this mosaic patchiness is easily discerned. For example, the patchiness of coat color in female calico cats is due to mosaicism in their tissues. One X chromosome carries the allele for black fur, and the other carries the allele for orange tiger-striped fur. Clones of each cell type express the allele they carry, resulting in patches of different fur colors. (The white color is carried on a separate chromosome.)

The Y chromosome contains few functional genes.

The Y chromosome includes few functional genes, with the most recent count coming to just 78 genes. It was previously assumed that there were no genes of consequence on the Y chromosome, but as the number of genes identified increases this seems illogical. Scientists are just beginning to understand the significance of the Y chromosome genes to the male. Only one, the **SRY** gene, codes for male anatomical traits. The remaining Y chromosome genes are "housekeeping" genes—genes that are active in most body cells and do not confer male characteristics.

None of these genes have specific homologous counterparts on the X chromosome. This is a potential problem during nuclear division, as the Y chromosome cannot condense and pair up with the X chromosome in the same fashion as autosomal chromosomes. Instead, the Y chromosome includes a series of **palindromes** that allow it to fold back on itself during cell division. With limited ability to cross over during meiosis or to silence dysfunctional genes on either the X or the Y chromosome during development, mutations are more often retained and expressed in the developing male. In females, having two copies of the X chromosome with all of its genes doubles the chance of expressing a functional allele. The male, however, has only one X chromosome. The alleles on that single chromosome must be used even if they are slightly defective.

> **palindrome** A group of nucleotides with the same sequence when read in either direction (for example, CGTTGC).

Genes carried on one sex chromosome with no counterpart on the other sex chromosome code for **sex-linked traits**. Because there are so many more functional genes on the X chromosome than on the Y, these are the genes usually referred to when discussing sex-linked traits. Characteristics carried on the X chromosome include color blindness and hemophilia. See **Figure 20.11**.

Females are mosaics, males are not.

As discussed, the X chromosome carries many more genes than the Y. The female embryo has two X chromosomes, but one randomly shuts down in each embryonic cell early in development. The same X chromosome is active in all daughter cells of any particular embryonic cell, creating a situation in which female body cells have two distinct genetic lineages.

Biologists call such a person a mosaic, and the different expression rates of alleles on the X chromosomes can have visible and invisible consequences. Female humans are mosaics, and this affects traits coded by the X chromosome. The varying proportion of each particular X chromosome in the adult tissues of the female may explain why the onset and intensity of X-linked genetic diseases vary more in women than in men.

Because males have only one X chromosome, any defective gene on it can cause disease. Scientists say this explains why males have higher rates of X-chromosome diseases, such as Duchenne muscular dystrophy and hemophilia. Paradoxically, having only one X chromosome may have accelerated evolution among males. X-linked diseases can be powerful enough to kill males in utero or before reproductive age, which helps remove the defective genes from the population. In evolutionary terms, a weakness for the individual becomes a strength for the group.

Pedigree of hemophilia in the royal family of Queen Victoria • Figure 20.11

People with hemophilia have blood that is deficient in a clotting factor necessary for proper wound healing. This deficiency leads to slower than normal blood clotting and is due to an X-chromosome disorder that results in a deficiency of blood-clotting compounds. Females are the carriers of the disorder, which shows up in males (most commonly). Queen Victoria was a carrier, so each of her daughters had a 50% chance of being a carrier as well, and 50% of her sons had a chance of being a hemophiliac. Her carrier daughter Alice introduced the allele into the Prussian and Russian royal dynasties, and her carrier daughter Beatrice brought the allele into the Spanish royal dynasty. The current British royal family is, fortunately, unaffected.

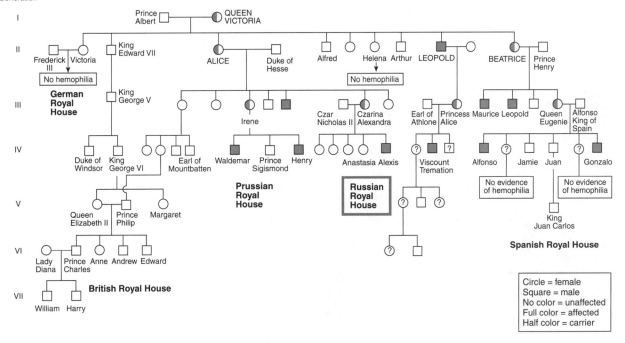

Sex-influenced traits are carried on autosomal chromosomes but are more common in one sex than in the other. Hormonal differences between the two genders are most often responsible for the altered expression of these genes.

Genetic Variations Are Usually Caused by Mutations

Many of the genetic variations we see in the human species are due to mutations that have been perpetuated in small, often isolated populations. Human populations, just like any animal population, will undergo more rapid **evolution** when they are reproductively isolated. Language and ethnicity can isolate human populations, even those that live in close physical proximity. Geographic structures, such as mountains, deep valleys, or broad deserts, can also isolate

evolution Descent with modification.

human populations. Despite isolation, humans exhibit a range of expected phenotypes. For example, natural skin tones range from extremely pale tan to very dark brown. People are NOT blue, right? Wrong! Amazingly, a group of people in Kentucky occasionally produce a blue child—see *What a Scientist Sees: The Blue People of Troublesome Creek*, on the next page.

Genetic Counseling Can Help Avoid Chromosomal Disorders

Genes and chromosomes can be damaged during cell division. Errors can occur in an entire chromosome, part of a chromosome, or a single gene. Gross errors, called chromosomal disorders, include variations in chromosome structure or number. These disorders include Down syndrome and fragile X mental retardation. According to the March of Dimes, chromosomal disorders affect about

WHAT A SCIENTIST SEES

The Blue People of Troublesome Creek

What is going on? These children are born the color of a bruised plum, and often they retain that color into adulthood. Some appear blue only when angry or cold.

The people of this area of Kentucky are all descendants of Martin Fugate, a French orphan, and his red-headed American wife. Against all odds, both Martin and his wife carried a reces-

sive gene coding for a nonfunctional enzyme in the blood. Methemoglobin is a blue precursor to normal hemoglobin that is present in small amounts in blood. Usually, the enzyme diaphorase converts methemoglobin to functional hemoglobin, restoring blood's red color. These people in Kentucky cannot convert methemoglobin to hemoglobin, resulting in that blue coloration to the skin and mucous membranes. Geographic barriers have isolated the population with the "blue gene" to the Troublesome and Ball Creek valleys.

Happily, modern medicine can correct the blue color, allowing these people to lead normal lives, but the allele remains in the population. This strange phenomenon clearly demonstrates that inheritance and evolution follow the same rules in humans as in other animals. Genes carry traits, and traits can be either lost or enhanced in populations.

Think Critically

1. Can you find any evidence in this description that the defective diaphorase gene is either a sex-linked or a sex-influenced trait? What type of evidence would you look for?
2. How might you help couples in this area determine their probability of producing a child with abnormal blue coloration?
3. How might scientists have discovered that both Martin Fugate and his wife carried this recessive gene? What tool could demonstrate the beginnings of this trait?

7.5% of fertilizations, but many cause extreme deformities. Because many defective embryos abort spontaneously, only about 0.6% of live births show genetic defects due to chromosomal disorders. Just as it can be heartbreaking to lose a baby during pregnancy, it can be difficult to raise a child born with a **congenital** defect. Most babies born with congenital defects can trace their problems to a single gene carrying a dangerous recessive or dominant allele. Therefore, the chances of conceiving a child with a congenital defect caused by alleles can be predicted with the Punnett square.

congenital A condition that is present at birth because of genetic or environmental factors; usually detrimental.

Genetic disorders may also result from the interaction of genes and the environment. Other genetic disorders are caused by a series of alleles spread over several genes, which, if present in one individual, lead to the expression of a genetic defect. These defects depend on the interaction between several genes and the environment. These **multifactorial disorders** include cleft lip and palate, rheumatoid arthritis, epilepsy, and bipolar disorder. Simple traits, such as skin color, hair color, and weight, are also multifactorial traits. As you know from observing these traits in your

multifactorial disorder Genetic disorder due to a combination of genetic and environmental factors.

Genetic disorders, their symptoms, and their predominant carriers   Table 20.3

Disorder	Type	Symptoms	Carriers/Type of disease
Huntington's disease	Chromosome abnormality	Affects the brain, causing poor memory, lack of coordination, mood swings, lack of fine motor control	Autosomal dominant disease
Turner syndrome	Chromosome abnormality	Short stature, improperly developed ovaries, stocky appearance, webbed neck, low hairline	Missing or incomplete X chromosome (XO female)
Klinefelter syndrome	Chromosome abnormality	After puberty, males develop breast tissue, have less muscle mass, and have little facial hair	XXY males
Cri-du-chat syndrome	Chromosome abnormality	Distinctive cry due to abnormal larynx development, low birth weight, microcephaly, heart defects, facial deformities	Deletion in chromosome 5
Phenylketonuria	Single-gene disorder	Severe brain damage, epilepsy, eczema, microcephaly, and a musty body odor	Autosomal recessive
Severe combined immunodeficiency disorder (SCID)	Single-gene disorder	High rate of infections soon after birth, including pneumonia and meningitis	X-linked recessive trait
Sickle cell disease	Single-gene disorder	Loss of function in organs where oxygen delivery is compromised; shortened life span	Autosomal recessive trait
Cystic fibrosis	Single-gene disorder	Coughing, wheezing, respiratory illnesses, salty-tasting skin, weight loss	Defective gene on chromosome 7; autosomal recessive
Marfan syndrome	Single-gene disorder	Connective tissue disorder causing excessive growth with little strength, long fingers, toes, and shins, weak heart valves	Autosomal dominant disease; defective gene on chromosome 15

own family, the inheritance of multifactorial traits is most apparent in the immediate generation. As individuals become farther removed from the affected individual (the carrier), the trait disappears. As an example, your hair color is probably closer to your parents' hair color than to your great-grandparents'.

Sometimes, unpredictable genetic disorders, caused by mutations or improper meiotic divisions, appear in families. Mutations occur with amazing frequency, at an estimated rate of about 1 misplaced base per 50 million nucleotides. That works out to 120 mutations per new cell. Although several enzymes "patrol" your DNA looking to repair these errors, and natural selection is constantly trying to delete defective genes from new generations, the system is not perfect. However, with our increasing knowledge of genetics, potential parents have tools at their disposal that take

some of the guesswork out of producing healthy children. One option is the time-tested "let's fall in love, get married, and take our chances" approach. Some couples, however, are more interested in taking control of their genetics. For these people, genetic counseling is a great choice.

Table 20.3 lists some of the many genetic disorders that are discussed in genetic counseling.

Tay-Sachs disease results from a defective allele.
Certain religious or ethnic groups have a higher proportion of detrimental recessive alleles than others, because their populations intermarry more than other groups. Ashkenazi (north European) Jews and French Canadians, for instance, have a higher likelihood of carrying the recessive allele for Tay-Sachs disease. Tay-Sachs is a fatal disease caused by a dysfunctional lysosomal enzyme in the brain.

Usually, neurons create fatty substances that are easily removed from the brain by lysosomes. In Tay-Sachs, the allele that codes for the enzyme that breaks down these fatty substances is defective, so the fats build up. The affected homozygous recessive individual develops normally until age 4, but brain function then deteriorates rapidly. The gene for this defective lysozomal enzyme is recessive, so phenotypically normal heterozygous carriers are not aware that they are carrying this potentially lethal mutation.

Sadly, up to 1 in 25 Ashkenazi Jews are thought to be carriers. When marrying within the faith, Ashkenazi Jews often request a compatibility score from a genetic counseling service, which will indicate the probability that their child would have Tay-Sachs. This type of testing has caused a dramatic reduction in deaths due to Tay-Sachs.

Prenatal Testing Raises Questions

Rapid advances in genetics have raised the promise—or the peril—of studying the genetics of children yet to be born. Already, prenatal ultrasound can reveal the sex of a fetus, and some parents in the many cultures that favor male babies have responded by aborting female fetuses. This practice has increased the ratio of male to female children in China and perhaps elsewhere.

As you remember from Chapter 19, prenatal genetic testing can take two forms: testing the developing baby with chorionic villus sampling or amniocentesis, and testing the genes of potential parents. Each process raises questions. See *I Wonder... Can We Create Super-Babies?* to investigate one such question.

Prenatal genetic sampling can detect chromosomal abnormalities. Prenatal genetic sampling is done primarily to detect chromosomal abnormalities, such as Down syndrome, and focuses on women age 35 or over who are more likely to have children with these abnormalities. These genetic problems cannot be corrected, and the parents must either abort the "defective" fetus or understand and accept the challenges of raising such a child. If a problem is discovered, at the very least the test results can alert the parents to their future child's special needs. Any benefits

I WONDER...
Can We Create Super-Babies?

Do you want a child with dark hair? Musical talent? Muscular stamina? As we learn more about the human genome, we come closer to understanding just how traits like these are inherited. Originally, the human genome was mapped in order to identify those genes related to disease. Once these genes were located, the genomes of at-risk people could be scanned to determine whether they carried the same deleterious gene. For many of these genes, identification amounted to looking for uncommon SNPs or single nucleotide polymorphisms. These are areas in the human genome that differ among individuals by only a single nucleotide (A, C, T, or G). SNPs normally occur every 300 bases or so. Researchers have found that SNPs occurring within genes or their regulatory areas often lead to a higher susceptibility of disease, and therefore they use these SNPs to "mark" disease susceptibility. With the human genome project completed over 8 years ago, scientists have had access to our genome and its many SNPs for almost a decade. We can now identify genes that code for traits and behaviors not related to disease. Most personality traits are produced by a group of genes, working together and interacting with the environment to produce phenotypic results. Despite this complication, some interesting traits have been linked to specific genes. As of late 2008, the genes that code for handedness, eye color, addictive behavior, and athleticism were identified. As recently as 2005, muscular strength was discovered to be "marked" by a series of SNPs, just like disease susceptibility. Of course, the manipulation of the human genome leads to many unexpected scientific questions. Genes often have more than one effect on phenotype. For example, the gene that codes for increased memory and enhanced learning was also discovered to code for increased pain sensitivity in laboratory mice. At the current time, we have the knowledge to identify many deleterious and beneficial traits. We also have the ability to select for or against these traits in pre-implanted embryos through the GIFT program. Can we create a super baby? Potentially, yes. But should we?

of these tests must be weighed against the chance that the invasive sampling itself will harm the fetus. In the future, as the knowledge of genetics increases, we may see sampling of the embryo itself, in the hope of intercepting genetic diseases even earlier.

Genetic testing can be used even before conception. A more complicated set of ethical questions arises when parents want to analyze their own genes before conception. In a few cases, the need for such analysis is clear and convincing. If a genetic disease like the deadly nerve disorder Huntington's disease runs in the family, parents might want assurance that they will not pass the gene to their children. If testing reveals a high probability of their passing on this disease, the would-be parents may want to avoid pregnancy.

Genetic situations can also present confusing ethical decisions, especially now that scientists are detecting the genetic components of dozens or even hundreds of diseases and conditions. Many of these genes do not amount to a death sentence. Would a genetic predisposi-

tion for cancer matter if the gene raised the child's risk of cancer by 10%? What if it doubled the risk of cancer?

The picture is complicated now, and the only thing we can say for sure is that better knowledge of genetics will make the issue of prenatal testing even more complex. A strong basic understanding of human genetics will help prepare you to answer the difficult questions you may confront during your reproductive years.

CONCEPT CHECK

1. **What** can be learned from a family pedigree?
2. **Which** chromosome carries the genes for sex-linked traits?
3. **What** is a chromosomal disorder and how does it relate to genetic counseling?
4. **What** are the values and costs associated with prenatal testing?

11.2 Cancer Has Many Causes and Effects

LEARNING OBJECTIVES

1. **List** the four major categories of factors that cause cancer.
2. **Define** what is known about each causal factor.
3. **Explain** how cancers are classified.

What causes cancer? The question has been at the top of the cancer research agenda almost since the beginning of the "War on Cancer" declared by President Richard Nixon in 1971. In the 40-some years of research since then, scientists have determined that a number of common occurrences, ranging from viruses to hereditary factors to exposure to radiation, play a part in causing cancer. Although it is statistically impossible to say that there is a single cause for an individual cancer, we now know that many factors play a role in initiating and promoting cancer. Scientists have identified several factors that create a predisposition to cancer, initiate the development of a cancerous tumor, or promote the growth and metastasis of a cancer. Amazingly, researchers are finding that most cancer-causing mutations are the result of the body's cells accidentally damaging their own genes in the normal course of cellular respiration. During the breakdown of nutrients within the cell, a molecule breaks loose and damages the cell's own DNA. As we have noted, these mutations occur all the time, so it is clear that mutations alone are not enough to cause cancer. There must be other factors involved in causing cancer. Scientists have identified many of these factors, and have found that they fall into four major categories: heredity, environment, viruses, and diet.

Certain Genes Are Linked to Cancer

It is probably not surprising that the sequence of genes you carry on your chromosomes can affect your body's ability to ward off cancer. Scientists have found a number of genetic markers that predispose individuals to one or another form of cancer. **Figure 11.5** shows a sequence describing genetic predispositions to cancer. The earliest discovery of a genetic association to a particular cancer occurred in 1990 with the identification of a gene that, when passed to a female child, greatly increases the likelihood that she will develop breast cancer. The gene was named **breast cancer gene 1**, or *BRCA1*. A second gene, discovered later, was called *BRCA2*. Both BRCA1 and BRCA2 are tumor-suppressor genes.

While some scientists believe that any woman who carries a mutant BRCA1 or BRCA2 gene will develop breast cancer, it seems that the situation is far more complicated. If a mutated BRCA1 or BRCA2 gene is inherited from either parent, the child carries that mutated gene in every cell in her body. Because she carries two copies of every gene in her cells (one from each parent), the mutated gene will not be expressed and her chances of developing breast cancer are no higher than for the rest of the population. Only if a second BRCA1 or BRCA2 mutation occurs through the natural process of genetic mutation does the child's chances of developing cancer increase over those of the general population. If the second mutation develops in breast tissue cells, the result is breast cancer. If the mutation develops in an ovary, the result is ovarian cancer.

Other genes have been definitively linked to an increased risk of contracting particular cancers. For example, the *RB* gene has been linked to **retinoblastoma**, a cancer of the retina. RB is another tumor-suppressor gene. Both copies of the RB gene must be mutated in order to increase an individual's risk of contracting this form of cancer.

The genetics of cancer • Figure 11.5 _____

The causes of cancer include genetic predisposition. Pedigree A is a general example, while Pedigree B is typical of retinoblastoma.

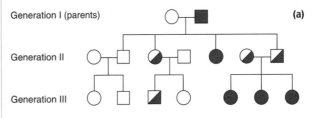

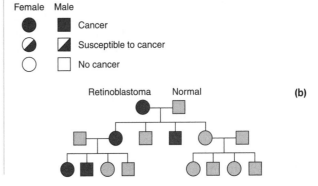

197

For some genes, only one mutated copy need be present to increase the risk of developing cancer. The risk of contracting thyroid cancer is greatly enhanced if the individual has a mutation in one of the two copies of the *RET* gene present in every cell. According to research from the Sloan Kettering Cancer Center, nearly everyone with one mutated RET gene develops medullary thyroid cancer.

Environmental Carcinogens Can Cause Cellular Mutations

As if the threat of naturally occurring, cancer-causing mutations were not enough, it appears that there are agents in the environment that increase our risk of developing cancer. **Carcinogens** are all around us—in the air we breathe, the water we drink, and the products we use in and around our homes. We can avoid contact with some, but not all, of these agents. Environmental carcinogens act by causing cellular mutation. These mutated genes can then be passed from parent to child in the egg or sperm, and they may then predispose the child to developing cancer. However, unlike the previously discussed mutations of oncogenes or mutator genes, some kind of **initiator** needs to be present to trigger the cellular activities and secondary mutations necessary for cancer to develop in these individuals. Some environmental carcinogens act only as initiators, whereas others act as both initiators and **promoters**.

Some cancer researchers have estimated that more than 50% of all cancers are caused by environmental carcinogens. However, that number is much smaller if we factor in only the environmental chemicals most people think of as causing cancer—smokestack pollution and chemicals in our drinking water or food. Additionally, there is a whole host of naturally occurring chemicals that have been proven to cause cancer in research studies, including tannins found in high concentrations in teas, safrole found in cinnamon, and even one of the major flavor-enhancing compounds in black pepper. In truth, multiple factors contribute to each cancer, with environmental agents factoring in many cases.

> **carcinogens** Environmental agents that can cause cancer.

> **initiator** An agent that causes cancerous changes in cellular functioning.

> **promoters** Environmental agents that increase the likelihood that an initiator will affect cellular functioning.

Some environmental carcinogens • Figure 11.6

We know a good deal about individual suspected carcinogens, but we know little about their interactions with each other. We know almost nothing about their interactions with hundreds of new chemicals introduced to our environment each year.

The two most prevalent forms of environmental carcinogens are chemicals and radiation. Some chemicals and some forms of radiation can be avoided, but not all. **Figure 11.6** shows some common environmental carcinogens. Among the chemical carcinogens that are most easily avoided are those associated with smoking organic compounds. The process of burning tobacco or any other organic material causes the release of multiple chemicals. Tobacco smoke, for example, contains N-nitrosonor-nicotine, vinyl chloride, benzo[a]pyrenes, and other chemicals, each of which has been identified as a carcinogen. Even the paper used in cigarettes includes harmful chemicals that are released when the cigarette is burned. Estimates of the percentage of cancer deaths linked to cigarette smoke run from 30% to 80%. This percentage includes deaths due both to smoking and to regular exposure to smoke (referred to as "passive smoking" or "secondhand smoke," and often occurring among family members and close co-workers of smokers). Since the 1990s, legislators at the local, state, and federal levels have enacted numerous laws to reduce passive smoke exposure by limiting the amount of smoking permitted in workplaces, schools, restaurants, public transportation, and entertainment venues.

To put the relationship between tobacco smoking and cancer in perspective, only about 2% of cancer deaths are linked to exposure to industrial pollutants. The majority of these cancers occur in people who work in an industry that uses the carcinogenic substances and not in people

who are exposed to diffuse environmental pollution. Many individuals wish to remain as healthy as possible and therefore try to reduce all risks of cancer in their lives. However, it is very difficult for some individuals to reduce their risk of contracting cancer through exposure to diffuse pollution. For example, although we are all exposed to some amount of diesel fuel exhaust (which is given off by trucks, buses, and trains), people in certain jobs, such as railyard workers, diesel mechanics, and miners, are exposed to far larger amounts. Also, while we are all exposed to some amount of pesticides on the produce we eat (unless we purchase only organically grown produce), we are not exposed to nearly as much as are farmers, farm workers, and packers, as shown in **Figure 11.7**. We are all exposed to a small amount of benzene that leaches out of paints, dyes, and furniture, but those who work in paint manufacturing, tanning and dyeing, and furniture manufacturing and finishing are exposed to far more.

See *Ethics and Issues: How Do We React to Cancer Clusters?* on the next page for some examples of environmental carcinogens and how we think about them.

Pregnant women and their fetuses are especially susceptible to some kinds of industrial pollution. During periods of active cellular growth and differentiation, the fetus can be negatively affected by even minute quantities of introduced carcinogen. As a matter of public policy, Americans have to decide how to balance protecting individuals from unusually high levels of carcinogens against people's right to live, work, and play as they wish. For instance, we know that many industrial solvents are highly carcinogenic and can also cause birth defects if a pregnant woman comes into contact with them, yet we still produce and use

these solvents in some occupations. Does this mean that a woman working at a job that is part of a manufacturing process using dangerous solvents must leave her job if she becomes pregnant? What rights does she have to transfer to a safer job within the same company? What obligations does the company have to her? Can a company refuse to hire women who may become pregnant for any job that requires contact with a carcinogen? What about refusing to hire people with a genetic predisposition to cancer for jobs that cause the worker to come in contact with carcinogens?

This issue is not merely an academic one. In the 1970s, some states mandated testing of African Americans for sickle cell anemia, a debilitating blood disorder that is especially prevalent among African Americans. This information was used to discriminate against African Americans in certain

A farm worker spraying a field • Figure 11.7

Even wearing protective clothing, this farmer is exposed to concentrated carcinogens while preparing and spraying pesticides. Many laborers suffer similar working conditions, often without a clear understanding of the dangers they face.

ETHICS AND ISSUES
How Do We React to Cancer Clusters?

From 1997 to 2001, doctors in Churchill County, Nevada, diagnosed 15 children with leukemia, a far higher rate of diagnosis than would be expected in a lightly populated, semirural region. Beginning in March 2000 and continuing through March 2001, the federal Centers for Disease Control and Prevention (CDC), working with Nevada health officials and university and industry consultants, conducted extensive studies of environmental conditions in the region. The goal was to see whether any environmental agent could have directly caused the statistically significant increase in cancer cases.

Since the 1970s, when a similar cancer cluster was diagnosed in Love Canal, New York, federal and state health officials have investigated a number of suspicious clusters and have found a potential link between environmental waste and increased levels of cancer. The most famous of these cases have become part of our culture through books and movies, such as *Erin Brockovich* and *A Civil Action*.

The Churchill County cluster came to light years after many other well-documented clusters, at a time when medical science had vastly increased its understanding of the genetic component of cancer. In the process of investigating this cluster, researchers uncovered new links between environmental and hereditary factors in promoting and initiating cancer. Researchers found that the soil and water of Churchill County contained elevated levels of the heavy metal tungsten, the chemical arsenic, and the breakdown product of the pesticide DDT. Despite this, the content of

environmental samples taken from inside and around the homes of cancer patients did not differ from the content of samples from the homes of other members of the community. Also, tissue and fluid samples taken from cancer patients did not contain higher levels of dangerous substances than similar samples from healthy children.

After these environmental and biological samples revealed no direct link between environmental agents and the cancer cluster, researchers turned to genetic analysis. From 2003 to 2006, they conducted extensive genetic tests of both ill and healthy children. The tests showed that all the ill children had a variation in a gene known as SUOX. The SUOX gene tells the body to make sulfite oxidase, a substance that acts to neutralize unsafe chemicals. It would make sense that if this gene were not producing functional sulfite oxidase, those individuals would be less able to handle the introduction of toxic compounds. However, a number of healthy children also carried a similar variation in the SUOX gene.

Critical Reasoning Issues The researchers concluded that, although a mutation in the SUOX gene leads to an increased risk of developing cancer in the presence of high levels of certain heavy metals and chemicals, it is not inevitable that exposure will cause the development of cancer. This complicated relationship of cause and effect is a familiar one for critical reasoners.

NATIONAL GEOGRAPHIC

Think Critically

1. What other cancer clusters have been in the news, and what causes and effects were found?

2. If a company's negligence leads to cancer clusters, how much responsibility does the company bear and how much responsibility does the local, state, or federal agency responsible for environmental protection bear?

3. Sometimes an industry or company will present studies of cancer clusters, often called *meta-studies*, to prove that their product or industry practice is not carcinogenic or is only weakly carcinogenic. Should you be skeptical about the inclusion of studies that follow an exposed population for only a few years or that include as many healthy workers as possible in their study?

situations. For example, some insurance companies refused coverage to those who carried the gene, and employers chose not to hire those with the sickle cell genetic predisposition. In response, Congress enacted the National Sickle Cell Anemia Control Act, which withheld federal health funding from states that mandated testing and created penalties for discrimination based on sickle cell status. In the spring of 2008, Congress proposed a similar law, the Genetic Information Nondiscrimination Act (GINA), which bans discrimination in hiring based on an individual's genetic profile.

Radiation is another carcinogenic agent.

Radiation takes two forms: ionizing and non-ionizing. The most prevalent source of ionizing radiation is sunlight. **Figure 11.8** illustrates the electromagnetic spectrum, showing the wavelengths of various forms of light energy. Over 80% of skin cancers, especially the highly dangerous melanoma, are caused by exposure to higher-frequency ultraviolet B (UVB) rays of sunlight. People with fair complexions are more prone to sunburn than are people with darker skin, but anyone can become sunburned. Frequent sunburn, especially in childhood and young adulthood, often leads to the development of skin cancers beginning in early middle age. Although it is nearly impossible to completely avoid the sun, knowing the dangers of ultraviolet radiation has changed the

habits of many people, who today are more likely to wear hats and use sunscreen than they might have been a generation or two ago.

Another form of environmental radiation is radon, a colorless, odorless gas that is released by water, soil, and rocks in varying amounts and intensities in different geographic areas. Homebuyers should always have their new house inspected for radon and equipped with radon detectors. The presence of radon cannot be detected by other means; moreover, the radiation patterns of radon change over time, necessitating constant surveillance. Radon is thought to be the second leading cause of lung cancer.

Nuclear fuel, whether used to generate power or to produce bombs, has been linked to cancer. Those at risk include workers who have been exposed to radioactive materials, either while mining raw uranium or processing uranium into fuel or bomb material. Others have been exposed to radiation as a result of nuclear power plant accidents, testing of nuclear bombs, and the two nuclear bombs used in World War II. Although those affected by nuclear blasts receive extremely high doses of radiation, fortunately most of us will not experience a bombing or a nuclear power plant accident. Our exposure is more likely to result from the use of diagnostic X-rays or radiation therapy to treat cancer. The benefits of these procedures generally far outweigh the harm done by such minimal

The electromagnetic spectrum • Figure 11.8

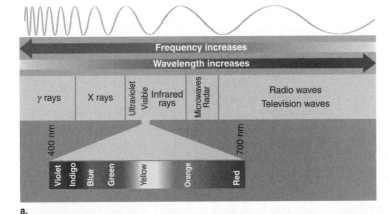

The electromagnetic spectrum is divided into various sections, depending on the wavelengths of the light energy/radiation. The ultraviolet rays cause most of the damage to our skin.

a.

b.

HEALTH, WELLNESS, AND DISEASE
Unraveling Genetic Links to Cancer Risks

Even in the 1950s, medical professionals were aware that there seemed to be a correlation between blood type and susceptibility to pancreatic cancer. People with blood type A, AB, or B developed pancreatic and gastric cancer at a higher rate than those with blood

NATIONAL GEOGRAPHIC

type O. It seemed preposterous that blood type would have any real connection with cancer risks, but now scientists have uncovered a possible explanation. In August 2009, the National Cancer Institute published a study indicating there is a genetic relationship between blood type and pancreatic cancer susceptibility. Working with 14 academic centers, they compared the nucleotide sequence (A,C,T, and G) of the entire genome of 4,353 patients with pancreatic cancer to that of 4,593 control individuals.

To do this, they look for a single base difference occurring in a gene with low frequency in the population—for example, in one gene, an adenine/thymine pair may be present instead of a cytosine/guanine pair in 25% of the population. If that difference is found in 76% of the patients with pancreatic cancer, it may indicate increased susceptibility to cancer. Amazingly, pancreatic cancer patients with A, B, or AB blood type had an increased frequency of changes on chromosome 9, immediately adjacent to the gene that codes for blood type. This type of comparative genetic screening is turning up many chromosomal "hotspots," each one linked to increased risk of a specific cancer. The more we learn about these genetic links to cancer risks, the more likely we will be able to prevent the development of cancer in predisposed individuals.

---

radiation exposure. However, there remains a slight risk, and X-rays should not be used without a good reason.

Many people believe that the non-ionizing radiation created by electric power lines, household appliances, and cell phones is also carcinogenic. There is, however, no scientific evidence to support this notion to date.

Viruses Can Promote the Development of Cancer

Some viruses have been linked to particular cancers. Since viruses must take command of a cell's genetic machinery in order to copy themselves, they can also promote cancerous mutations. A few viruses are known to cause cancer in humans by just this process. For example, there are several forms of human papilloma virus (HPV) that together are the most common causes of cervical cancer, according to the Mayo Clinic. Although we aren't always successful in creating long-term vaccines against viral diseases because of the high rate of change in the viral coat, occasionally medical researchers are able to produce an effective one. An example is Gardasil, a recently released vaccine against HPV.

Other viruses linked to specific cancers include the Epstein–Barr virus (EBV), which is linked to both Hodgkin's and non-Hodgkin's lymphoma; the hepatitis B and C viruses, linked to liver cancer; HIV/AIDS, linked to non-Hodgkin's lymphoma and Kaposi's sarcoma; and the human T-cell leukemia/lymphoma virus, linked to T-cell non-Hodgkin's lymphoma.

How do viruses initiate cancers? We do not know exactly how viruses initiate cancer, but we do know that viruses reproduce by inserting their DNA into that of a host cell. If, in this process, the host cell's functioning is either increased or decreased, the risk of developing cancer will be increased. Viruses may also promote the development of cancer by adversely affecting the immune system and altering the natural balance between cancer cells and the cells that defend the body from them.

Together, these viruses probably account for the initiation of a very small percentage of cancers, far smaller than the percentage initiated by environmental agents. Often, the chances of developing a specific type of cancer are increased by having a genetic predisposition for that cancer. See *Health, Wellness, and Disease: Unraveling Genetic Links to Cancer Risks* to learn more.

Certain Diets May Contribute to Cancer

Statistical studies have shown that certain diets promote the growth of cancers that have been initiated either by inherited or environmental factors. Obesity has been linked with an increase of 50% or more in the incidence of colon cancer among both men and women and to an increase of 50% or more in the risk of breast and uterine cancer among women. Diets high in animal fat from beef, pork, and dairy foods have also been associated with an increased risk of colon cancer.

One 2007 study showed that colon cancer patients who continued their traditional Western diet (high in fats and red meat and low in fruits and raw vegetables) were three times as likely to have a recurrence of their cancer after surgery than colon cancer patients who altered their diet by decreasing their fat intake and increasing their vegetable and fruit intake after surgery. Somehow, the typical Western diet seemed to fuel those few cancer cells that remained in the body after surgery.

Chemicals called *nitrites*, which are converted into nitrosamines in the digestive process, are often used as a preservative in luncheon meats and other foods. A diet high in nitrites has been linked to a higher risk of cancer, as have diets high in nitrates and smoked meats, which contain chemical carcinogens similar to those found in tobacco smoke.

Fish and mollusks that feed in waters contaminated by chemicals or heavy metals often store some of these carcinogenic substances in their flesh. Therefore, it is important to limit consumption of fish caught off coastal waters, especially fatty fish, such as bluefish and bass. The Monterey Bay Aquarium has recently published a listing of seafood selections indicating which fishes are considered healthiest and which traditionally carry the highest levels of potential carcinogens. This important information is available to anyone with an Internet connection.

Excessive alcohol consumption (more than two drinks per day or on a single occasion) has also been linked to increases in many forms of cancer, especially cancers of the mouth, throat, and esophagus. Breast and liver cancers have also been linked to excessive alcohol use.

Certain Foods May Help Guard Against Cancer

While some foods are thought to promote cancer, other foods help to guard against cancer. Green, leafy vegetables contain a precursor to vitamin A called *beta-carotene*, which is an antioxidant. Antioxidant vitamins counteract the effects of the **free radicals** that are a normal byproduct of cellular metabolism. Free radicals are generally detoxified by the body's natural processes, but if that cleansing is inefficient, free radicals that build up in the body can damage other molecules, including DNA. Vitamin C, found in citrus fruit, is another antioxidant.

> **free radicals** Highly reactive organic ions that have an unpaired electron, such as oxygen ions.

Cancer Can Strike Almost Any Part of the Body

Cancers are classified according to their location and the type of tissue in which they appear. See **Figure 11.9**.

Some classes of cancer • Figure 11.9

Cancers are named for the tissue from which the tumor originated. Most new cancer cases in the United States every year are carcinomas, with non-melanoma skin cancers leading the way followed closely by lung and breast cancer. Leukemias are the second most common class of cancer, but they are a distant second. According to the National Cancer Institute, NIH, total new cases of leukemia in 2008 were a mere one-thirtieth of the total new cases of carcinomas.

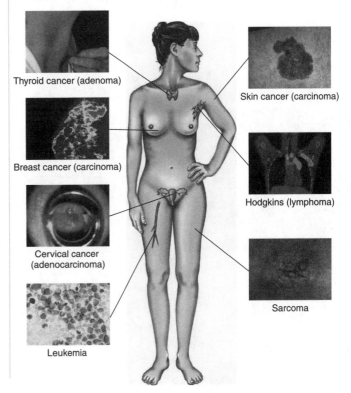

Thyroid cancer (adenoma)

Breast cancer (carcinoma)

Cervical cancer (adenocarcinoma)

Leukemia

Skin cancer (carcinoma)

Hodgkins (lymphoma)

Sarcoma

11.2 Cancer Has Many Causes and Effects 291

- **Carcinomas** are cancers of the epithelial tissues. Skin, breast, liver, lung, prostate, and intestinal cancers are carcinomas.

> **carcinoma** Cancer of epithelial tissue.

- **Adenomas** are cancers of the glandular tissues, such as tumors on the thyroid or adrenal gland.
- **Adenocarcinomas** are cancers of the glandular epithelial cells, such as an adenocarcinoma of the uterine cervix.
- **Sarcomas** are cancers of the connective and muscular tissues, including cancers of the bone, muscle, and fibrous connective tissues.

> **sarcoma** Cancer of soft tissue, such as connective tissue.
>
> **leukemia** Cancer involving blood.
>
> **lymphoma** Cancer involving the lymphatic system.

- **Blastomas** are cancers of the embryonic tissues, such as retinoblastoma.
- **Leukemias** are cancers involving the blood.
- **Lymphomas** are cancers involving the lymphatic system.

Cancer can occur anywhere in the body, but some parts are more susceptible to cancer than others. Three of the most common cancers—of the lung, the colon and rectum, and the breast—are also three of the most deadly. Survival often depends on the nature of the organ in which the cancer originates. Cancers in organs with a large blood supply, such as the lungs and liver, are usually more aggressive, and, at least in the United States, survival rates for these cancers are lower.

Lung cancer diagnosis is based on symptoms. Cigarette smoking is by far the leading factor in the development of lung cancer. All other risk factors—household, workplace, or environmental exposure to chemicals, asbestos, and radiation—pale by comparison. There is no screening test for lung cancer; it is diagnosed based on symptoms, which include persistent cough, frequent pneumonia or bronchitis, and changes in the voice. In the United States, the one-year survival rate is under 50%, and the five-year survival rate is only about 15%. Early detection improves these rates somewhat. Lung cancer causes more deaths than the next five most deadly cancers combined.

Most colorectal cancers start as benign polyps. Unlike for lung cancer, there is a screening test for colorectal cancer. Additionally, an initial diagnostic **colonoscopy** at age 50 is recommended for most people; earlier screening is recommended for those at higher risk, such as people with a family history of inflammatory bowel disease. Colonoscopy is done under sedation and involves snaking a fiberoptic tube and camera through the anus and the length of the colon, or large intestine, to the junction of the small and large intestines. See **Figure 11.10**. Rectal bleeding or bloody

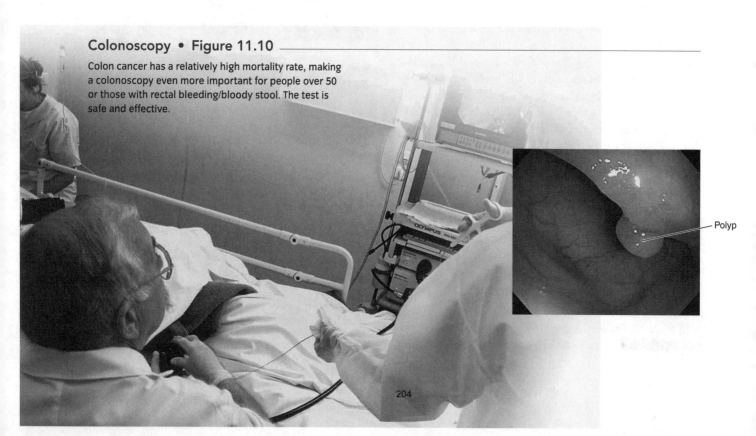

Colonoscopy • Figure 11.10

Colon cancer has a relatively high mortality rate, making a colonoscopy even more important for people over 50 or those with rectal bleeding/bloody stool. The test is safe and effective.

Polyp

stool, even in a younger person, necessitates a colonoscopy to rule out cancer. A high-fat, low-fiber diet and a sedentary lifestyle have been linked to increased risk of colon cancer.

Most colorectal cancers start as benign polyps that protrude from the lining of the colon. Fortunately, most polyps never develop into malignancies; when they do, the process usually takes years. Early detection is important: The five-year survival rate for colon cancers is 64%, but the five-year survival rate for those in whom the cancer has spread is only 10%.

There are several risk factors for breast cancer. Breast cancer is almost solely a woman's cancer, although about 1,700 cases of male breast cancer are diagnosed each year in the United States. Age is a major risk factor: 1 in 200 women will develop breast cancer before age 40, but 1 in 26 will develop breast cancer before she reaches her 60s. Other risk factors are early menarche (the first menstrual cycle) or late menopause; obesity, especially after menopause; use of hormonal contraceptives, such as birth control pills or patches; and hormone replacement therapy after menopause.

Most breast cancer is diagnosed by means of a *mammogram*, an X-ray of breast tissue like the one shown in **Figure 11.11**. Women over age 40 are encouraged to have an annual or biannual mammogram, depending on their risk factors and family history. In recent decades, significant improvements have been made in the detection, treatment, and outcome of breast cancer. Many tumors can be removed with far less invasive surgeries than in the past. In the United States, the five-year survival rate for women with tumors that have not yet spread is 98%, and the overall ten-year survival rate is around 80%. For those with metastatic breast cancer, which has spread to the lymph nodes, the five-year survival rate is much lower.

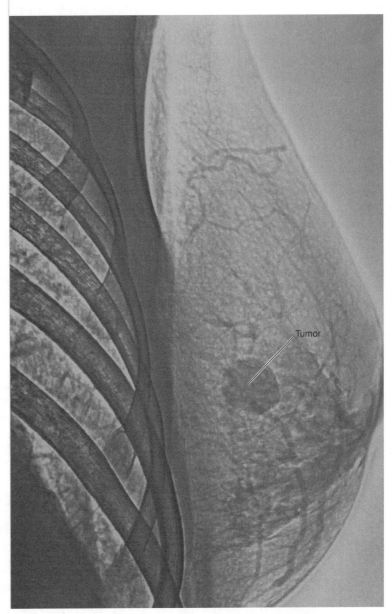

Tumor

A mammogram • Figure 11.11 ⎯⎯⎯⎯

Mammograms are an invaluable tool for breast cancer detection. However, they carry a small chance of both false positives (finding a growth that is not a tumor) and false negatives (missing a tumor). New imaging techniques are improving the accuracy of mammograms yearly.

11.2 Cancer Has Many Causes and Effects 293

There are three kinds of skin cancer. Skin cancer is the most common type of cancer for both men and women. There are three types of skin cancer: basal cell carcinoma, squamous cell carcinoma, and melanoma, as shown in **Figure 11.12**. Both basal cell carcinoma, which affects the basal cells of the epithelium, and squamous cell carcinoma, which affects the epithelial cells produced by the basal cells, appear as small, abnormal patches on the skin. Although they spread quite slowly if they spread at all, these cancers should be surgically removed. If these two types of skin cancer are not considered, the rate of skin cancer in the population drops dramatically from representing the most common type of cancer all the way down to between 4% and 5%.

Melanomas are very dangerous. They occur much less frequently than basal cell or squamous cell carcinomas, but they can metastasize very quickly. The five-year survival rate is 98% for individuals with melanomas that have been detected and removed; for those with melanomas that have metastasized, the five-year survival rate is under 20%.

Prostate cancer occurs in men, most commonly after age 50. Because prostate cancer is quite common, men over age 50 are recommended to have either a digital rectal exam or a prostate-specific antigen (PSA) blood test, or both, annually. Symptoms of prostate cancer include difficulty or inability to urinate, blood in the urine, or pain in the pelvic area. However, these are also symptoms of an enlarged noncancerous prostate, known as benign prostate **hyperplasia**, or even of a bladder infection. Prostate cancer is a slow-growing cancer, and many men who are diagnosed with the disease after age 65 or 70 may choose not to undergo any treatment. Treatments include surgical removal of the prostate gland, radiation, and hormonal therapy. Although these treatments may seem radical, they are well worth the pain, as in the United States the 15-year survival rate for men choosing to treat their prostate cancer is over 75%. Moreover, these surgical procedures have been improved so that nerve functioning, urine control, and sexual abilities are preserved.

Leukemia is cancer of the white blood cells. Leukemia can strike anyone, at any age—even children are susceptible to this form of cancer. Unlike prostate or breast cancer, leukemia is usually a diagnosis of exclusion (that is, it is made after tests have excluded other possible conditions). The reason is that the symptoms are nonspecific, including fatigue, weight loss, and frequent infections, which are similar to the symptoms of many other diseases. A definitive diagnosis is made after a blood test and a bone marrow biopsy. See **Figure 11.13**. Scientists remain unclear about the factors involved in the causes of leukemia, but there are some correlations. For example, increased exposure to high levels of ionizing radiation and/or benzene has been linked to a higher rate of leukemia, although the link is statistically weaker than other accepted links between environment and cancer. The most common treatment for leukemia is chemotherapy to destroy cancerous white cells, often followed by a bone marrow transplant to replace the destroyed cells.

Skin cancers • Figure 11.12

Know your own skin well enough to recognize suspicious areas, and consult a medical professional if any of these descriptions apply.

a. Basal cell carcinoma (BCC) usually develops in places routinely exposed to the sun.

b. Squamous cell carcinoma (SCC) is a tumor of the upper layers of the skin. Roughly 16% of skin cancer cases are SCC.

c. Melanomas are the most aggressive, and can be marked by "ABCD" guidelines: asymmetry (growing irregularly), borders that are indistinct, color that is not uniform, and diameters that are larger than those of noncancerous blemishes.

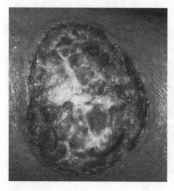
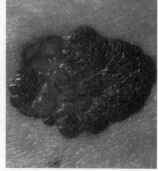
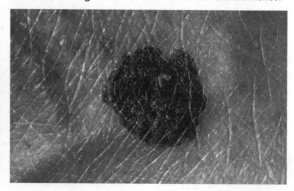

294 CHAPTER 11 Cancer

Lymphoma is cancer of the lymphatic tissue.

Lymphoma is a form of cancer that attacks the lymph nodes. There are two main categories of lymphoma: Hodgkin's disease and non-Hodgkin's lymphoma. In both of these, enlarged lymph nodes are most frequently recognized in the groin, armpits, and neck. Other symptoms include intermittent fever, weight loss, and night sweats. As with leukemia, a diagnosis of lymphoma is often made after excluding more common causes of these symptoms. A weakened immune system, from HIV or human T-cell leukemia/lymphoma virus, or from immunosuppressive drugs taken by organ transplant recipients and sufferers of autoimmune diseases, increases the risk of developing lymphoma. Typically, treatment consists of high-dose radiation treatment or chemotherapy, sometimes followed by bone-marrow transplant. Newer treatments, such as specific antibodies to lymphoma cells, have shown promise. Boston Red Sox pitcher Jon Lester is a well-known lymphoma survivor. Read more about Lester in *What a Scientist Sees: Getting Back to Work After Cancer.*

Leukemia cells • Figure 11.13

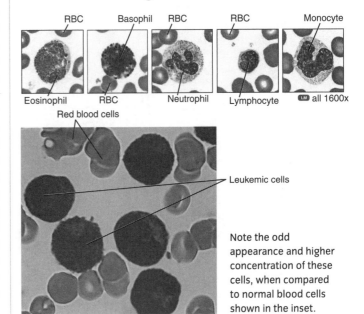

Note the odd appearance and higher concentration of these cells, when compared to normal blood cells shown in the inset.

WHAT A SCIENTIST SEES

Getting Back to Work After Cancer

Non-Hodgkin's lymphoma was once rare, but it is now the fifth most common form of cancer in the United States. One kind of non-Hodgkin's lymphoma, called anaplastic large-cell lymphoma, strikes young males more often than others. Boston Red Sox pitcher Jon Lester was diagnosed with this type of cancer on September 6, 2006, at age 22. A very specific form of chemotherapy, combining four drugs administered every two or three weeks, succeeded in sending his cancer into remission, and a year later Lester was pitching for the Red Sox in the final game of the 2007 World Series. On May 19, 2008, Lester threw a no-hitter against the Kansas City Royals, only 18 months after being diagnosed and treated.

Younger patients have been showing the greatest improvement in five-year survival rates for lymphoma. Those survival rates have risen from roughly 50% to over 66%.

Think Critically

1. Why might a specific type of cancer—for example, anaplastic large-cell lymphoma—be more common in one gender than the other?
2. What is meant by the phrase "a very specific form of chemotherapy"? How can chemotherapy be tailored to one specific cancer?

Types and frequency of cancer in the United States • Figure 11.14

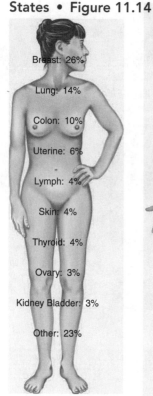

Breast: 26%
Lung: 14%
Colon: 10%
Uterine: 6%
Lymph: 4%
Skin: 4%
Thyroid: 4%
Ovary: 3%
Kidney Bladder: 3%
Other: 23%

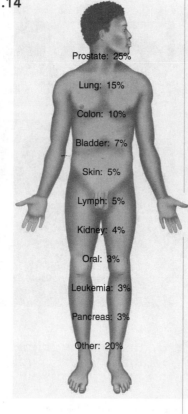

Prostate: 25%
Lung: 15%
Colon: 10%
Bladder: 7%
Skin: 5%
Lymph: 5%
Kidney: 4%
Oral: 3%
Leukemia: 3%
Pancreas: 3%
Other: 20%

Other, less common cancers occur in the liver, kidney, pancreas, bladder, and reproductive organs. Brain cancers are infrequent but are usually fatal after a short time. A **primary cancer** does not usually form in the brain; brain cancer is usually a sign

> **primary cancer** The original site of tumor development; can metastasize to form secondary cancers.

of metastatic disease that has spread from a primary cancer of the breast, colon, or lung. It is very difficult to treat brain cancers, since cancerous tissue must be totally separated from healthy tissue in order to maintain the highest possible level of brain functioning. See **Figure 11.14** for types of cancer and their rates of frequency.

The incidence of most cancers increases with age. As we age, our risk of cancer increases. With increased life expectancies across the population comes an increase in the number of new cancer diagnoses and cancer deaths each year. Although it is tempting to look at statistics over time and determine that not much progress has been made in the fight against cancer, that would be an error. Long-term survival rates for many cancers continue to rise, and the seeming lack of progress in defeating cancer is actually due to an increasing proportion of cancer cases being diagnosed in the elderly. Because these people are advanced in age, and perhaps not physically able to withstand the rigors of surgery or chemotherapy, they often choose not to treat the cancer. In truth, medical science has made incredible advances in treating this series of diseases, and there are many exciting new techniques on the horizon.

CONCEPT CHECK **STOP**

1. **What** are the four major categories of factors that cause cancer?
2. **What** is known about each causal factor?
3. **How** are cancers classified?

11.3 Cancer Can Be Diagnosed and Treated Effectively

LEARNING OBJECTIVES

1. **List** the most common ways in which cancer is diagnosed.
2. **Define** the difference between traditional and newer approaches to treating cancer.
3. **Describe** the steps individuals can take to help remain cancer-free.

Although some cancers are easy to detect and diagnose, others require more thorough investigation. Some are diagnosed based on a set of symptoms, and others can be detected through routine screening. When diagnosed, however, all cancers can be treated. There are often a few different

Self-examinations by men and women • Figure 11.15

Self-examination is an important first step in cancer identification and control. Guidelines such as these can be obtained from your physician and should be followed routinely.

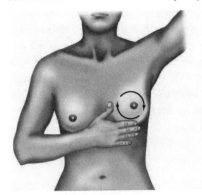

Shower check for breast self-exam

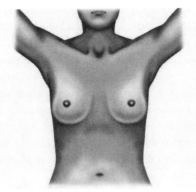

Mirror check for breast self-exam

Shower check for testicular self-exam

methods of treatment available, and the choice of how best to proceed rests with the patient and the attending physicians. Together, they consider the potential effectiveness of conventional and experimental treatments in extending and improving the quality of life for each individual patient. What works for one person may not be acceptable for the next.

Diagnosing Cancer Requires Many Tools

There are four ways to make a definitive diagnosis of cancer:

- Screening tests
- Imaging
- Tumor enzyme tests
- Genetic tests

There are several routine screening tests. Routine screening tests include manual self-tests, manual tests performed by a doctor or other health care provider, and visual examinations. The self-tests are important, because women performing breast self-examination and men performing testicle self-examination often find irregular lumps in these organs. On further medical examination, many of these turn out to be benign, but some are found to be cancerous. Because early detection is key to surviving these cancers, self-tests are literally life-saving activities. **Figure 11.15** presents accepted methods for performing these self-examinations.

We all know that good health care includes routine physical examinations by a medical professional. Cancer screening is built into these exams. Part of a full physical examination for a man includes a testicular examination by the provider. For men over 50, the physical should include a digital rectal examination of the prostate. For women, a full physical examination includes a manual breast examination. The American Cancer Society recommends that women between 20 and 40 have a manual pelvic exam performed at least once each three years, and annually after age 40, along with a manual breast examination by a provider.

At the same time that your medical professional is examining your blood pressure and heart and lung sounds, he or she is also screening for cancers. A physical examination includes a visual examination for skin cancers of areas commonly exposed to the sun (neck, face, scalp, behind the ears, forearms, and hands). A manual examination of lymph nodes of the neck, armpit, and groin can also be performed. A digital rectal exam and card smear for occult blood in the stool should be performed every year after age 50, beginning earlier for those with risk factors for colorectal cancer. If any of these manual or visual exams reveals abnormalities, further tests should be performed to determine whether the abnormality is cancerous.

Some screening requires the use of various instruments, and therefore may be scheduled for a separate doctor's visit. For instance, it is recommended that women have a Pap smear performed by a provider annually beginning at age 18 or at the onset of sexual activity. The Pap test examines cervical cells for cancer or precancerous changes (known as **dysplasia**). A flexible **sigmoidoscopy**, which examines just the final portion of the colon, or a full colonoscopy, should be performed every five years beginning at age 50, and more frequently if the individual has a family history of colorectal cancer or polyps or has inflammatory bowel disease.

The mammogram is a key diagnostic tool.

The mammogram, a special X-ray technology for breast imaging, is perhaps the most significant improvement in cancer diagnosis in recent history. Mammograms can detect cancerous tumors that are too small or too deep in the breast tissue to be detected in a manual examination. It is recommended that women have their first mammogram between ages 35 and 40 with annual mammograms beginning at age 40. Breast cancers diagnosed at an early stage can often be removed in a procedure that spares essentially all breast tissue.

Cancer specialists use a wide variety of imaging techniques.

In addition to mammography, simple X-rays can show large anomalies and masses in soft tissues, such as those associated with lung cancers. Doctors can also use a host of other imaging techniques to diagnose cancer; one technique is shown in **Figure 11.16**. Computerized axial tomography (CAT or CT) scanning uses computerized analysis of continuously scanning X-

Liver cancer • Figure 11.16

This X-ray image with false color added shows the axial section of an abdomen with a cancerous liver. The liver is shown in red, and the cancerous liver tumors are shown as lighter sections on the liver.

rays to create a "cross section" of the area being scanned. This scan depicts organs and any tumors present in three dimensions. From this computer-generated image, a physician can infer a tumor's size and position relative to body organs. Magnetic resonance imaging (MRI) is particularly helpful in pinpointing and identifying tumors in connective tissues as well as tumors of the brain or spinal cord. Ultrasound uses high-frequency sound, which bounces off tissues of different densities at different rates, helping to distinguish between healthy tissue and tumors. It can provide a visualization of the size, shape, and location of tumors in the prostate, ovary, kidney, pancreas, and intestinal tract.

Tumor markers and genetic tests can also be used to diagnose cancer.

Tumor markers are chemicals produced by the body in response to the development of a tumor. When they are present in the blood, they "mark" or indicate the presence of a tumor. For example, prostate-specific antigen (PSA) is produced by prostate cells. At present, it is the only tumor marker that can be confidently used to make a diagnosis of cancer. Other tumor markers can be used to determine whether certain cancers have spread or recurred after initial treatment.

Currently, genetic tests can only determine whether an individual has a predisposition to cancer. Genetic testing cannot determine the presence of a growing tumor in the body. Recall that genetic testing can identify a woman's susceptibility to breast cancer by identifying mutated BRCA1 and BRCA2 genes. However, DNA analysis of released substances, such as urine and saliva, can sometimes identify gene mutations associated with certain cancers. For instance, cell mutations associated with lung cancer can sometimes be found in cast-off cells released in sputum; mutations associated with bladder cancer can sometimes be found in cells floating in urine; and mutations associated with colon cancer can sometimes be found in cells removed from the colon along with the feces.

Treating Cancer Is a Multistage Process

Cancer treatment has long focused on killing or removing the primary tumor and then attacking any metastatic tumors that may be present. In following this general procedure, there are three standard treatments for cancer:

surgery, radiation therapy, and chemotherapy. Because of the "sledgehammer," whole-body approach that these techniques employ, they are often called the brute force methods. Fortunately, there are also some newer, more delicate forms of cancer therapy that reflect the fact that cancer is actually many different diseases. These new methods usually use one of three refined techniques for controlling cancer:

- Attacking the tumor cells with specifically designed or selected immune cells or antibodies. This is called immunotherapy.
- Crippling the proteins that promote the cancer.
- Cutting off the blood supply to the tumor—this is called anti-angiogenesis.

These highly targeted therapies can either identify cells more precisely so that the killing treatment is applied only to cancerous cells, or block the signals that cause cancerous growth while not affecting the growth of normal body cells. These methods are called "intelligent" because they are targeted so precisely. There are also other types of treatment, often experimental, that include genetic therapy, magnetism, and phototherapy.

Surgery is still a key tool in fighting cancer. Surgical removal of cancerous tumors was performed even before the discovery of anesthetics. Surgery is the logical solution to a growth, especially one with easily identified borders—simply remove it! If a cancer appears to be contained in one small area, it is referred to as *in situ*. If detected early, completely localized *in situ* cancers, such as basal cell and squamous cell skin cancer, as well as some colon and other cancers, can be removed surgically with no follow-up treatment. However, even if it appears that a cancer is *in situ*, most cancer spe-

oncologist
A physician who specializes in the treatment of cancer.

cialists—**oncologists**—will recommend either radiation therapy or chemotherapy after surgery to kill any cells that may have broken away from the primary tumor or been left behind after the removal of the tumor.

Radiation can be deadly to dividing cells.
Radiation was first employed as a medical aid soon after the discovery of X-rays in 1895. It is deadly to cells that are dividing because it damages DNA, and damaged DNA in cells typically prevents cellular divisions and leads to cell death through apoptosis. Radiation therapy is gener-

ally used if the cancer has spread from its original site but is still localized—for example, radiation may be used as a secondary treatment during breast cancer recovery if lymph nodes removed during surgery show no evidence of metastasis. In that case, radiation is used to ensure that no cancerous cells remain to begin a new tumor. Radiation is also used as the primary therapy for those cancers for which surgery is especially difficult (such as cancers of the larynx or brain) or may have undesirable side effects (such as prostate cancer).

Unfortunately, radiation does not distinguish between cancer cells and the cells of healthy tissue surrounding the cancer being irradiated. For that reason, it is one of the "sledgehammer" methods, killing every cell in its path. Depending on where the radiation beam is aimed, there may be various localized side effects, such as hair loss, irritated skin, and even blistering burns at the treatment site. Often, there are also systemic side effects, including dry mouth, fatigue, and nausea. Both local and systemic side effects generally disappear soon after treatment is ended.

Chemotherapy disrupts cells throughout the body. Chemotherapy uses compounds that specialize in killing fast-growing cells, so it is used to attack cancers that have spread. Unlike radiation, which interrupts cell growth only where the radiation beam is aimed, chemotherapy interrupts cell growth throughout the entire body. These drugs will prevent cell division in normal healthy cells as well as cancer cells. The hope is that the growth of the cancerous tumor will be stopped before the drug causes death of healthy organs. Cancer drugs given either orally or by infusion travel throughout the body and damage rapidly dividing cells wherever they are (think attack squad with general killing orders). Some drugs damage cellular DNA; others interfere with DNA synthesis; and still others attack cancerous cellular processes—all with the aim of killing those quickly dividing cancer cells. Different drug "cocktails" are created to attack different types of cancers, with the hope of killing cancer cells while killing or damaging as few healthy cells as possible. Using many different chemicals also prevents the cancer from developing a resistance to one particular medication. The side effects of chemotherapy are the same as those of radiation: nausea and lack of appetite, fatigue, hair loss, and dry mouth, as well as anemia due to the killing of red

blood cells and reduced immune system functioning due to the killing of white blood cells. See **Figure 11.17** for an example of a chemotherapy infusion session.

Bone marrow transplants are another tool.
Bone marrow transplants are sometimes performed in conjunction with chemotherapy or high-dose radiation therapy that destroys fast-dividing bone marrow cells. If possible, a bone marrow transplant is undertaken using a process called *autotransplantation*. Healthy bone marrow is located within the skeleton of the cancer patient (not all of the bone marrow is diseased even in cancers of the blood, such as leukemia). The healthy marrow is removed from the patient prior to treatment, and the stem cells that will form red and white blood cells are harvested and stored. After high-dose radiation therapy or chemotherapy has

IV is the typical chemotherapy delivery method • Figure 11.17

Chemotherapy is often a customized combination of drugs, delivered via IV. Some of the drugs in the cocktail cut down on the debilitating side effects of the other drugs. More effort is now being devoted to making the chemotherapy experience as non-threatening as possible.

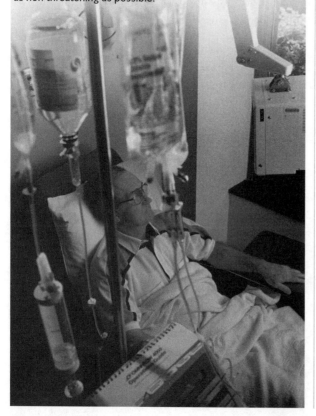

destroyed the patient's remaining bone marrow cells, the stored stem cells are transplanted back into the patient, where they begin to make new, healthy blood cells again. In cases such as sickle cell anemia, where all of the bone marrow carries the disease-causing gene, marrow will be transplanted from a closely matching donor.

Immunotherapy boosts the immune system.
When cancer occurs, it indicates that the body's immune system is failing to kill cancer cells or is failing to kill them faster than they are reproducing. The goal of immunotherapy is to boost the immune system in an effort to help it fight the cancer more effectively. This is done in one of two ways: either by assisting in the killing of the cancer cell through creating vaccines against the cancer or by increasing the amount and activity of certain types of killer cells. Adding compounds, such as interleukin-2, interferons, and tumor necrosis factor, will assist the body's natural immune cells in fighting the disease.

Anti-angiogenesis drugs can starve a tumor.
When cancerous tumors reach a certain size (about 1 to 2 million cells), angiogenesis begins. The tumor develops its own blood supply through the formation of new blood vessels. Researchers are currently studying a number of drugs that stop the process of angiogenesis, stopping the formation of these new vessels and essentially starving the tumor of nutrition. In theory, once the tumor runs out of nutrients, it should shrink and die. Also, without a blood supply the tumor cells cannot remove their waste products, resulting in toxic buildup and further cell death.

Genetic therapy holds great promise.
Since the 1960s, scientists have known how genes work. Since the 1980s, they have been able to introduce genetic material into organisms to change them. This process has been done most often in agriculture, in order to create food products that are more robust or produce larger yields. Even with the lessons learned from repeated successes in altering the genetic makeup of agriculturally significant crops, correcting genetic mutations that cause disease has proven to be much more difficult. Gene therapy is still mostly the stuff of science fiction. Amazingly, in 2008, scientists at the University of Iowa and the Children's Hospital of Philadelphia announced that they had successfully used genetic therapy to correct a type of inherited blindness. Currently, work is progressing on genetic therapies for diseases that are caused by only a few genetic mutations. Unfortunately, this does

not include most cancers. Cancer gene therapy is rendered almost incomprehensibly complicated by the sheer number of genetic mutations that must be corrected and also by the complex relationship between the mutation and later promotors of disease. Despite these seemingly insurmountable obstacles, scientists continue to hope that by changing the genetic structure of cells they can reduce the incidence of certain types of cancer.

Magnetism and phototherapy are in the early stages of experimentation. Magnets may hold a key to directed cancer treatments. Powerful magnets are being experimented with in an attempt to target chemotherapy more precisely. As you know, magnets attract metal. In experiments with liver cancer, tiny metallic beads coated with chemotherapy drugs are injected into the patient. Powerful magnets are then positioned directly over the tumor, in the hope that their magnetic force will pull the drug-coated beads deeply into the tumor tissue.

Lasers and light-sensitive drugs are being used in a similar fashion to insert chemotherapy deep into tumors embedded in organs. The patient receives light-sensitive drugs that are drawn into the tumor cells in the usual fashion; they are carried through the bloodstream and eventually find their way to the tumor. The difference between these drugs and previously discussed chemotherapy is that the light-sensitive drugs are inactive as they travel the body. Laser light directed at the tumor and focused to a particular frequency sets off a chemical reaction in the drugs that enhances their ability to kill tumor cells.

Personal Choices Help Fight Cancer

We know that personal choices matter in every area of our lives. There is mounting evidence that our personal choices increase or decrease our risks of getting cancer.

We need to support cancer research and cancer awareness. Every year, scientists learn more about cancer. As a result, people who develop cancer are able to live longer, healthier, and more rewarding lives after diagnosis and treatment. From the time we print this to the time you read this, thousands of cancer professionals will have put in millions of additional hours improving our knowledge and our odds of living well should we develop cancer. It is important that we all support research into cancer prevention and treatment. It may save our lives. See **Figure 11.18**.

Cancer researchers at work • Figure 11.18

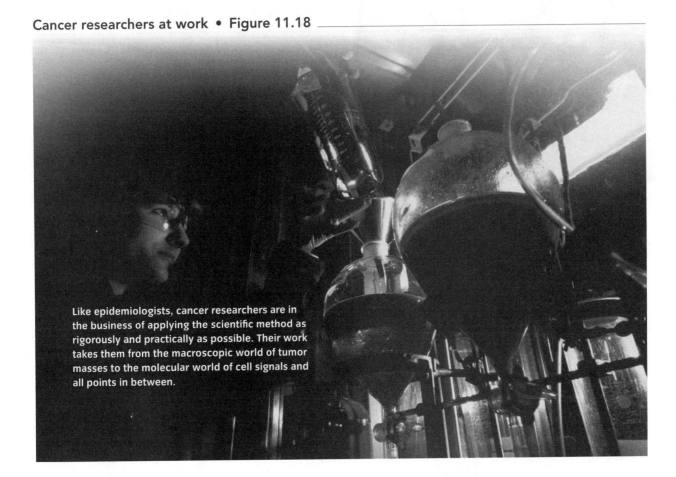

Like epidemiologists, cancer researchers are in the business of applying the scientific method as rigorously and practically as possible. Their work takes them from the macroscopic world of tumor masses to the molecular world of cell signals and all points in between.

I WONDER...
How Can I Lower My Cancer Risks?

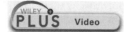

- *Don't use tobacco.* Tobacco, especially when smoked but also when chewed or "dipped," is the most frequent cause of preventable cancers. Research shows that tobacco use leads to cancer and, in combination with environmental and other hazards, greatly magnifies the chances of developing cancer.

- *Be careful about exposure to sun.* As the protective layers of ozone have been depleted by pollution and greenhouse gases, the sun's ultraviolet rays have become more dangerous than ever before. Use sunscreen or sunblock liberally, and wear protective clothing whenever you go out in the sun.

- *Eat a healthy diet.* Such a diet is low in trans- and saturated fat, which comes primarily from animal products, and includes lots of vitamins A and D. Eat whole grains instead of processed foods. Fresh fruits and vegetables, especially green leafy vegetables, are high in fiber and potentially cancer-fighting agents.

NATIONAL GEOGRAPHIC

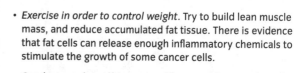

- *Exercise in order to control weight.* Try to build lean muscle mass, and reduce accumulated fat tissue. There is evidence that fat cells can release enough inflammatory chemicals to stimulate the growth of some cancer cells.

- *Conduct regular self-exams,* and have regular complete check-ups during which a doctor or other health-care provider conducts a thorough visual and manual cancer screening.

- *Try to limit your exposure to environmental toxins.* At home, at work, and at school, take available precautions if needed—wear protective equipment, and wash thoroughly immediately after exposure to any toxins.

We need to be aware of the ways our lifestyles affect our cancer risks. You can't do anything about your genetic makeup. However, you can engage in certain behaviors that will reduce your chances of developing cancer, as seen in *I Wonder… How Can I Lower My Cancer Risks?*

CONCEPT CHECK   STOP

1. **What** are some ways to diagnose cancer?
2. **How** have cancer treatments changed in the past 20 years?
3. **What** steps can individuals take to help them remain cancer-free?